GUID

Guide to Mechanics

Philip Dyke

*Head of the Department of Mathematics and Statistics,
Polytechnic South West*

and

Roger Whitworth

Head of Mathematics, Droitwich High School

MACMILLAN

First published 1992 by
THE MACMILLAN PRESS LTD
Houndmills, Basingstoke, Hampshire RG21 2XS
and London
Companies and representatives
throughout the world

ISBN 0–333–51072–0

A catalogue record for this book is available
from the British Library.

Printed in Hong Kong

To Ottilie and Tom

CONTENTS

EDITOR'S FOREWORD

Wide concern has been expressed in tertiary education about the difficulties experienced by students during their first year of an undergraduate course containing a substantial component of mathematics. These difficulties have a number of underlying causes, including the change of emphasis from an algorithmic approach at school to a more rigorous and abstract approach in undergraduate studies, the greater expectation of independent study, and the increased pace at which material is presented. The books in this series are intended to be sensitive to these problems.

Each book is a carefully selected, short, introductory text on a key area of the first-year syllabus; the areas are complementary and largely self-contained. Throughout, the pace of development is gentle, sympathetic and carefully motivated. Clear and detailed explanations are provided, and important concepts and results are stressed.

As mathematics is a practical subject which is best learned by doing it, rather than watching or reading about someone else doing it, a particular effort has been made to include a plentiful supply of worked examples, together with appropriate exercises, ranging in difficulty from the straightforward to the challenging.

When one goes fellwalking, the most breathtaking views require some expenditure of effort in order to gain access to them: nevertheless, the peak is more likely to be reached if a gentle and interesting route is chosen. The mathematical peaks attainable in these books are every bit as exhilarating, the paths are as gentle as we could find, and the interest and expectation are maintained throughout to prevent the spirits from flagging on the journey.

Lancaster, 1987

David A. Towers
Consultant Editor

PREFACE

Many students in higher education will be experiencing courses in mechanics for the first time or may have found the option of mechanics difficult when it was studied as part of an A-level mathematics course. In recognition of these factors, this text progresses at a gentle pace and requires no previous knowledge of mechanics. The approach adopted throughout is to motivate particular areas of mechanics through the reflection of real-life problems and practical activities. The amount of algebraic manipulation required at any stage is kept to a minimum, which we feel will allow students to work with the mechanics concepts with greater confidence. This type of approach will go some way to accommodating the changes that have occurred in the teaching of mathematics in schools in GCSE courses and at A-level.

The number of students who have studied mechanics at school or in further education has decreased in the past few years with the introduction of other options at A-level. For those who have studied mechanics before, we feel confident that the approach we have adopted will offer a refreshing contrast to their experience of older texts.

In writing this book, we have had to take the decision to omit any study of rigid body mechanics, so that the text would be short but still accommodate a range of courses in higher education. The course of study here is based on particle mechanics, which we feel will establish a sound foundation for the later study of rigid body mechanics.

As with other guides in this series, this text is suitable for self-study. Answers to exercises are provided, as well as hints on how to solve the more demanding problems.

P.D. & R.W.

1 KINEMATICS

1.1 INTRODUCTION

The study of the motion of bodies requires a structured understanding of the fundamental quantities of displacement and time. This study is called *kinematics* and it will provide a basis for later modelling in other branches of mechanics. From time and displacement, we derive the quantities velocity and acceleration. All of these, with the exception of time, are vector quantities and can be expressed in an algebraic vector form. Not surprisingly, therefore, the study of vectors is crucial to the study of kinematics and all mechanics.

We shall start our study by considering some kinematic quantities with which you may already be familiar. Everyday language provides us with an intuitive comprehension of these quantities, but in some cases can lead to serious misunderstanding, particularly when considering vectors.

When a car is travelling along a road, and the speedometer reads an unchanging 30 km per hour, the driver naturally assumes that the speed is constant. The fact is that if the car is cornering, or going down or climbing up a hill, it *is* accelerating despite the constant speed shown on the speedometer. In the following section, we begin to establish the concepts of displacement, velocity and acceleration. In particular, we clarify the distinction between speed and velocity, often used as synonyms by non-mathematicians, and the cause of the apparent contradiction of the accelerating car with its constant speedometer reading.

1.2 DEFINITION OF KINEMATIC QUANTITIES

The following formal definitions of displacement, distance, velocity, speed and acceleration should help us to make a start in overcoming the aforementioned misconceptions.

Consider the fixed points P and Q, illustrated in Figure 1.1. The

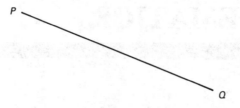

Fig. 1.1

displacement from P to Q represented by the vector **PQ** = **s** is the translation that is needed to move the point P to the point Q. The inverse of this operation, the displacement from Q to P, is represented by the vector **QP**. Thus:

$$\mathbf{QP} = -\mathbf{PQ}$$

The magnitude of the displacement from P to Q is the distance PQ and the orientation of the line segment PQ is its direction. It follows, therefore, that the displacement from Q to P has equal magnitude but that its direction differs by π radians or 180°. Displacement clearly satisfies the requirements of a vector in having both magnitude and direction. Displacement vectors must of course obey the law of vector addition. Thus, as illustrated in Figure 1.2, the displacement **PQ** + **QR** is equivalent to the displacement **PR** and so we can write:

$$\mathbf{PQ} + \mathbf{QR} = \mathbf{PR}$$

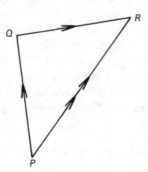

Fig. 1.2

The *velocity*, **v**, of a body is the rate of change of its displacement with respect to time. Using the notation of calculus, we have that:

$$v = \frac{dx}{dt}$$

As velocity depends on displacement, then velocity is a derived vector and has a dependent magnitude and direction. The magnitude of velocity is *speed*. Speed, a scalar, is thus not dependent on direction.

The *acceleration*, **a**, of a body is the rate of change of its velocity with respect to time. Again, calculus notation gives:

$$\mathbf{a} = \frac{d\mathbf{v}}{dt} = \frac{d^2\mathbf{x}}{dt^2}$$

Acceleration is derived from a vector so it must be a vector itself, possessing both magnitude and direction.

Acceleration is the most difficult concept to appreciate intuitively. It can be non-zero when the speed of a body is unchanged but the direction of motion varies. There are numerous examples of motion with constant speed but non-zero acceleration and some will be discussed in later chapters. In Figure 1.3, which illustrates the process of cornering with constant speed, the velocities of motion at points P and Q, which occur at a one-second interval, are given as $\mathbf{v}_1$ and $\mathbf{v}_2$. Note that $\mathbf{v}_1 \neq \mathbf{v}_2$.

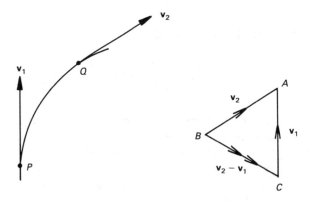

Fig. 1.3

Figure 1.3 also shows the vector triangle for $\mathbf{v}_2 - \mathbf{v}_1$. The triangle ABC formed is isosceles as $|\mathbf{v}_1| = |\mathbf{v}_2|$. The acceleration over the one-second interval is $\mathbf{v}_2 - \mathbf{v}_1$, the direction BC represents the direction of this acceleration and the length BC is its magnitude, which is non-zero. Note that the direction of the acceleration is not the same direction as $\mathbf{v}_1$ or $\mathbf{v}_2$.

Our first consideration will be the study of one-dimensional models of motion. The understanding that is developed from this study can then be easily rendered to two and three dimensions, using vector notation, with the algebra unchanged. This is an important advantage of using vector notation in mechanics.

1.3 ONE-DIMENSIONAL MODELS

The special case of motion in a straight line is a usual starting point for the study of kinematics. Examples are the motion of a body falling vertically under gravity or that of a particle attached to a spring lying on a smooth horizontal table.

Although we still maintain our vector approach, we can see that all quantities can be expressed as negative and positive values along the direction of motion, the x-axis say, represented by the unit vector $\mathbf{i}$. The position vector $\mathbf{r}$ with respect to the origin, at time t, is:

$$\mathbf{r} = x(t)\mathbf{i}$$

The velocity vector is then:

$$\frac{\mathrm{d}\mathbf{r}}{\mathrm{d}t} = \frac{\mathrm{d}x}{\mathrm{d}t}\mathbf{i} = \dot{x}\mathbf{i}$$

The acceleration vector is similarly represented as:

$$\frac{\mathrm{d}^2\mathbf{r}}{\mathrm{d}t^2} = \frac{\mathrm{d}^2x}{\mathrm{d}t^2}\mathbf{i} = \ddot{x}\mathbf{i}$$

It is usual for the vector formulation in terms of $\mathbf{i}$ to be omitted and for the direction to be represented by a $+$ or $-$ sign. The following definitions will apply: Given that the displacement of a body from the origin at time t is $x(t)$ in a given direction, then velocity, v, is $\dot{x}(t)$ and the acceleration, a, is $\ddot{x}(t)$ or $\dot{v}$. (Note that, in one dimension, it is not necessary to use bold face for vectors as there is no ambiguity.)

1.4 GRAPHICAL REPRESENTATION

It is common practice to express one-dimensional motion in graphical form. Consider the following simple example.

Two cars A and B are moving at constant speeds in the same direction along parallel straight traffic lanes. Car A has a speed of 10 ms^{-1}. Car B has a speed of 12 ms^{-1} and passes an observer 2 s after A. At what time and at

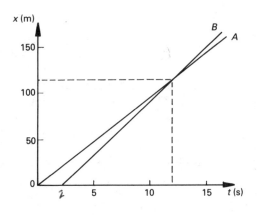

Fig. 1.4

what distance from the observer will car *B* overtake car *A*?

The solution of problems of this type shows the value of representing journeys in a graphical form. For example, Figure 1.4 shows the journeys for both *A* and *B*. The origin *O* (*t* = 0) is taken to be the point when *A* passes the observer. The point of intersection of the two straight lines represents the time and place when *A* and *B* meet. Accurate drawing of the figure will lead to the correct solution; the time is 12 s after car *A* passes the observer, and the distance is 120 m away from the observer.

This type of diagram, called a *displacement–time graph*, can be used to determine timing and scheduling of events, and is thus valuable in creating timetables. It provides direct pictorial representation of journeys and events. It should be noted that the gradient of each curve, represented by $\dot{x}$, is the velocity, where negative gradients represent reverse motion. In cases like the one shown in Figure 1.4, where the speed is constant, the graphs are straight lines.

Mathematically, the *velocity–time curve* is a more rewarding graphical representation of the journey of a body in a straight line. Consider the following example of a train journey from Leicester to Nottingham, which for our purposes has been divided into five parts *A*, *B*, *C*, *D* and *E*. The motion can be assumed to be a straight line. Note that the gradient at any point on these curves is a measure of the acceleration of the train at that instant, and the area below the curve is the distance travelled.

The journey is represented by the velocity–time curve in Figure 1.5:

A: Starting from rest, the train travels with constant acceleration for the first 10 minutes of the journey.

B: It then moves with constant velocity of 70 kmh⁻¹ (that is, its acceleration is zero) for 40 minutes.

5

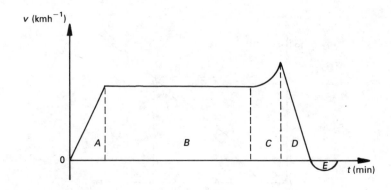

Fig. 1.5

C: The train undergoes non-uniform acceleration for 5 minutes, reaching a maximum speed of 100 kmh⁻¹.

D: Braking results in a constant retardation from its speed of 100 kmh⁻¹ but this results in the train overshooting the station.

E: Having first come to rest, it then reverses into the station, achieving a maximum reversing velocity of 10 kmh⁻¹. This time it comes to rest at the platform.

The interpretation of this type of graph is not as easy as it was for displacement–time graphs. You may find it helpful to consider other journeys that you have experienced in the same way. A journey across a busy town is clearly a highly complex version of this example. You will find it constructive to try to develop a velocity–time graph for such a journey.

It should be noted that in velocity–time graphs the acceleration is represented by the gradient of the curve. Negative gradients represent retardations. Constant accelerations are represented by straight lines.

Example 1.4

A body moves along a straight line with an initial velocity of 5 ms⁻¹. It then accelerates at 7 ms⁻² for a certain period. For the next 10 s, it has a retardation of 1 ms⁻². The total distance travelled during the motion is 450.0 m. Find the length of time for which the body has an acceleration of 7 ms⁻².

Solution Figure 1.6 shows a sketch of the velocity–time graph for the completed journey. For the purpose of our analysis, the journey has been divided into three parts A, B and C. The velocity at the end of A is u and at

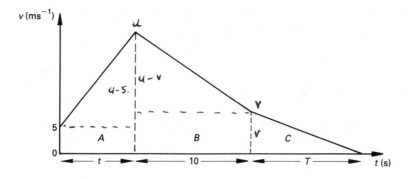

Fig. 1.6

the end of B is v. The times of the first and last periods of acceleration are t and T respectively.

Using the fact that acceleration is represented by the gradient of the curve, we can write:

$$7 = \frac{u - 5}{t} \quad \text{for } A$$

$$-4 = \frac{v - u}{10} \quad \text{for } B$$

$$-1 = \frac{-v}{T} \quad \text{for } C$$

Solution of these equations for u, v and T in terms of t gives:

$$u = 7t + 5 \qquad v = T = 7t - 35$$

Using the fact that total distance travelled equals the area under the graph for the completed journey, we obtain:

$$450.5 = \frac{1}{2}(u + 5)t + \frac{1}{2}(u + v)10 + \frac{1}{2}vT$$

Substituting for u and v gives:

$$0 = 56t^2 - 340t + 24$$

and by factorising we see that:

$$0 = 4(14t - 1)(t - 6)$$

7

The solution $t = 1/14$ gives $T < 0$, so this can be disregarded. The time of the initial acceleration is therefore 6 s.

EXERCISES 1.4

1 Describe, in words, the motion illustrated in the displacement–time graph shown in Figure 1.7.

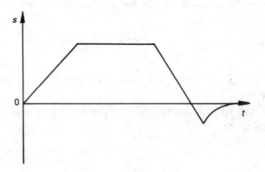

Fig. 1.7

2 Figure 1.8 shows the velocity–time graphs for the motion of four different bodies. Describe what might be happening in each case and, for each one, sketch the corresponding displacement–time curve.

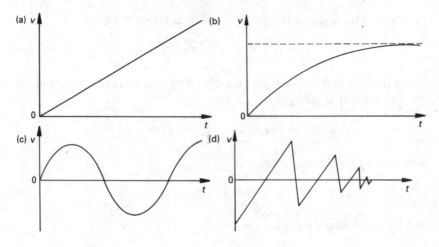

Fig. 1.8

3 A hovercraft crosses the English Channel, a distance of 52 km, in a time of 40 minutes. It is capable of a top cruising speed of 80 kmh⁻¹. Choose the velocity–time curve from those shown in Figure 1.9 that best illustrates the journey, explaining your choice and completing the scales on both axes.

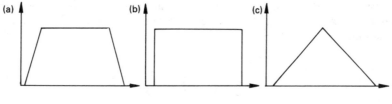

Fig. 1.9

4 A tube train travels a distance of 432 m, starting and finishing at rest, in 1 minute. It first accelerates at $1/3$ ms⁻², then travels with constant velocity and finally retards at 1 ms⁻². Find the time taken in each of the three stages of the journey.

5 Two cars start to move from a point on a road. Car A starts first, from rest, and moves with a constant acceleration of 3 ms⁻². Two seconds later, car B starts and maintains a uniform velocity of 16 ms⁻¹. Show that the cars will be level twice and find the time during which car B leads car A.

1.5. CALCULUS AND RATES OF CHANGE

Let us consider the relationship:

$$\frac{dx}{dt} = v$$

where v is written as a function of t. To find x in terms of t, we simply integrate both sides to give:

$$x = \int v \, dt$$

Clearly, the indefinite integration here results in the introduction of an arbitrary constant. This constant is evaluated by knowing the value of x for some t.

If we require the distance travelled in the time interval $a \leqslant t \leqslant b$, we can

9

find this, its value being that of the definite integral:

$$\int_a^b v \, dt$$

It should be noted that if v changes sign, the integral over the whole range does not represent the actual distance travelled. The value of the area is the distance, but the process of integration means that areas below the t-axis are negative and will be subtracted from those areas above the t-axis.

A similar approach for:

$$\frac{dv}{dt} = a$$

where a, the acceleration, is a function of t, leads to a solution for velocity, v, in terms of t given by:

$$v = \int a \, dt$$

Alternatively, considering a as a function of x, we can write:

$$\frac{dv}{dt} = v \frac{dv}{dx}$$

This gives a solution for the velocity, this time in terms of x, as:

$$\frac{1}{2}v^2 = \int a \, dx$$

Examples 1.5

1. The velocity, v, of a body moving along a straight line at time t is given by:

$$v = 3t^2 - 2t + 3$$

Find (a) the initial acceleration and (b) the displacement when $t = 2$ if the displacement is 5 m when $t = 1$.

Solution
(a) acceleration $= \dfrac{dv}{dt} = 6t - 2$

When $t = 0$ the acceleration is -2 ms^{-2}.

(b) displacement $= x = \int v \, dt = t^3 - t^2 + 3t + c$ $(c = \text{constant})$

When $t = 1$, $x = 5$ and $5 = (1)^3 - (1)^2 + 3(1) + c$. This gives $c = 3$; so when $t = 2$ we have:

$$x = (2)^3 - (2)^2 + 3(2) + 3 = 11$$

The displacement is thus 11 m.

2. The acceleration of a block on a table when attached to a spring is given by:

$$a = 5 - 10x$$

where x is the block's distance from the spring's fixed end ($x = 0$). If, at the start of the motion, $x = 0$ and the velocity is then $\sqrt{20}$ ms⁻¹, find the distance of the block from the spring's fixed end when the block is first at rest.

Solution   As suggested, we express the acceleration as:

$$v \frac{dv}{dx} = 5 - 10x \qquad (1)$$

Integration then gives:

$$\frac{1}{2}v^2 = 5x - 5x^2 + c \qquad (c = \text{constant}) \qquad (2)$$

When $x = 0$, we are given that $v = \sqrt{20}$, whence:

$$10 = 0 - 0 + c \quad \text{or} \quad c = 10$$

When the block is at rest, $v = 0$. Thus, equation (2) becomes:

$$0 = 5x - 5x^2 + 10$$
$$0 = 5(x - 2)(x + 1)$$

The solution $x = -1$ is not feasible as the block must stay on one side of the origin; hence, the block first comes to rest at $x = 2$ m.

EXERCISES 1.5

1 The acceleration, a ms^{-2}, of a particle moving in a straight line is $a = 7 - 2t$, where t is the time in seconds. If the velocity, v, is 12 ms^{-1} when $t = 2$, then calculate:

(a) the time when $a = 3$ ms^{-2};
(b) v in terms of t;
(c) the maximum velocity;
(d) the distance travelled in the first second.

2 A body is x metres from a point after t seconds where $x = t^{-2}$. Find the speed and acceleration of the body after 2 s.

3 A body starts from A and its displacement from A after a time t seconds is given by $x = 2t^3 - 5t^2 + 20t + 4$. Find the acceleration when the velocity of the body is 24 ms^{-1}. What will be the body's displacement from A when the velocity is 24 ms^{-1}?

4 The acceleration of a body is given by $a = x\sqrt{(4 - x^2)}$, where x represents the body's displacement from its starting position O. If, at the start of the body's motion, its velocity is 2 ms^{-1}, find:

(a) v in terms of x;
(b) the distance of the body from O when at rest;
(c) the maximum velocity of the body.

1.6 CONSTANT ACCELERATION

Constant acceleration is a special case of motion. It rarely occurs in real problems, as we will find when we look at resistance models in later chapters. As a guide, it is best to consider acceleration to be non-constant, unless we have evidence or justification to the contrary.

It is usual to derive three equations to model motion with constant acceleration. A simple example of such motion with constant acceleration is illustrated in the velocity–time graph in Figure 1.10. This allows us to derive three constant acceleration formulae.

If the acceleration, a, has a constant value a_0, then we have:

$$\frac{dv}{dt} = a_0$$

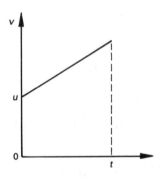

Fig. 1.10

Solution of this equation gives $v = a_0 t + c$, where c is a constant. It is usual to define the initial velocity as u. Thus, when $t = 0$, $v = u$, and this gives:

$$v = u + a_0 t \tag{3}$$

The displacement, s, is then given by a second integration as:

$$s = ut + \frac{1}{2}a_0 t^2 + \text{constant}$$

It is usual to take an origin such that the displacement, s, at time $t = 0$ is zero to give:

$$s = ut + \frac{1}{2}a_0 t^2 \tag{4}$$

(Note that s replaces the usual notation for displacement, x, in the constant acceleration formulae.)

A third equation giving the velocity, v, as a function of displacement, s, can be obtained by eliminating t from equations (3) and (4). The same equation can also be derived using integration, by considering a_0 to be a function of s:

$$\frac{1}{2}v^2 = a_0 s + \text{constant}$$

Together with the condition that $v = u$ when $s = 0$, this gives:

$$v^2 = u^2 + 2a_0 s \tag{5}$$

Equations (3), (4) and (5) are usually termed the constant acceleration formulae. The notation is standard, except that f is often used for acceleration.

All three equations can also be obtained easily from the geometry of the velocity–time curve in Figure 1.10, as follows.

13

Using the fact that acceleration is the gradient of the velocity–time graph gives:

$$a_0 = \frac{v - u}{t}$$

This is equation (3).

Using the fact that displacement is the area under the velocity–time graph gives:

$$s = \frac{1}{2}(u + v)t$$

This is also obtained by eliminating a_0 between equations (3) and (5).

Example 1.6

The driver of a car is approaching a set of traffic lights. When he is 50 m away from them and travelling with a speed of 72 kmh^{-1}, he notices they are red. He immediately applies the brakes. If the maximum retardation that his brakes can create is 1.5 ms^{-2}, can the car come to rest before it arrives at the lights?

Solution   The car comes to rest if its final velocity, v, is zero, and we shall assume that the retardation is constant at -1.5 ms^{-1}. Given that the acceleration is constant, we can apply equations (3), (4) and (5) with $v = 0$, $a_0 = -1.5$ and $u = 72$ kmh^{-1} or 20 ms^{-1} to find s.

The equation that links these quantities is equation (4). Thus, inserting the values for u, v and a_0 gives:

$$0 = 20^2 + 2(-1.5)s$$

Hence, $s = 133.3$ m. Clearly, the car does not come to rest in time.

EXERCISES 1.6

1 The brakes of a train are able to produce a retardation of 1.5 ms^{-2}. The train is approaching a station and is scheduled to stop at a platform there. How far away from the station must the train apply its brakes if it is travelling at 100 kmh^{-1}? If the brakes are applied 50 m beyond this point, at what speed will the train enter the station?

2 A ball is projected vertically downwards and describes 100 m in the

tenth second of its motion. Calculate its velocity of projection if its acceleration can be assumed to be 10 ms^{-2}.

3 A train P sets off from a station A and travels directly towards a station B, accelerating uniformly at 2 ms^{-2}. At the same time, a second train Q is passing through station B, travelling towards station A, with uniform speed 30 ms^{-1}. After what time will the trains meet if the stations are 4 km apart?

The trains meet at C. Determine the acceleration required by Q at C in order for it to arrive at station A at the same time that P arrives at station B.

4 Two trains A and B are standing in a station on adjacent tracks ready to leave in opposite directions. A man is sitting in train A opposite the engine of train B. Both trains start to move: A accelerates uniformly to a speed of 72 kmh^{-1} in 200 m; B accelerates uniformly to a speed of 54 kmh^{-1} in 50 s. If the man notes that it takes 15 s before the end of train B passes him, how long is train B?

5 A relay runner running at a speed u begins to slow down at the constant rate of a when approaching her team mate, who is at rest. Her team mate sets off with acceleration b. What is the greatest distance that can separate them at the time the team mate starts if they are to exchange the baton? (Assume that the two runners meet in order to exchange the baton.)

1.7 CONCLUSIONS FROM EXPERIMENTAL DATA

Experimentation allows us to test the mathematical models we use in mechanics against what can be expected in practice. This process is called *validation*. Involvement in experimental work is an integral part of the study of kinematics. It allows models to assume greater purpose. The following example is an experimental test for uniform acceleration.

Example 1.7

The following table gives the results obtained from an experiment. Here s represents the vertical distance upwards from the observer, in metres, of a body after a time t in seconds.

t	0	1	2	3	4
s	2.0	3.5	4.0	−2.5	−22.0

Is this data consistent with uniform acceleration?

Solution   If we look at the results graphically, we obtain the displacement–time graph shown in Figure 1.11(a). Estimating gradients at the times given leads to the velocity–time graph shown in Figure 1.11(b).

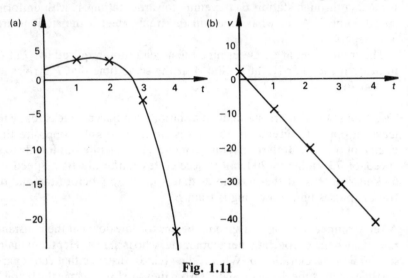

Fig. 1.11

It appears clear from our estimates that the data is the result of uniform acceleration. Estimation of the acceleration from the velocity–time graph confirms this.

An alternative approach to this same problem is to assume that the data is a result of uniform acceleration and to seek a contradiction. We write:

$$s = s_0 + ut + \frac{1}{2}at^2$$

where s_0, u and a are constants that must be determined from the data. The fact that $s_0 = 2.0$ follows immediately from the value of s at $t = 0$ and we are then required to find unique solutions for u and a from the other values. This results in our solving simultaneous equations in unknowns. Note that at least four sets of values of s and t are required to confirm constant acceleration for this particular time interval.

It is possible to adopt a similar approach when the experimental data consists of pairs of values of the velocity, v, and the distance, s, from the observer.

In the following table, we have used our estimate of the gradients of the graph in Figure 1.12(a) to determine the acceleration using the relation:

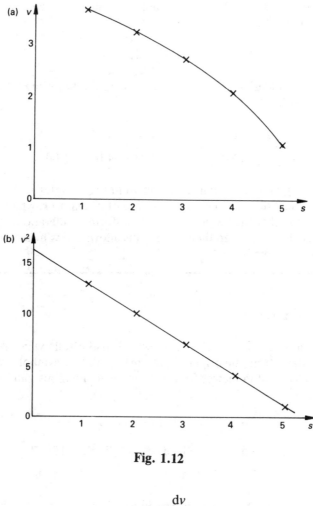

Fig. 1.12

$$a = v \frac{dv}{ds}$$

s	1	2	3	4	5
v	3.61	3.16	2.65	2.00	1.00
$\dfrac{dv}{dt}$	−0.42	−0.47	−0.57	−0.75	−1.50
a	−1.5	−1.5	−1.5	−1.5	−1.5

To a degree of accuracy of one decimal place, this appears to confirm that the data is consistent with constant acceleration.

17

Alternatively, as before, if we are able to assume uniform acceleration so that equation (5):

$$v^2 = u^2 + 2as$$

is valid, then tabulating values of v^2 and s as in the following table should give a straight line.

s	1	2	3	4	5
v^2	13.0	9.99	7.02	4.00	1.00

The resulting graph of v^2 against s is shown in Figure 1.12(b). We see that the graph indeed shows a linear relationship of v^2 against s, which confirms our assumption that the motion is due to uniform acceleration. It cuts the vertical axis at u^2 and its gradient is $2a$. This allows the values of a and u to be determined directly.

EXERCISES 1.7

1 The motion of two particles is described in the following table. Each particle starts from the origin, O, at time $t = 0$. The symbol s represents the displacement in metres from O, v the velocity in ms^{-1} and t the time in seconds.

	Particle 1					Particle 2			
v	−2.5	−2	−1	1	s	7	15	15	7
t	1	2	4	8	t	1	3	5	7

Confirm that each particle is moving with constant acceleration and determine the acceleration and initial velocity of both particles.

2 A car starts from rest and covers s metres in t seconds. The following table represents the motion of the car for the first 8 s.

t	1	2	3	4	5	6	7	8
s	4	11	21	34	50	69	91	116

Plot the displacement–time graph and from it plot the velocity–time graph for values of t as described in the table. Is the data consistent with constant acceleration?

1.8 TWO- AND THREE-DIMENSIONAL MODELS

Many of the comments made here apply to all vectors but we will use velocity as our example of a vector.

From the definition of a vector quantity, the velocity of a body can be represented simply as a directed line segment, its magnitude being proportional to its length and its orientation representing the direction. This allows velocities of 30 ms^{-1} north, 20 ms^{-1} on a bearing of 120°, 40 ms^{-1} SW and 25 ms^{-1} on a bearing of 320° to be represented as shown in Figure 1.13. Note that the north direction here has been defined by the direction allocated to the first case; all other directions have then been measured relative to it. It is just as easy to relate the velocities of, for example, football players on a field of play to the direction of play.

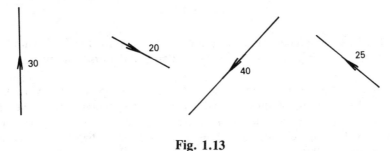

Fig. 1.13

Similarly, an acceleration of 2 ms^{-2} NW or a displacement of 10 m on a bearing of 80° can be represented as line segments as shown in Figure 1.14.

Fig. 1.14

Any vector quantity, as well as having magnitude and direction, will also satisfy the triangle law of addition, which was illustrated earlier. Using velocity, we can consider the following examples of the triangle law.

Examples 1.8.1

1. An airplane wishes to fly north in a wind whose speed is 50 kmh^{-1} from

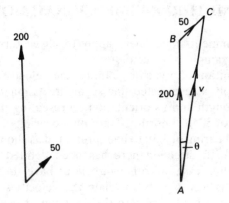

Fig. 1.15

the SW. If the plane's engines create a forward velocity of 200 kmh⁻¹ in still air, what happens to the plane if it steers a course due north?

Solution Figure 1.15 shows the velocities of the plane and wind and also the addition of these velocities using the triangle law of vector addition. The velocity that results, from the addition of the plane and wind velocities, is represented in magnitude and direction as a line segment parallel to and equal in length to AC. It is possible to determine the magnitude of the resulting velocity, v $(= AC)$, and its direction, θ, approximately by scale drawing. However, it is best done by calculation, because greater accuracy is obtained. Simple use of the sine and cosine rules gives:

$$v^2 = 50^2 + 200^2 - 2 \times 50 \times 200 \times \cos 45°$$

$$v = 238.0 \text{ kmh}^{-1}$$

and:

$$\frac{50}{\sin \theta} = \frac{238.0}{\sin 135°}$$

$$\theta = 8.5°$$

The result is that the plane will follow a course of 8.5° with speed 238.0 kmh⁻¹.

2. The pilot in our example needs to find the direction that she should steer to travel north.

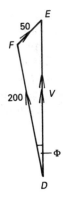

Fig. 1.16

Solution The velocities are shown in Figure 1.16. In this case, the combined effects of the wind and plane velocities must be V, as shown in Figure 1.16. The magnitude of V (= DE) can be found, but more important for the pilot, the angle Φ will tell her the direction that she must travel. The calculation involves the repeated use of the sine rule:

$$\frac{\sin \Phi}{50} = \frac{\sin 45°}{200}$$

$$\Phi = 10.2°$$

and:

$$\frac{V}{\sin 124.8°} = \frac{200}{\sin 45°}$$

$$V = 232.3 \text{ kmh}^{-1}$$

The pilot must steer a course of 349.8° and completes her journey at a speed of 232.3 kmh⁻¹. In this case, the wind has assisted her on her journey and she can predict an earlier than expected arrival time.

Observers at an airport may reflect on the time discrepancies between outward and return journeys on flights (not just due to crossing time zones!). This is a consequence of the effect just considered. They may also notice that, during take-off in a high wind, an aircraft appears not to be steering in the direction of travel. To an observer on the ground, it will usually travel in a crab-like motion across the sky. This is also predicted by our model example. These problems are called *relative* velocity problems. In the example, the velocity of the plane relative to the air in which it travels was used to find its true velocity for a given wind speed. Other sources for relative velocity problems are: swimmers in fast flowing rivers; the direction of steam from a moving train; wind assistance in athletics events; the direction assumed by the sail of a yacht.

EXERCISES 1.8

1   A swimmer who can swim at a speed of 5 ms⁻¹ in the still water of a swimming pool needs to cross a river whose width is 20 m. The river flows at 3 ms⁻¹ and she sets off directly across the river. Find the time it takes her to cross and the distance she drifts down the river while crossing. What direction would she need to set off in if she is to cross the river directly? Why is it not possible for her to cross the river directly if it flows at a speed greater than 5 ms⁻¹?

2   The time taken for an airplane to fly between two cities A and B, a distance of 600 km, is about 2.5 h when the plane steers a course of 30° to AB. If the plane's speed in still air is 250 kmh⁻¹, find the direction it must steer and the time taken to do the return journey.

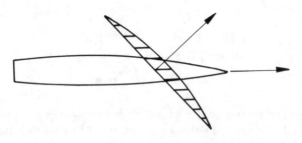

Fig. 1.17

3   On a sailing boat, the direction set by the sail is that of the velocity of the wind relative to the boat, as illustrated in Figure 1.17. The sail is set at an angle of 45° to the boat's motion and an observer on the shore measures the boat's speed to be 6 ms⁻¹. Find the wind speed if its direction, shown from flags on the shore, is at 30° to the boat's motion.

1.9 RESOLUTION OF VECTORS

The triangle law of addition that we have already discussed can also lead to a procedure for the resolution of vectors. In the previous section, we combined the component velocities of the wind and the plane in still air to find the resultant true velocity. An alternative viewpoint is to consider velocities in their component parts, which will be our aim here. In later problems, involving any vector quantity, you may find that much of the algebraic manipulation is removed by adopting this process.

It is common practice, in all branches of mechanics, to consider the resolution of the vector quantities using vector addition in a right-angled triangle. In Figure 1.18, we consider a velocity of 20 ms^{-1} in a direction of 60° represented by OP, so that OA is in an eastwards direction and AP a northwards direction. This gives the velocities represented by OA and AP as components of the original velocity. In this case, we say that they are resolved components, the triangle OAP being right-angled.

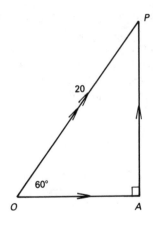

Fig. 1.18

The original velocity is equivalent to the velocity represented by OA, together with the velocity represented by AP. These resolved components are:

$$20 \cos 30° = 17.32 \text{ ms}^{-1} \text{ east} \quad \text{and} \quad 20 \sin 30° = 10.00 \text{ ms}^{-1} \text{ north}$$

It is convenient, and standard notation, to introduce unit vectors **i** and **j** defined in the east and north directions respectively. These allow a velocity of 20 ms^{-1} in the direction of 60° to be written as:

$$17.32\mathbf{i} + 10.00\mathbf{j}$$

23

EXERCISES 1.9

1 Using **i** and **j** component unit vectors in the east and north directions, represent the following velocities in vector form:

(a) 40 kmh^{-1}, 45°; (b) 12 ms^{-1}, 300°;
(c) 20 ms^{-1}, east; (d) 5 kmh^{-1}, SW.

2 If **i** and **j** are defined as in exercise 1.9.1, find the magnitude and direction of the velocities represented by:

(a) 50**i**; (b) 12**i** − 9**j**; (c) −10**i** + 10**j**; (d) −12**j**.

1.10 TWO-DIMENSIONAL PARAMETRIC MOTION

It is possible to examine many of the two-dimensional (2D) vector concepts of kinematics easily using a micro's graphics mode and the motion of its cursor. Position on a micro's screen requires the use of a Cartesian coordinate system and, as a result, it is not surprising to find **i** and **j** component vectors being easily adapted for use.

If, for example, we consider the motion of a cursor whose position vector for time $t \geq 0$ is:

$$\mathbf{r} = 2t\mathbf{i} - 2t^2\mathbf{j}$$

then simulation of the cursor's motion describes the path as illustrated in Figure 1.19. The velocity vector of the cursor is given by:

$$\mathbf{v} = \frac{d\mathbf{r}}{dt} = 2\mathbf{i} - 4t\mathbf{j}$$

Note that differentiation has been carried out term by term for each of the **i** and **j** components. A second differentiation gives the acceleration as a constant vector:

$$\mathbf{a} = \frac{d\mathbf{v}}{dt} = -4\mathbf{j}$$

In general, for a body whose position vector is described by the vector:

$$\mathbf{r}(t) = x(t)\mathbf{i} + y(t)\mathbf{j}$$

24

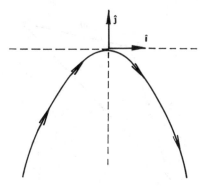

Fig. 1.19

the velocity vector is:

$$\mathbf{v} = \frac{d\mathbf{r}}{dt} = \frac{dx}{dt}\,\mathbf{i} + \frac{dy}{dt}\,\mathbf{j}$$

and the acceleration vector is:

$$\mathbf{a} = \frac{d^2\mathbf{r}}{dt^2} = \frac{d^2x}{dt^2}\,\mathbf{i} + \frac{d^2y}{dt^2}\,\mathbf{j}$$

The direction of the velocity vector relative to the x-axis is given as:

$$\tan^{-1}\left(\frac{dy}{dt}\bigg/\frac{dx}{dt}\right) = \tan^{-1}\left(\frac{dy}{dx}\right)$$

This is just the direction of the tangent at that point of the path. We conclude that the velocity of a body at any instant is along the tangent to its path at that point. The magnitude of its velocity is given by:

$$\left[\left(\frac{dx}{dt}\right)^2 + \left(\frac{dy}{dt}\right)^2\right]^{1/2}$$

Consider a ship at a point A whose vector position is $\mathbf{a}$ at time $t = 0$. If the constant velocity vector of the ship is $\mathbf{u}$, then Figure 1.20 shows the position P of the ship at subsequent times when $t > 0$. The position vector of the ship at time t is, as a result, given by:

$$\mathbf{r} = \mathbf{a} + t\mathbf{u}$$

25

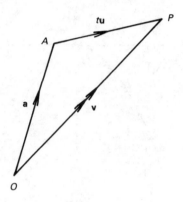

Fig. 1.20

This is the vector equation of a straight line passing through A in a direction $\mathbf{u}$. Expressing the position in terms of the parameter t can help in the solution of many problems. For example, the closest approach (the position when they are nearest) of two bodies, travelling with a constant velocity, can easily be studied using this vector formulation.

Examples 1.10

1. Two ships P and Q sail at the same time from ports A and B respectively. Port B is 25 km due north of A. If the ship P sails with a velocity of 10 kmh⁻¹ on a bearing of 30° and ship Q sails with a velocity of 10 kmh⁻¹ due east, find:

   (a) after what time they are closest to each other;
   (b) their distance of closest approach;
   (c) the bearing of Q from P at this time.

   Solution If we take port A as the origin of coordinates, then the positions of P and Q, after a further t hours, will be given by:

   $$\mathbf{r}_P = (10 \sin 30°\mathbf{i} + 10 \cos 30°\mathbf{j})t \quad \text{and} \quad \mathbf{r}_Q = 10t\mathbf{i} + 25\mathbf{j}$$

   (Figure 1.21). This gives the position vector of Q relative to P at time t as:

   $$\mathbf{r}_Q - \mathbf{r}_P = 5t\mathbf{i} + (25 - 5\sqrt{3}t)\mathbf{j}$$

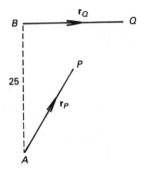

Fig. 1.21

The distance, D, between P and Q at time t is given by the magnitude of this vector and its direction represents the bearing of Q from P:

$$D^2 = (25 - 5\sqrt{3}t)^2 + (5t)^2 = 625 - 250\sqrt{3}t + 100t^2$$

(a) This quadratic function has a minimum value when $t = 5\sqrt{3}/4$, which gives the time of closest approach after 2.165 h or 2 h 9 minutes 54 s.

(b) The distance of closest approach is then given by substituting this value of t in the equation for D^2 to give:

$$D^2 = \frac{625}{4}$$

$$D = 12.5 \text{ km}$$

The distance of closest approach is thus 12.5 km.

(c) The vector position of Q relative to P is then:

$$\mathbf{r}_Q - \mathbf{r}_P = 6.25\sqrt{3}\mathbf{i} + 6.25\mathbf{j}$$

The bearing of Q from P at closest approach is then:

$$\tan^{-1}(\sqrt{3}) = 60° \text{ W of S}$$

An alternative solution of this problem is achieved by drawing a relative velocity diagram. We proceed as in Figure 1.22 for both the ships

27

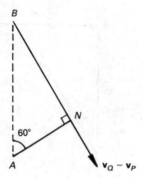

Fig. 1.22

motion relative to the ship P. The velocities of the ships are:

$$\mathbf{v}_P = 10\mathbf{i} \quad \text{and} \quad \mathbf{v}_Q = 5\mathbf{i} + 5\sqrt{3}\mathbf{j}$$

so that:

$$\mathbf{v}_Q - \mathbf{v}_P = 5\mathbf{i} - 5\sqrt{3}\mathbf{j}$$

This velocity has a bearing of 150° and its magnitude is 10 kmh⁻¹. The closest approach is represented by the distance:

$$AN = 25 \cos 60° = 12.5 \text{ km}$$

2. A ship sails from a port with a velocity of 10 kmh⁻¹ due north out to sea. At the same time, a customs patrol boat, at sea 50 km due east of the port, is radioed and instructed to intercept it. If the patrol boat travels at its top speed of 15 kmh⁻¹, what course must it steer to intercept the ship as soon as possible? Can the patrol boat intercept the ship before it enters international waters, 50 km from port?

Solution If we define the direction of travel of the patrol boat to be $\theta°$ W of north, then the velocities of the ship and patrol boat can be illustrated as in Figure 1.23. Using **i** and **j** unit vectors, the velocities of the ship and patrol boat can be written as:

$$\mathbf{v}_s = 10\mathbf{j} \quad \text{and} \quad \mathbf{v}_P = -15 \sin \theta\mathbf{i} + 15 \cos \theta\mathbf{j}$$

The velocity of the patrol boat relative to the ship is given by:

$$\mathbf{v}_P - \mathbf{v}_s = -15 \sin \theta\mathbf{i} + (15 \cos \theta - 10)\mathbf{j}$$

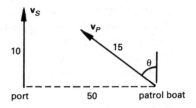

Fig. 1.23

For interception, this velocity relative to the ship must be eastwards, towards the ship. This can only happen if the **j** component of the relative velocity is zero, which requires that $\cos \theta = 2/3$, that is $\theta = 48.2°$. The patrol boat thus steers a course N 48.2° W to intercept the ship.

The distance to sea of the ship at the time of interception is:

$$\frac{50}{\tan \theta} = 44.72 \text{ km}$$

The ship will, as a result, be intercepted before it reaches international waters.

EXERCISES 1.10

1 With distances measured in nautical miles and velocities measured in knots, three ships A, B and C are observed from a coastguard station. At noon, they have the following position and velocity vectors relative to the station:

$$\mathbf{r}_A = -\mathbf{i} + \mathbf{j} \qquad \mathbf{v}_A = \mathbf{i} + \mathbf{j}$$
$$\mathbf{r}_B = -3\mathbf{i} + 4\mathbf{j} \qquad \mathbf{v}_B = 2\mathbf{i}$$
$$\mathbf{r}_C = 9\mathbf{i} + \mathbf{j} \qquad \mathbf{v}_C = -6\mathbf{i} + \mathbf{j}$$

(a) Find the position vector of the three ships after an hour.
(b) Prove that, if the ships continue with the same velocities, two of them will collide, and find the time when this happens.

2 A ship P is travelling due east at 12 kmh^{-1} and at a certain instant a ship Q is 4 km due south of P. If the velocity of Q is 16.5 kmh^{-1} on a bearing of 75°, find the time taken until the ships are closest. Find the bearing of Q from P a further hour later.

3 Two roads intersect at 90° at a point P. A man A is cycling at 10 km along one of the roads towards P and at a certain instant is 400 m fr. P. A then observes a second man B, 300 m from the junction a running towards it at 6 kmh⁻¹. Find the time when the men are nearest each other and the distance between them.

4 A ship sails due north at 20 kmh⁻¹. It observes another ship, sailing o bearing of 45° at 15 kmh⁻¹ and at a distance of 5 km due west. Find t distance of closest approach between the ships.

Radio contact can only be maintained between the ships when t distance between them does not exceed 5 km. How long after the fi sighting will radio contact be maintained?

2 FORCES AND NEWTON'S LAWS IN ONE DIMENSION

2.1 THE NATURE OF FORCE

We now introduce the concept of force. When forces are studied alone, the study is called *statics*; when they are studied in conjunction with kinematics, then the area of study is called *dynamics*.

If a body changes its velocity, we conclude that a force acts on it. Consider the motion of parachutists falling from an airplane:

(a) At first, they fall vertically downwards as a result of the force acting on them in that direction (Figure 2.1(a)). Their speed increases as they move downwards. The vertical force involved is principally the *weight*, which is the force of the Earth's attraction acting on the parachutist. In addition, there are *resistance forces*. Resistance forces will always oppose motion when they occur.

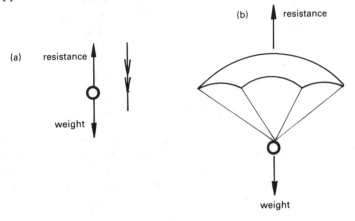

Fig. 2.1

(b) After the parachute opens (Figure 2.1(b)), the parachutist's speed will eventually reach a stage when it stops increasing. In this case, the velocity is no longer changing and all forces acting on the body must cancel out. In fact, the magnitude of the resistance force is then equal to the magnitude of the weight (see Chapter 6).

In the case of a body in a state of *equilibrium*, that is, at rest, the total force acting on a body must also be zero. Consider the following cases of a body *P* in equilibrium:

(a) When the body is suspended by a string to hang freely (Figure 2.2(a)), the weight is supported by an upward force in the string, the *tension*.

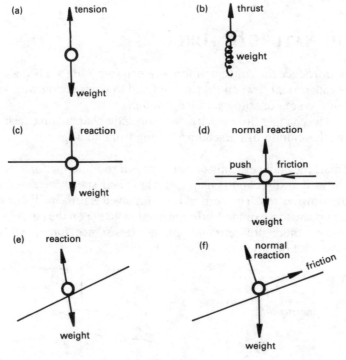

Fig. 2.2

(b) When the body is supported on a spring from below (Figure 2.2(b)), the weight is supported by an upward force in the spring, the *thrust*.
(c) When the body is resting on a horizontal surface, the weight is supported by an upward force supplied by the surface, the *reaction* or *normal reaction* (Figure 2.2(c)).
(d) When the body is resting on a horizontal surface while being pushed by a horizontal force, the weight is again balanced by the normal reaction.

An additional resistance force, *friction*, acts to balance the pushing force. The friction force acts tangentially between the surface and *P* and opposes the motion that the pushing force is trying to create (Figure 2.2(d)).

(e) When the body is resting on a rough inclined plane, the weight will pull the particle down the plane, if unopposed by a friction force acting up the plane. The normal reaction again opposes the pulling effect of the weight towards the plane (Figure 2.2(e)).

An alternative way of viewing this problem (Figure 2.2(f)) is to consider one reaction force applied by the plane. This supports the body on which the weight acts and must act vertically. Clearly, this single force combines the effect of the normal reaction and friction forces.

When forces do not balance, motion will result. In the last example, if the friction force is removed, motion occurs down the plane; that is, in the opposite direction to which the force of friction acts.

Example 2.1

Figures 2.3(a) and (b) show two cases of forces not in equilibrium. Draw diagrams to indicate the direction of motion of a body *P* when (a) on a string and (b) being dragged along a rough inclined plane.

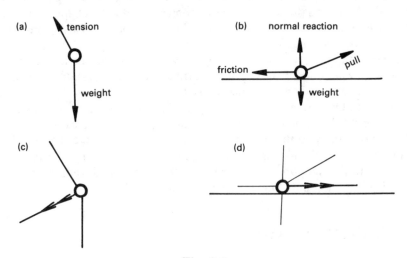

Fig. 2.3

Solution Figures 2.3(c) and (d) show the resultant forces, shown as double-headed arrows.

We know that, in reality, bodies have finite rather than infinitesimal dimensions. In order to appreciate the important consequences that arise from this, consider the rectangular packing case, illustrated in Figure 2.4, resting on a rough horizontal floor.

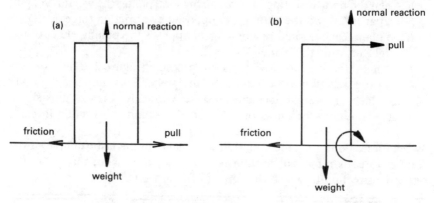

Fig. 2.4

In Figure 2.4(a), the force of reaction balances the weight and the pulling force, P, is exactly balanced by the force of friction, F. The result is that the case remains in equilibrium.

In Figure 2.4(b), all the forces are maintained in the same magnitude but we find that, in this situation, the case topples. What in fact happens is that the case rotates about the bottom right-hand corner. This cannot be predicted by resolving forces.

Clearly, the final motion of any body, whether we are concerned with statics or dynamics, depends upon both translation and rotation. The finite dimensions of a body make it necessary to take into account the effects of its rotation. One method of restricting equilibrium to translation only is to eliminate the dimensions of a body. For these purposes, we usually reduce the size of a body so that it does not possess any finite dimension – it has only position. This assumption is fundamental to the *particle model*, as opposed to the *rigid body model* when both rotation and translation must be taken into account. This text is based on particle models.

2.2 NEWTON'S LAWS

Newton's three laws of motion cannot be proved. They were arrived at by painstaking observation and measurement, and a great deal of inspiration by Sir Isaac Newton in 1687. We will consider them one by one through illustrative examples.

Ice hockey players use a 'puck', a small disc that slides virtually without friction on the ice. Once it is hit, it travels in a straight line at a constant speed until another player stops it or deflects it, or the puck hits a wall or the goal net. This is an example of Newton's first law.

NEWTON'S FIRST LAW   Every body will remain at rest or continue to move with uniform velocity unless an external force is applied to it.

Another illustration of this law is the spacecraft Pioneer 1 which is leaving the solar system and will soon be so far from all other planets and stars that no forces will act upon it. It will then carry on in a straight line until acted upon by an external force, possibly another civilisation that can read the message on it! Although the first section of this chapter discussed the nature of forces, 'force' has not been formally defined. In fact, Newton's first law is the nearest we get to a definition. A force is that which moves a previously stationary mass or changes the velocity of a moving one.

Newton's second law tells us something more about the nature of force. A ball falling freely in air (without air resistance) is subject to the force of gravity. It accelerates with a constant value, called the *gravitational acceleration*, given the letter g. The force of gravity is a constant, so is g, the acceleration it causes on a falling body. This illustrates Newton's second law.

NEWTON'S SECOND LAW   When an external force is applied to a body, the force produces an acceleration. This acceleration is directly proportional to the force. The constant of proportionality is the (constant) mass of the body, that is:

$$\text{force} = \text{mass} \times \text{acceleration}$$

Mathematically, this law can be expressed as follows:

$$F = m \, \frac{\mathrm{d}^2 x}{\mathrm{d}t^2}$$

Until Chapter 10, the mass, m, will always be taken as a constant.

Newton's third law is easily illustrated by you, the reader. Unless you are reading this while travelling, you are assumed to be stationary. You do not fall, so the chair or floor must be exerting a force equal, but in the opposite direction, to your weight. If you push against a wall, the wall must be exerting a resistive force on your push. A glance back at Section 2.1 will provide further illustrations of Newton's third law, which can be expressed as follows.

NEWTON'S THIRD LAW   When a body *A* exerts a force on a body *B*, *B* exerts an equal and opposite force on *A*.

A body resting in equilibrium on a table has zero acceleration. From Newton's second law, the net force on the body must be zero. Hence, the weight of the body, acting downwards (Figure 2.2(c)), must exactly match the normal reaction of the table, acting upwards. Similarly, a train moving on a straight track at a constant speed has no net force acting on it. The tractive force of the engine is just enough to overcome all the different resistive forces acting upon it.

These remarkable laws, recently celebrating their 300th anniversary, still adequately describe all mechanics, except the innermost workings of the atom and the motion of objects whose speed approaches that of light itself (3×10^8 ms^{-1}). Before considering an example, a brief word needs to be said about units.

Most of us, these days, use SI units (Système International d'Unités). Distance is measured in metres, and the units of velocity and acceleration follow straightforwardly from kinematics. Velocity is the rate of change of distance with respect to time, and hence is measured in metres per second (ms^{-1}). Acceleration is the rate of change of velocity with respect to time, and hence is measured in metres per second (ms^{-2}, read as metres per second squared). Newton's second law of motion tells us that force is equal to the product of mass and acceleration. The SI unit of mass is the kilogram (kg), hence the unit of force is kilogram metre per second squared (kgms^{-2}). This is considered rather clumsy, hence a new name, the newton (N), is used instead. One newton is the force required to give a mass of 1 kg an acceleration of 1 ms^{-2}. Units do not tell us about direction; however, all units can be expressed in terms of mass, length and time, and an equation is certainly wrong if the units of both sides, calculated in terms of mass, length and time, do not balance. If there is a balance, however, the equation may or may not be correct. Only in some imprecise sense is the likelihood of correctness increased.

The momentum of a particle is a vector quantity equal to the product of its mass and its velocity. The units of momentum are kgms^{-1}. If the velocity of a particle is constant, then so is its momentum, for constant mass.

Newton's second law is:

$$\mathbf{F} = m \, \frac{d\mathbf{v}}{dt}$$

or for a constant mass:

$$\mathbf{F} = \frac{d(m\mathbf{v})}{dt}$$

36

This relationship, in words, is that force equals the rate of change of momentum. Integrating both sides of this equation with respect to time between the limits $t = t_1$ and $t = t_2$ gives:

$$\int_{t_1}^{t_2} \mathbf{F} \, dt = \left[m\mathbf{v} \right]_{t_1}^{t_2} = m\mathbf{v}(t_2) - m\mathbf{v}(t_1) \qquad (1)$$

The right-hand side is the change in momentum brought about by the force $\mathbf{F}$. The integral of the force with respect to time is called *impulse*, and the integration of Newton's second law shows that <u>impulse is equal to the change in momentum</u>. The SI units of impulse are <u>newton seconds</u> (Ns). From the foregoing equation, these are also the units of momentum. Since the newton, when expressed in more fundamental units, is kgms^{-2}, this is consistent with momentum being expressed in these same units as kgms^{-1}.

Example 2.2.1

Figure 2.5 shows the 'executive toy' known as Newton's cradle. Analyse and describe what happens when ball 1 is pulled aside and released.

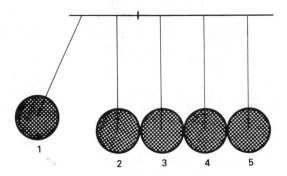

Fig. 2.5

Solution   Each ball has equal mass, m. When ball 1 is pulled aside and released, it swings down and hits ball 2, which is of course stationary. Ball 1 stops, but what has happened to its momentum? Usually, the balls are made of metal, which can be assumed to be perfectly elastic. As ball 1 swings down, its speed increases, and so does the magnitude of its momentum as a result. (This increase in speed is due to an increase in kinetic energy, a term explained in Chapter 4.) Ball 1 collides with ball 2. The impact produces an impulse which must be equal to the momentum lost by ball 1 on impact, from the integral of Newton's second law, equation (1). This impulse is transmitted across all the balls in turn, but balls 2, 3 and 4 cannot move. The impulse is thus given to ball 5 which moves off with the same momentum as was lost by ball 1 on impact. Ball 5 then swings up and back down, and the process is reversed and repeated indefinitely. In reality, the balls eventually come to rest due to the air resistance on balls 1 and 5, and the balls not being perfectly elastic.

Momentum is a very important concept, especially when considering the impact of masses (see Chapter 5). We will meet other concepts such as work and energy. However, all of these mechanical quantities can be expressed in terms of the fundamental units, mass, length and time. Let us break here to consider a purely computational example based on Newton's second law.

Example 2.2.2

A mass of 4 kg is displaced a distance x from the origin, O, according to the law:

$$x = 3 \sin 2t \quad (m)$$

What is the force acting on the mass that produces this displacement:

(a) at time $t = 0$;
(b) after $t = \pi/4$ s;
(c) after $t = \pi/2$ s?

Solution Newton's second law gives:

$$\text{force} = \text{mass} \times \text{acceleration} \quad ✓$$

$$= m \frac{d^2x}{dt^2} \quad ✓$$

Differentiating $x = 3 \sin 2t$ gives:

$$\frac{dx}{dt} = 6 \cos 2t \quad (ms^{-1}) \quad ✓$$

A second differentiation gives:

$$\frac{d^2x}{dt^2} = -12 \sin 2t \quad (ms^{-2}) \quad ✓$$

From Newton's second law:

$$\text{force} = m\frac{d^2x}{dt^2} = 4x(-12 \sin 2t)$$

$$= -48 \sin 2t \quad \text{(newtons)} \quad \checkmark$$

We can now substitute any value of t to obtain the force at that time:

(a) $t = 0$ gives force $= -48 \sin 0 = 0$ N;
(b) $t = \pi/4$ gives force $= -48 \sin (\pi/2) = -48$ N;
(c) $t = \pi/2$ gives force $= -48 \sin (\pi/1) = 0$ N.

This answers the question fully. Note here that $x = 3 \sin 2t$ is an oscillatory function of the type that is studied extensively in Chapter 9 (vibrations).

Apart from enabling us to compute the force, as in the foregoing example, Newton's second law provides an explanation for many everyday occurrences. A car travelling at high speed hits a brick wall. Its (negative) acceleration is very large. Some data might be: velocity before impact $=$ 90 kmh^{-1} (250 ms^{-1}), velocity after impact $= 0$ ms^{-1}, mass of car $=$ 1500 kg, duration of impact $= 1$ s. We calculate acceleration from the change in velocity per unit time:

$$\text{acceleration} = \frac{0 - 250}{1} = -250 \text{ ms}^{-2}$$

Newton's second law then gives:

$$\text{force} = 1500 \times (-250) = -3.75 \times 10^5 \text{ N}$$

This very large force suggests the kind of damage that might be expected by driving into a brick wall. Here is another example.

When a lorry is on a slope, making angle θ with the horizontal (Figure 2.6), then there is a component of weight, $mg \sin \theta$, in the direction down the slope. If the lorry weighs 10 tonnes (or 10 000 kg) and the slope is 10° (or 0.174 radians), then the net force down the slope is:

$$mg \sin \theta = 10\ 000 \times 9.81 \times 0.174$$

$$= 1703 \text{ N}$$

If the lorry is parked, by Newton's third law, the brakes must exert 1703 N

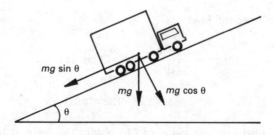

Fig. 2.6

of force in order to stop the lorry from rolling or sliding down the slope. (Friction of course is an aid here since it prevents motion, so if F_B is the force of the brakes, then strictly:

$$1703 = F_B + \text{friction}$$

and 1703 is a safe value for F_B in that it is the most F_B has to be.)

When you stand in a lift, how much do you weigh? If the lift is stationary or moving with constant speed, then your weight is the same as it is now (assuming that you are not reading this in an accelerating lift!). If the lift is accelerating, then the situation is as shown in Figure 2.7. R is the reaction, mg your weight and a is the acceleration of the lift. You may be forgiven

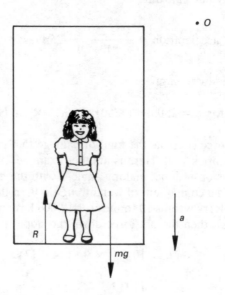

Fig. 2.7

for thinking that $R = mg$ and that your weight is the same, no matter what the value of a. However, you would be wrong! What we have to do is to relate a, the acceleration, to a fixed origin. This is shown as O. The floor of the lift is then travelling with acceleration a relative to O, and Newton's second law applied to the occupant is:

$$mg - R = ma$$

Rearranging this equation gives:

$$m(g - a) = R$$

and we have a statement of Newton's third law (as far as you, the occupant of the lift, are concerned). If $a = 0$, $mg = R$, as expected. If $a > 0$, the lift is accelerating downwards, $mg > R$, so the reaction of the floor of the lift, which is after all what you actually feel, is less than your weight. If the lift cable snaps and $a = g$, you become 'weightless', not because you actually are but because $R = 0$ and you feel as if you are. If $a < 0$, the lift is accelerating upwards, $mg < R$, and you feel heavier because $R > mg$.

EXERCISES 2.2

1 It is winter and a stone is thrown across the surface of a frozen pond. Neglecting friction, what will be the path of the stone?

2 A ball is falling through the air towards the Earth. It is travelling with a constant velocity. Explain this in terms of Newton's first law.

3 A geostationary satellite is one that remains above the same point on the Earth's surface. It is thus not moving from the point of view of an earth dweller. How can this be explained from Newton's first law?

4 Newton's cradle was introduced in example 2.2.1 (Figure 2.5). Analyse what happens if:

(a) balls 1 and 2 are drawn aside and released simultaneously;
(b) balls 1 and 5 are pulled aside to the same height and released simultaneously;
(c) balls 1 and 2 are drawn aside, as is ball 5, all to the same height and released simultaneously. (All motion may be assumed to be one dimensional.)

5 Show that, if the displacement of a mass is a quadratic function of time, it is being subjected to a constant force.

6 The displacement of a mass of 5 kg is given by the formula:

$$x(t) = t^3 - 6t^2 + 4t + 7 \quad \text{(m)}$$

Find the force in newtons that gives rise to this displacement and deduce at what value of time this force is momentarily zero.

7 The 'wall of death' is a fairground attraction where the 'victim' stands on the inside of a large spinning cylinder, facing the axis. As the spin increases, the 'victim' is pressed against the wall. The floor then falls away, but the 'victim' remains pinned to the wall. Explain this in terms of Newton's third law. (*Hint*: You need the definition of friction.)

8 A window cleaner sometimes uses a cradle with pulleys to haul himself to different floors of a tall office block. If the weight of the window cleaner and the cradle is W, and this is supported by four light inextensible ropes of equal tension, find this tension in terms of W if the cradle plus window cleaner:

(a) is stationary;
(b) moves upwards at a constant speed of 0.5 ms^{-1};
(c) moves downwards at a constant speed of 0.5 ms^{-1};
(d) moves upwards at 0.5 ms^{-1} after starting from rest a second earlier.

(Take $g = 9.81$ ms^{-2}. The effects of friction may be neglected.)

9 Discuss how the answer to exercise 2.2.8 will be modified by the inclusion of friction.

2.3 RESISTANCE AND THE PARTICLE MODEL

Only in a highly idealised world do balls slide or roll on a horizontal table and never stop. In reality, resistance acts so as to slow down motion. For solid objects, we can distinguish two kinds of resistance. There is friction between solid surfaces, which is treated fully in Chapter 3, and there is friction between an object and its fluid surroundings – this friction is usually called *drag*. Almost all of the time, we will be concerned with bodies moving through air or water. As a solid object does this, it needs to push fluid aside in order to make progress. The more streamlined an

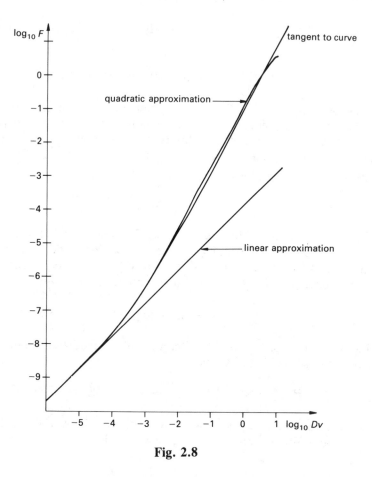

Fig. 2.8

object, the easier the progress. As the body moves forwards, the fluid pressure at the front is greater than the fluid pressure behind. The difference in pressure creates a resistive force that always opposes motion. Clearly, the bigger the volume of an object, the greater this drag.

However, in using Newton's laws, we are treating all masses as particles which have zero volume. Thus, we have no hope of representing shape or volume in our drag law. Instead, we rely on experimentation. Figure 2.8 shows a graph of the drag force experienced by a ball moving through air for various diameters of ball and at various speeds. We can see how drag depends upon speed by plotting drag against speed. However, in order to obtain a useful curve from the data, Figure 2.8 plots log (force) against log (diameter × speed). Fortunately, the data gives two reasonably linear portions of the graph. The fact that drag may be proportional to velocity

43

squared can also be argued rather loosely on dimensional grounds as follows:

$$\text{force} = MLT^{-2} \quad (\text{mass} \times \text{length} \times (\text{time})^{-2})$$

whereas velocity $= LT^{-1}$. There is no time dependence in any other variable we may consider appropriate (volume of object and shape of object are the possible candidates, but these involve lengths only). Thus, we are forced to conclude that we must square LT^{-1} to obtain $L^2 T^{-2}$, which at least means assuming that:

$$\text{force} \propto (\text{velocity})^2$$

since this gives the correct time dimensions. The other variables (M and L) can be sorted out with the appropriate constants (density for example).

Square laws become linear for very small values. Figure 2.8 bears this out with a linear portion at very small velocities. The straight line:

$$\log_{10} F = -3.77 + \log_{10} Dv$$

fits the data well. Taking anti-logarithms results in the linear relationship between drag force, F, and speed, v:

$$F = 1.7 \times 10^{-4} Dv \qquad 0 \leqslant Dv < 3 \times 10^{-5}$$

There is another linear portion, but with double the slope, valid for larger diameters and forces. This straight line has equation:

$$\log_{10} F = -0.70 + 2 \log_{10} Dv$$

This time, taking anti-logarithms gives a quadratic relationship between F and v:

$$F = 0.2(Dv)^2 \qquad 10^{-2} < Dv < 1$$

We return to these drag laws when we look at projectiles in Chapter 7. As we have demonstrated, the quadratic law can be established using dimensional analysis. This gives drag proportional to (speed)^2, and the constant of proportionality will depend upon the shape. For small enough values of F and v, a linear law will apply. The use of quadratic and linear laws for drag can be deduced from experiment and suggested from dimensional analysis. They cannot be derived from mathematics.

Here is an example using resistance and Newton's second law. Note that all masses are treated as particles.

Example 2.3

A harpoon is fired horizontally under water. Assuming it is neutrally buoyant and travels in a straight line, find the distance travelled by the harpoon before its speed is reduced to one-tenth of its initial value, if the resistance is $mv^2/100$ (m = mass of harpoon, v = speed of harpoon). In addition, find the time taken for this to happen if the harpoon is launched at 40 ms^{-1}.

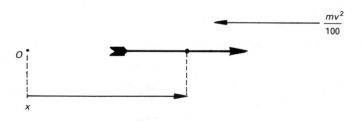

Fig. 2.9

Solution   From Newton's second law:

$$\text{mass} \times \text{acceleration} = \text{force}$$

Since resistance always opposes motion (Figure 2.9):

$$mv\frac{dv}{dx} = -\frac{mv^2}{100}$$

where acceleration = $v\,dv/dx$.

$$\int \frac{dv}{v} = -\int \frac{dx}{100}$$

$$\ln v = -\frac{x}{100} + \text{constant}$$

$$v = Ae^{-x/100}$$

When $x = 0$, $v = u$ (say) the initial velocity. Hence:

$$v = ue^{-x/100}$$

so $v = u/10$ when:

$$\frac{u}{10} = ue^{-x/100}$$

$$\frac{1}{10} = e^{-x/100}$$

Solving for x by taking logs (to base e):

$$\ln 10 = \frac{x}{100}$$

$$x = 230 \text{ m}$$

Using acceleration dv/dt, Newton's law is now:

$$\frac{dv}{dt} = -\frac{v^2}{100}$$

Hence:

$$-\int \frac{dv}{v^2} = \int \frac{1}{100} \, dt$$

which upon integration gives:

$$\frac{1}{v} = \frac{t}{100} + A$$

When $t = 0$, $v = 40 \text{ ms}^{-1}$, so:

$$\frac{1}{40} = A$$

Thus, when $v = 4 \text{ ms}^{-1}$, a tenth of its initial value:

$$\frac{1}{4} = \frac{t}{100} + \frac{1}{40}$$

whence:

$$\frac{t}{100} - \frac{1}{4} - \frac{1}{40} = \frac{9}{40}$$

therefore:

$$t = 22.5 \text{ s}$$

Alternatively, we could have used:

$$v = \frac{dx}{dt} = ue^{-x/100}$$

with $u = 40 \text{ ms}^{-1}$:

$$\int e^{x/100} \, dx = \int 40 \, dt$$

$$100e^{x/100} + B = 40t$$

$x = 0$ when $t = 0$, so $100 + B = 0$, therefore:

$$B = -100$$

From the first part of the question, $x = 230$:

$$100e^{230/100} - 100 = 40t$$

so:

$$t = \frac{10}{4}(e^{2.3} - 1) = 22.4 \text{ s}$$

This is the same, within round-off error, as was obtained before.

EXERCISES 2.3

1 Calculate the dimensions of the following quantities in terms of mass, M, length, L, and time, T, hence deduce their SI units:

(a) volume;

(b) density;

(c) pressure (force per unit area);

(d) tension.

2 If $F = mDv^2$, where F = force, m = mass and v = speed, calculate the dimensions of the drag constant D. In addition, find the dimensions of k if $F = mkv$.

3 The force in a spring is proportional to its extension. What are the dimensions of the constant of proportionality?

4 A bullet is travelling at a constant speed of 400 ms^{-1} when it hits a stone wall. On examination, the bullet has penetrated a distance of 0.1 m. Assuming that the resistance of the wall is mkv, where m is the mass of the bullet and v its speed, estimate the value of the constant k. (You may neglect gravity.)

3 FORCE AS A VECTOR

3.1 MODELLING FORCES

The term force was defined in Chapter 2. We saw there how this definition was adequate to use when modelling motion in one dimension. However, whenever we wish to introduce a force into a problem in mechanics in two or three dimensions, we need to be specific in its description in terms of its magnitude, direction and point of application. While we are concerned with the particle model, the point of application will have no significance, as it is described as the particle's position. Here are some examples:

(a) A force of 10 N which pushes a cart along a horizontal plane: Its magnitude is 10 N and its direction is specified to be horizontal and in the direction of the push.

(b) A weight of 500 N: Automatically, in specifying weight, we have allocated a vertically downwards direction to the magnitude of 500 N.

(c) A tension of 10 N in a string: By the definition of tension, the force of magnitude 10 N is directed away from the centre of the string along its length.

Various guises are used to indicate direction. They can be compass bearings, or fixed planes or lines, and it is common to see the words vertical and horizontal being used as reference.

As stated in Section 1.2, force, in order to be defined as a vector, must, as well as having magnitude and direction, satisfy the vector law of addition. This means that, if two forces act at a point, they can be combined to produce a single force, i.e. a *resultant* whose magnitude and direction are obtained from a vector triangle.

49

Example 3.1.1

Consider the following experiment, which you are advised to attempt if you have not done so previously. The apparatus consists of two fixed pulleys A and B which rotate freely. An inextensible string (that is, one whose length remains constant, as opposed to an elastic string which can be stretched) hangs over the pulleys. Forces of magnitude P and Q are applied, one at each end of the string, and the midpoint, M, of the string is pegged to a fixed point as shown in Figure 3.1(a).

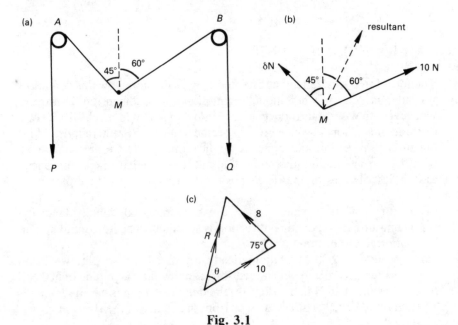

Fig. 3.1

Choose P as 8 N and Q as 10 N. Since the pulleys at A and B are smooth, this leads to the tensions at M being as shown in Figure 3.1(b). Using the triangle law for adding vectors (Figure 3.1(c)), we can determine the resultant force acting at M. Simple use of the sine and cosine rules will then allow us to calculate the magnitude, R, and direction, θ, of the resultant force on the peg.

Solution

$$R^2 = 8^2 + 10^2 - 2 \times 8 \times 10 \times \cos 75°$$

$$R = 11.07 \text{ N}$$

and:

$$\frac{8}{\sin\theta} = \frac{11.07}{\sin 75°}$$

$$\sin\theta = \frac{8\sin 75°}{11.07}$$

$$\theta = 44.3°$$

The magnitude of the resultant is 11.07 N and it acts in a direction of 44.3° with the string *MB*. We can say that, if we apply a force of equal magnitude but in an opposite direction at *M*, then we can remove the peg and the point *M* will remain in the same position. Practically, this is achieved by attaching a second string at *M*, which supports a weight whose magnitude is equal to the resultant's magnitude. The correct direction is then achieved by inserting a smooth peg at *L*, so that the force acts along *ML* in the opposite direction to the resultant, as shown in Figure 3.2.

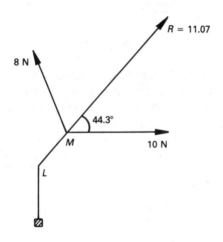

Fig. 3.2

The experiment just outlined is usually successful and leads us to conclude that force can be modelled as a vector. This allows us to calculate the resultant force **R** of two forces **P** and **Q** applied at a point by the law of vector addition:

$$\mathbf{R} = \mathbf{P} + \mathbf{Q}$$

usually called the *law of triangle*. It provides a foundation for the future modelling of force.

Example 3.1.2

Consider two tugs used to pull a heavy ship through still water. If they are to apply respective forces of 2×10^{10} N and 3×10^{10} N along chains, as illustrated in Figure 3.3(a), can you predict the direction the ship will start to move?

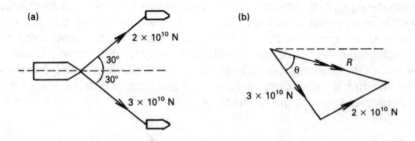

Fig. 3.3

Solution The ship will first move along the direction of the resultant force acting upon it. If the resultant has magnitude R and acts at $\theta°$ to the chain with the largest pulling force, then we can use the triangle of forces illustrated in Figure 3.3(b). This gives:

$$R^2 = 3^2 \times 10^{20} + 2^2 \times 10^{20} - 2 \times 3 \times 10^{10} \times 2 \times 10^{10} \times \cos 120°$$

$$R = 4.36 \times 10^{10} \text{ N}$$

and:

$$\frac{2 \times 10^{10}}{\sin \theta} = \frac{4.36 \times 10^{10}}{\sin 120°}$$

$$\theta = 23.4°$$

The ship starts to move in a direction of 6.6° with a force of 3×10^{10} N. As any water resistance would directly oppose this resultant force, it would not change this initial direction of travel.

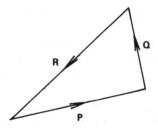

Fig. 3.4

If the resultant force on a body is zero, then the body is in equilibrium. We can apply the triangular addition law here to say that, if three forces **P**, **Q** and **R** are acting on a body which is in equilibrium, then:

$$\mathbf{P} + \mathbf{Q} + \mathbf{R} = 0$$

This is illustrated in Figure 3.4. Note that, if any of the three forces have their directions reversed, they will be equal to the resultant of the other two. If you then solve the resulting one-dimensional problem, the equilibrium condition follows directly.

Example 3.1.3

A heavy weight of 20 N is suspended using an inextensible string. The weight is then pulled by a horizontal force so that the string makes an angle of 30° with the vertical, as illustrated in Figure 3.5(a). Find (a) the horizontal force and (b) the tension in the string.

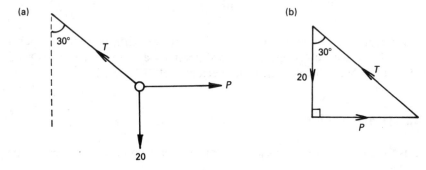

Fig. 3.5

Solution From the triangle of forces (Figure 3.5(b)), we have:

(a) the horizontal force $P = 20 \tan 30° = 15.5$ N;
(b) the tension in the string $T = 20/\cos 30° = 32.1$ N.

Most classical work on systems of forces was done using trigonometric and geometric methods on the resulting triangle of forces, and we too have followed this path. This method is very useful for such problems. However, when more than three forces are involved in a system, it can be very tedious combining forces using the triangular law of addition. For instance, to find the resultant of five forces would require as many as four applications of the addition law. One refinement of the triangle law which is achieved by its repeated application is the law of polygon of forces. This allows us to find the resultant **R** of any number of forces $\mathbf{F}_1, \mathbf{F}_2, \mathbf{F}_3 \ldots$ by:

$$\mathbf{R} = \mathbf{F}_1 + \mathbf{F}_2 + \mathbf{F}_3 + \ldots$$

The relationship is illustrated in Figure 3.6.

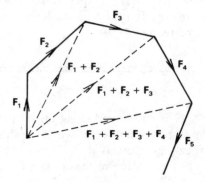

Fig. 3.6

However, the trigonometric and geometric working of such problems can become overpowering, so a more compact and more easily worked method has been developed, using vector algebra methods.

3.2 RESOLUTION

As is the case with velocities and any other vector quantities, forces can be resolved.

Consider Figure 3.7(a), where a particle rests on an inclined smooth plane supported by a string which is fastened to a point on the plane. The

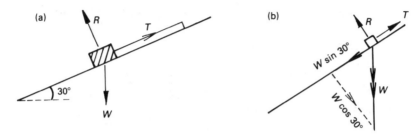

Fig. 3.7

string rests along the line of greatest slope of the plane. All forces acting on the body are as illustrated.

Clearly, the weight of the body has an effect on the plane, which is balanced by the reaction, R, perpendicular to the plane and the tension, T, along the plane. If we complete a vector triangle for W, so that it has sides along and perpendicular to the plane, as shown in Figure 3.7(b), then we can see the effect of the weight as that represented by $W \sin 30°$ along and down the plane and $W \cos 30°$ perpendicular to the plane and downwards. It seems safe to assume that, in this case:

$$T = W \sin 30° \quad \text{and} \quad R = W \cos 30°$$

It is usual to consider the resolution of forces in terms of the unit vectors **i**, **j** and **k** defined in suitable directions. By so doing, the transition from one dimension to two dimensions and then to three dimensions is made considerably easier.

We first consider two dimensions using unit vectors **i** and **j**. In Figure 3.8, four forces are illustrated, **P**, **Q**, **R** and **S** with **i** and **j** defined as shown. The reader should confirm that the forces can be written as:

$$\mathbf{P} = 5 \cos 30°\mathbf{i} + 5 \sin 30°\mathbf{j} \qquad \mathbf{Q} = -3\mathbf{i}$$

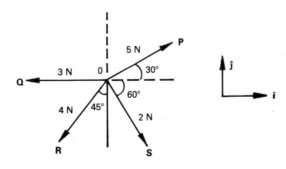

Fig. 3.8

$$R = -4 \cos 45°i - 4 \sin 45°j \qquad S = 2 \cos 60°i - 2 \sin 60°j$$

In a reverse process, the forces:

$$F = 3i + 5j \quad \text{and} \quad G = -2i + 3j$$

can be shown to have magnitude and direction as:

$$F: \quad \sqrt{34} \text{ N}; \quad \tan^{-1}(5/3) \text{ with } i$$

$$G: \quad \sqrt{13} \text{ N}; \quad -\tan^{-1}(3/2) \text{ with } i$$

3.3 RESULTANT FORCE

Consider the simple problem of finding the resultant of the following forces, which have been written in terms of i and j:

$$F = 4i + 2j \quad \text{and} \quad G = 3i + 5j$$

The triangle law can be applied as shown in Figure 3.9. It should immediately be seen that the resultant can be found as:

$$R = (4 + 3)i + (2 + 5)j = 7i + 7j$$

This component-wise addition results in a simple but effective method for combining any number of forces. It is then an easy calculation to find its magnitude and direction.

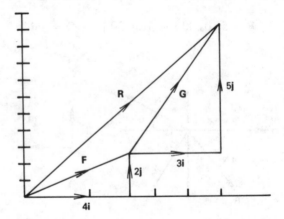

Fig. 3.9

Example 3.3

Find the magnitude of the resultant of the following system of forces:

$$\mathbf{F_1} = 3\mathbf{i} + 2\mathbf{j} \qquad \mathbf{F_2} = -4\mathbf{j} \qquad \mathbf{F_3} = -2\mathbf{i} + 5\mathbf{j}$$

The resultant is:

$$\mathbf{R} = (3 - 2)\mathbf{i} + (2 - 4 + 5)\mathbf{j} = \mathbf{i} + 3\mathbf{j}$$

Its magnitude is given as:

$$\sqrt{(1^2 + 3^2)} = 3.162 \text{ N}$$

in a direction $\tan^{-1}(3)$ with the direction of $\mathbf{i}$.

3.4 EQUILIBRIUM

If a system of forces is in equilibrium, then the resultant force of the system is zero. This simple concept when applied to forces in the $\mathbf{i}$, $\mathbf{j}$ form allows us to solve any problem in statics when the system of forces acts at a *single point*.

Example 3.4

A small body of mass 3 kg is suspended from a string. It is then pushed by a force of 20 N, always acting at right angles to the string, until the body rests in equilibrium, as illustrated in Figure 3.10. Find (a) the tension in the string and (b) the direction made by the string.

Solution $\mathbf{i}$ and $\mathbf{j}$ are defined along and perpendicular to the string as indicated in Figure 3.10. We write the forces in terms of $\mathbf{i}$ and $\mathbf{j}$:

$$\text{tension in the string} = T\mathbf{j}$$

$$\text{pushing force} = 20\mathbf{i}$$

$$\text{weight} = -30 \sin \theta \mathbf{i} - 30 \cos \theta \mathbf{j}$$

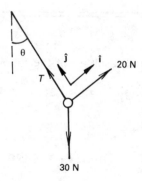

Fig. 3.10

Equilibrium gives that:

$$T\mathbf{j} + 20\mathbf{i} - 30 \sin \theta \mathbf{i} - 30 \cos \theta \mathbf{j} = 0$$

Considering **i** and **j** in turn gives:

$$20 - 30 \cos \theta = 0$$

so that:

$$\theta = \sin^{-1}(2/3) = 41.8°$$

and:

$$T - 30 \cos \theta = 0$$

so that:

$$T = 10\sqrt{5} \text{ N} = 22.4 \text{ N}$$

EXERCISES 3.4

1 A ship is towed at a constant speed by the cables from two tugs. If the tensions in the cables are 5×10^6 N and the water supplies a resistance force of magnitude 11×10^6 N, find the directions that the towing cables will make with the direction of motion.

2 A pulley of mass 3 kg is free to move up or down in a smooth vertical track. It is held in position by a string passing round the pulley so that the two parts make angles of 30° and 60° with the horizontal. Draw a

diagram of the system, showing all the forces acting on the pulley. Use the diagram to find the tension in the string.

3 A light inextensible string of length 2.4 m is fastened at its ends A and B to two pegs 2 m apart in the same horizontal line. A mass of 5 kg is attached to the string at C, 0.5 m along the string from A, and an equal mass at D, 0.5 m from B. Draw a diagram of the system, showing all the forces acting on the particles and use it to find the tensions in each part of the string.

4 The jack illustrated in Figure 3.11 is a screw type which is used for raising cars. The screw at B provides enough resistance to allow large loads to be supported. The rods AB, BC, CD, AD and the screw are light compared with the load W that the jack supports at A. When all rods make an angle of 30° with the horizontal, find, by considering all the forces acting at A and then B, the forces in each rod and the screw.

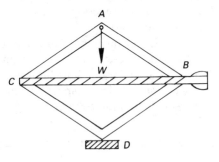

Fig. 3.11

3.5 FRICTION

To date, we have only mentioned the effects of resistance forces and how important they are in real problems. Here we will discuss friction.

You may like to carry out the following experiment with an object lying on a rough surface like a carpet. Consider Figure 3.12 in which a small body of weight W rests on a rough horizontal surface. If no other forces act, then the normal reaction R of the plane will have a constant magnitude W and will act vertically upwards (normal reaction).

If we now introduce a horizontal force P, then, as you should experience, the body will not move initially. We can, as a result, assume that some resistance force is opposing P, which must be equal in magnitude to P and opposite in direction. This force is *static friction*. It results from two rough (not smooth) surfaces trying to move relative to each other. The

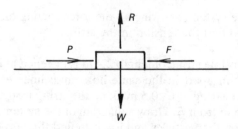

Fig. 3.12

force F of static friction will always act so as just to maintain equilibrium.

If we continue to increase P, then when a value, P_0 say, is reached, the body will begin to slide over the surface. When $P = P_0$, we say the system is at limiting equilibrium, where P_0 is the limit of friction. The value P_0 can be shown experimentally to be equal to μR, where μ is called the *coefficient of friction* for the two surfaces. You should consider for yourself various experiments involving friction to try to determine whether the friction force only depends on the normal reaction or whether other factors, such as the area of contact, are involved.

If the force P is increased still further, then the body will move in the direction of P. Using Newton's second law, the friction force will continue to act and we shall model it as maintaining its limiting value. In fact, it can be shown to assume a value slightly less than its limiting value. The friction in this stage is usually called *dynamic friction*.

Example 3.5.1

Have you ever tried to take a reluctant dog for a walk? If the dog has a mass of 25 kg and lays on the floor refusing to move, you find that, when you pull the lead with a force of 100 N, holding the lead at an angle of 30° with the horizontal, the dog slides along the floor. Calculate the coefficient of friction between the dog and the floor. (Take $g = 10 \text{ ms}^{-2}$.)

Solution Unit vectors **i** and **j** are as indicated in Figure 3.13:

$$\text{friction force} = -F\mathbf{i}$$

$$\text{normal reaction} = R\mathbf{j}$$

$$\text{force in lead} = 100 \cos 30°\mathbf{i} + 100 \sin 30°\mathbf{j}$$

$$\text{weight} = -250\,\mathbf{j}$$

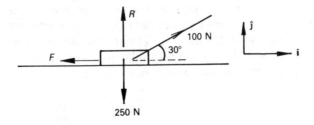

Fig. 3.13

For equilibrium:

$$-F\mathbf{i} + R\mathbf{j} + 100 \cos 30°\mathbf{i} + 100 \sin 30°\mathbf{j} - 250\mathbf{j} = 0$$

Hence:

$$100 \sin 30° - F = 0$$

so that:

$$F = 86.6 \text{ N}$$

and:

$$R + 100 \sin 30° - 250 = 0$$

so that:

$$R = 200.0 \text{ N}$$

Since friction will be limiting:

$$\mu = \frac{F}{R} = 0.433$$

When forces are considered in three dimensions, they present few problems if we analyse the system in terms of $\mathbf{i}, \mathbf{j}, \mathbf{k}$ component vectors, as the following example will show.

Example 3.5.2

A light post AP of length 1 m stands vertically on a smooth plane at the corner of a square $ABCD$ of side 2 m. The post is supported in this position by a tie PC and a string which passes through a smooth ring at P so that its two parts are parallel to DA and BA. The arrangement is shown in Figure 3.14. If the tension in the string through the ring has magnitude 100 N, find (a) the tension in the tie and (b) the thrust in the post.

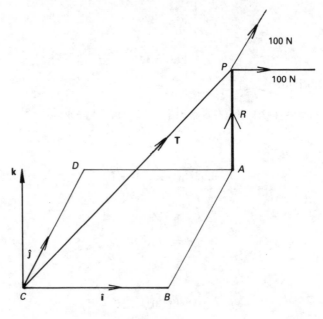

Fig. 3.14

Solution The unit vectors **i**, **j** and **k** are as shown in Figure 3.14. Tensions in the two parts of the string are 100**i** and 100**j**. Let the thrust in the post be **R** = *R***k**. We can write the unit vector along the tie as:

$$-\frac{(2\mathbf{i} + 2\mathbf{j} + \mathbf{k})}{3}$$

and the tension, **T**, in the tie is then:

$$\mathbf{T} = -\frac{T}{3}(2\mathbf{i} + 2\mathbf{j} + \mathbf{k})$$

As the forces at P are in equilibrium, we have:

$$100\mathbf{i} + 100\mathbf{j} + R\mathbf{k} - \frac{T}{3}(2\mathbf{i} + 2\mathbf{j} + \mathbf{k}) = 0$$

to give:

$$100 - \frac{2T}{3} = 0$$

$$T = 150 \text{ N}$$

and:

$$R - \frac{T}{3} = 0$$

$$R = 50 \text{ N}$$

EXERCISES 3.5

1 Three forces $\mathbf{F}_1$, $\mathbf{F}_2$ and $\mathbf{F}_3$ act at the top of a radio mast as illustrated in Figure 3.15. The mast is in equilibrium. If:

$$\mathbf{F}_1 = 5\mathbf{i} - 2\mathbf{j} - 12\mathbf{k} \quad \text{and} \quad \mathbf{F}_2 = -5\mathbf{i} - 2\mathbf{j} - 12\mathbf{k}$$

and the magnitude of the thrust in the mast is 32 N, find $\mathbf{F}_3$ in terms of the component vectors $\mathbf{i}$, $\mathbf{j}$ and $\mathbf{k}$ where $\mathbf{k}$ is the vertically upwards unit vector.

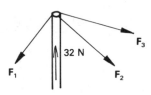

Fig. 3.15

2 An injured climber is being lowered down a mountain slope inclined at 50° to the horizontal by two ropes which, at an instant when the climber is at rest, make angles of 30° and 45° to the line of greatest slope. The climber and his stretcher have a mass of 200 kg. Define $\mathbf{i}$, $\mathbf{j}$ and $\mathbf{k}$ vectors so that $\mathbf{i}$ and $\mathbf{j}$ lie in the plane of the slope, and find the tension in each rope if no forces of resistance act.

3 A particle of weight W lies on the inner surface of a smooth sphere of radius a. It is supported by two light inextensible strings, each of length a, which are attached to points a distance a apart on the circumference of the horizontal equator of the sphere. Find the tension in the strings. (*Hint*: Show that reaction = tension.)

3.6 NEWTON'S LAWS IN VECTOR NOTATION

If a vector **a** determines the line along which a particle P is travelling with a constant speed v, then the velocity of the particle is $\hat{\mathbf{a}}v = \mathbf{v}$ where $\hat{\mathbf{a}} = \mathbf{a}/|\mathbf{a}|$, the unit vector in the direction of **a**. Newton's first law states that the particle will remain forever along **a**, travelling with velocity **v**, unless acted on by an external force **F**. Only if **F** is parallel to **a** (that is, $\mathbf{F} = F\hat{\mathbf{a}}$) does the particle P remain in the direction of the vector **a**. Otherwise it changes to another direction. To find this other direction, we use Newton's second law and the law of composition of vectors. In vector form, Newton's second law states that:

$$\mathbf{F} = m\,\frac{d^2\mathbf{r}}{dt^2}$$

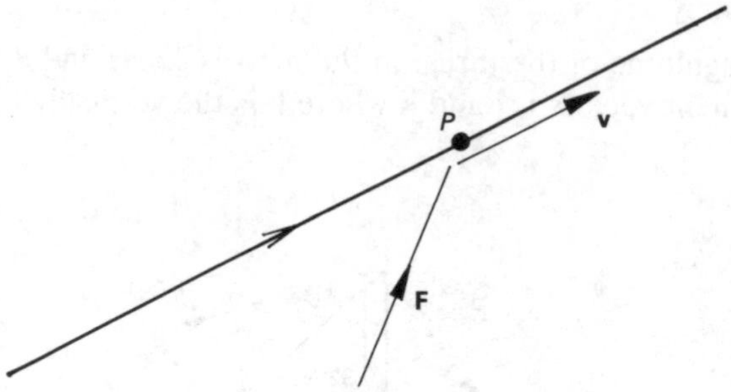

Fig. 3.16

An example should make using vectors with Newton's first two laws clearer.

Example 3.6.1

An insect of mass 0.001 kg is flying along the line $\mathbf{a} = 3\mathbf{i} + 2\mathbf{j}$ with constant speed $\sqrt{13}\ \mathrm{ms^{-1}}$ (**i** is due east and **j** is due north). A wind springs up from a

Fig. 3.17

westerly direction and lasts for 40 s. This wind subjects the insect to a constant force of 10^{-4} N for its duration (Figure 3.17). What velocity is the insect flying at (a) after 20 s, (b) after 40 s and (c) when there is no longer any wind?

Solution Before the wind starts, the velocity of the insect is:

$$\mathbf{u} = \sqrt{13} \times \frac{\mathbf{a}}{|\mathbf{a}|}$$

$$= \sqrt{13} \times \frac{(3\mathbf{i} + 2\mathbf{j})}{\sqrt{13}} = (3\mathbf{i} + 2\mathbf{j}) \text{ ms}^{-1}$$

Newton's second law is:

$$\mathbf{F} = m \frac{d^2\mathbf{r}}{dt^2} \quad \text{or} \quad 10^{-4}\mathbf{i} = 10^{-3} \frac{d^2\mathbf{r}}{dt^2}$$

so that:

$$0.1\mathbf{i} = \frac{d^2\mathbf{r}}{dt^2}$$

Integrating with respect to t gives:

$$\frac{d\mathbf{r}}{dt} = 0.1t\mathbf{i} + \mathbf{U}$$

where **U** is an arbitrary constant vector. At time $t = 0$,

$$\mathbf{U} = \frac{d\mathbf{r}}{dt} = \mathbf{u} = 3\mathbf{i} + 2\mathbf{j}$$

so that:

$$\frac{d\mathbf{r}}{dt} = 0.1t\mathbf{i} + 3\mathbf{i} + 2\mathbf{j}$$

This gives the velocity at any time t after the wind starts blowing. We can thus answer the three parts of the question.

(a) After 20 s:

$$\frac{d\mathbf{r}}{dt} = 0.1 \times 20\mathbf{i} + 3\mathbf{i} + 2\mathbf{j} = 5\mathbf{i} + 2\mathbf{j} \text{ ms}^{-1}$$

(b) After 40 s:

$$\frac{d\mathbf{r}}{dt} = 0.1 \times 40\mathbf{i} + 3\mathbf{i} + 2\mathbf{j} = 7\mathbf{i} + 2\mathbf{j} \text{ ms}^{-1}$$

(c) When there is no longer any wind, the net force on the insect is zero. By Newton's first law, it carries on with the velocity $7\mathbf{i} + 2\mathbf{j}$ ms^{-1}.

When explaining the nature of force in the last chapter, a particle resting on an inclined plane was considered. This is in fact a good illustration of Newton's third law in vector notation. Figure 3.18(a) shows a plane that can be made to incline at any angle θ, where $0 < \theta < 90°$. The particle P will be at rest when $\theta = 0$, its weight **W** being exactly counterbalanced by the *normal* reaction **N**. As θ is increased by adjusting the mechanism M, then P will still remain at rest, certainly for small θ, the weight **W** being equal and opposite to the reaction **R**. **R** can be thought of as consisting of a component **N**, normal to the plane, the normal reaction and a component **F**, parallel to the plane, the friction. This is illustrated in Figure 3.18(a), and is similar to the situation addressed in Section 3.2.

As θ is increased further, a point will be reached when the particle P begins to move. At this point, **W** is no longer balanced by **R** because **F** is not large enough. Figures 3.18(b) and (c) illustrate this, and indicate that **R** is no longer vertical. There is now a net force down the plane and so, according to Newton's second law, the particle begins to accelerate in that direction.

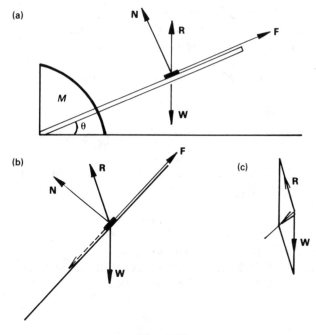

(a)

(b)

(c)

Fig. 3.18

Example 3.6.2

A block of mass 2 kg is situated on an inclined plane and held steady. The coefficient of friction between the block and the plane is 0.5. Determine whether or not the block moves when released if the angle the plane makes with the horizontal is (a) 20° and (b) 40°. If the block moves, determine its acceleration.

Solution   Take vectors **i** and **j** parallel and perpendicular to the plane as indicated in Figure 3.19. The forces acting are the normal reaction $R\mathbf{j}$, the

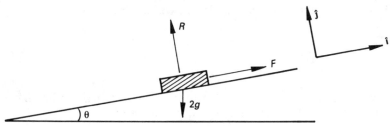

Fig. 3.19

67

frictional force $F\mathbf{i}$ and the weight of the block $-2g\sin\theta\mathbf{i} - 2g\cos\theta\mathbf{j}$, where θ is the angle the plane makes with the horizontal, as indicated. For equilibrium, the net force on the block is zero, hence:

$$R\mathbf{j} + F\mathbf{i} - 2g\sin\theta\mathbf{i} - 2g\cos\theta\mathbf{j} = 0$$

so that, equating components:

$$R - 2g\cos\theta = 0 \quad \text{and} \quad F - 2g\sin\theta = 0$$

If, on the other hand, the block moves down the plane, then the last equation no longer holds. Instead:

$$F - 2g\sin\theta < 0$$

since there is a net force in the $-\mathbf{i}$ direction.

When the block is about to slide, that is, the magnitude of F is just enough (but no more) to hold the block, then:

$$F = \mu R$$

where μ is the coefficient of (static) friction. We are given that $\mu = 0.5$, hence we can calculate at what angle the block begins to slide. Since:

$$F = 0.5R$$

using:

$$R = 2g\cos\theta$$

which is always true, we obtain, upon elimination of R:

$$F = g\cos\theta$$

If $F = 2g\sin\theta$ too, then eliminating F, we obtain:

$$\tan\theta = 0.5$$
$$\theta = 26°\ 34'$$

Hence, if (a) $\theta = 20°$, the block will not move. On the other hand, if (b) $\theta = 40°$, the block *will* slide down the plane and:

$$F < 2g\sin\theta$$

With $\theta = 40°$ and $g = 9.81$ ms^{-2}, this inequality is:

$$F < 12.61 \text{ N}$$

Now:

$$R = 2g \cos 40° \quad \text{and} \quad F = 0.5R$$

hence:

$$F = g \cos 40°$$
$$= 7.51 \text{ N}$$

The net force down the plane is:

$$12.61 - 7.51 = 5.10 \text{ N}$$

To find the acceleration, we divide by the mass of the block, which is 2 kg. Hence, the acceleration of the block down the plane is 2.56 ms^{-2}.

EXERCISES 3.6

1 A woman of mass 50 kg is skiing at a constant speed of 20 ms^{-1}. Throughout her ski run, a constant wind is blowing in a direction perpendicular to her initial direction of movement. At the end of her 200 m ski, she finds that she has been turned through 10° by the wind. Calculate the force of the wind.

2 A particle of mass 5 kg moves according to the law:

$$\mathbf{r}\ (t) = \left(\frac{t^3}{6} - \frac{t^2}{2} \right) \mathbf{i} + 3t\mathbf{j} - t^2\mathbf{k}$$

Find the force that acts on the particle at any time t. At what time is this force parallel to the z-axis?

3 A man is walking his dog, which weighs 10 kg. The man and dog together are walking in a straight line along the x-axis, at a constant speed of 1.5 ms^{-1}. At $x = 30$ m, the dog sees a sleeping cat at the point $x = 0$, $y = 30$ m. The dog dashes off, directly towards the cat (which

69

continues to sleep). The man continues to walk until the lead becomes taut, after 1 s. If the dog is travelling with an acceleration of 4 ms^{-2} towards the cat, find the force the man needs to exert in order to stop the dog.

4 USING ENERGY

4.1 INTRODUCTION

Energy is the capability of a body to do work. It can take many forms: heat, light, sound, electricity, magnetism, nuclear and so on. However, our concern is with mechanical energy. Mechanical energy is of two types: kinetic energy and potential energy. *Kinetic energy* is the energy of a body by virtue of its motion. *Potential energy* is the energy of a body by virtue of its position. A body is held so that it is stationary and then released; if it moves then it possesses potential energy. Examples include a stone dropped out of a window or the release of a stretched catapult. In order to develop results systematically from our knowledge of forces, we shall first define work.

4.2 WORK

If a mass m is acted on by a force $\mathbf{F}$, then the *work done* by the force $\mathbf{F}$ on the mass m is the component of $\mathbf{F}$ in the direction of the motion multiplied by the distance travelled by the mass m. If the vector $\mathbf{a}$ represents the direction and magnitude of movement of m, and θ is the angle between $\mathbf{F}$ and $\mathbf{a}$, then the work done by the force $\mathbf{F}$ is $|\mathbf{F}|\,|\mathbf{a}|\cos\theta$, which is $\mathbf{F}\cdot\mathbf{a}$, the scalar dot product of the two vectors.

(For those familiar with line integrals, the work done by the force $\mathbf{F}$ moving along the curve C is:

$$\int_c \mathbf{F}\cdot d\mathbf{r}$$

We will, however, not make use of line integrals.)

Figure 4.1 demonstrates that $\mathbf{F}\cdot\mathbf{a}$ is the distance travelled by the mass m multiplied by the component of $\mathbf{F}$ in the direction of $\mathbf{a}$. Here, $|\mathbf{F}|\cos\theta \times AB$ is the work done by $\mathbf{F}$ on moving the mass m from point A to point B.

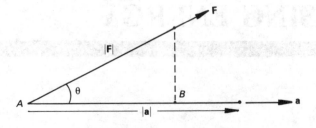

Fig. 4.1

The unit of work is the newton metre which is called the joule, named after the British physicist James Prescott Joule (1818–89), and abbreviated to J.

Example 4.2.1

A force of magnitude 5 N acts in the direction $0.6i + 0.8j$. What is the work done in (a) moving a mass 5 m in the **i** direction, (b) moving a mass 5 m in the **j** direction and (c) moving a mass 5 m in the $-i$ direction?

Solution The force vector is:

$$\mathbf{F} = 5\,(0.6\mathbf{i} + 0.8\mathbf{j})\ \text{N}$$

$$= (3\mathbf{i} + 4\mathbf{j})\ \text{N}$$

(*Note*: The vector $0.6\mathbf{i} + 0.8\mathbf{j}$ is already a unit vector. If it were not so, we would have to divide by its magnitude to ensure that the magnitude of **F** remains 5 N.)

(a) From the definition of work, the work done moving a mass 5 m in the **i** direction is:

$$\mathbf{F} \cdot 5\mathbf{i} = 15\ \text{J}$$

(b) Similarly, the work done moving a mass 5 m in the **j** direction is:

$$\mathbf{F} \cdot 5\mathbf{j} = 20\ \text{J}$$

(c) If the mass were moved 5 m in the $-i$ direction, the work done would be:

$$\mathbf{F} \cdot (-5\mathbf{i}) = -15 \text{ J}$$

Hence, if (a) then (c) were undertaken sequentially, no work would have been done. This may seem a strange use of the English word 'work' since, irrefutably, effort has been expended in moving a mass 5 m one way and 5 m back again. However, under the mathematical definition of work, there is no contradiction.

The term *power* is given to the rate at which work is being done. In general:

$$\text{power} = \frac{d(\text{work})}{dt}$$

We are perhaps familiar with the term power from everyday use. For example, we talk of a machine being powerful or the power output of a generating station. Everyday units of power are the watt (W), the kilowatt (kW = 1000 W), the megawatt (MW = 10^6 W) or indeed the gigawatt (GW = 10^9 W). Old-fashioned books talk about horsepower (still, unfortunately, found in glossy car brochures, 1 horsepower = 746 W). A watt is a joule per second, and is the SI unit of power. In fundamental units:

$$\text{power} = \frac{\text{force} \times \text{distance}}{\text{time}}$$

$$= \text{MLT}^{-2} \times \text{LT}^{-1} = \text{ML}^2\text{T}^{-3}$$

Under a unidirectional constant force, the power can be calculated by computing the product of force and speed. We can see this immediately from the above equation. This is useful, for example, when computing the maximum speed of a vehicle driven by an engine of known power up an incline.

Example 4.2.2

A lorry of mass 10 tonnes is travelling up an incline α where $\sin \alpha = 1/10$. Its top speed is found to be 20 ms^{-1}. Estimate the power of the engine. Why is this estimate not accurate? (Take $g = 10$ ms^{-2}.)

Solution Figure 4.2 shows the lorry of mass 10 tonnes = 10^4 kg. The

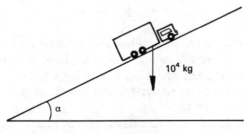

Fig. 4.2

component of weight down the slope is:

$$10^4 \, g \, \times \, \frac{1}{10} \, \approx \, 10^4 \, \text{N}$$

The power required to overcome this force and keep the lorry at a steady speed of 20 ms^{-1} is given by the product of force and speed, that is, $10^4 \times 20 \, \text{W} = 2 \times 10^5 \, \text{W} \, (= 200 \, \text{kW})$. This estimate is not accurate because we have totally ignored friction. The actual power of the lorry would probably be double this.

In fact, work and power are only incidental to the real point of this chapter, which is to use energy as a problem-solving technique. After some exercises on work and power, we will be ready to introduce these techniques.

Example 4.2.3

A locomotive of mass M, travelling along a straight track, is supplied with constant power MP and is subjected to a resistance Mkv^2, where v is its speed and k is a constant. Find the greatest possible value of the speed if it starts from rest. Show also that the locomotive acquires one-half of this speed after travelling a distance $(1/3k) \ln (8/7)$.

Solution Since the power, P, is the product of force and velocity and all motion is one dimensional, we have that, if F is the force:

$$MP = Fv \quad \text{or} \quad F = \frac{MP}{v}$$

Newton's second law thus gives:

74

$$\frac{MP}{v} -- Mkv^2 = M \frac{dv}{dt} = Mv \frac{dv}{dx}$$

Here we choose the v dv/dx form of acceleration since the problem involves distance. Cancelling the Ms and rearranging gives:

$$P - kv^3 = v^2 \frac{dv}{dx}$$

This equation separates and integrates to:

$$x + C = - \frac{1}{3k} \ln (P - kv^3)$$

where C is an arbitrary constant. When $x = 0$, $v = 0$, therefore:

$$C = - \frac{1}{3k} \ln P$$

hence:

$$x = \frac{1}{3k} \ln \left(\frac{P}{P - kv^3} \right)$$

From this equation for distance, x, we must have:

$$P - kv^3 > 0 \quad \text{or} \quad v < \left(\frac{P}{k} \right)^{1/3}$$

Hence $(P/k)^{1/3}$ is the maximum speed.

Half this speed is $1/2 (P/k)^{1/3}$, and putting v equal to this value in the expression for x gives:

$$x = \frac{1}{3k} \ln \left(\frac{8}{7} \right)$$

as required.

EXERCISES 4.2

1 A force of 10 N acts in the direction $i + j + k$. Find the work done in

moving a mass 3 m in the following directions:

(a) $\mathbf{i} + \mathbf{j} + \mathbf{k}$;
(b) $-0.5\mathbf{i} + \mathbf{j} - 0.5\mathbf{k}$;
(c) $-\mathbf{i} - \mathbf{j} - \mathbf{k}$.

What is the total work done in performing (a), (b) and (c)?

2 A pyramid of height h with a square base of side a is resting on one of its triangular faces on a horizontal table. Its weight is W. Find the work done in righting it so that it is resting on its square base.

3 A car of mass 1000 kg climbs a hill of gradient α where $\sin \alpha = 1/8$. Its maximum speed is 40 ms^{-1}. If the power of the car is 100 kW, what is the frictional force acting on the car? After lubrication, this frictional force is halved. What is the new top speed of the car up this hill?

4 A lorry of weight W kg can generate a power P and has a maximum speed of u ms^{-1} on level ground, but v ms^{-1} on an upslope α. If the power and resistance remain unchanged, prove that:

$$uvW \sin \alpha = P(u - v)$$

5 A car of mass M kg works at a constant rate of Mk Nm^{-1}. If there is constant frictional resistance and the maximum speed attainable is u ms^{-1}, show that the speed, v, of the car at time t satisfies the equation:

$$\frac{1}{v} - \frac{1}{u} = \frac{1}{k}\frac{dv}{dt}$$

If the car starts from rest, integrate this to show that:

$$t = \frac{u}{k}\left[u \ln\left(\frac{u}{u - v}\right) - v\right]$$

If $u = 50$ ms^{-1} and $k = 100$ m^{2}s^{-3}, show that the time taken for the car to attain a speed of 30 ms^{-1} from rest is approximately 8 s.

4.3 ENERGY

The notion of conservation is one with which most of us are familiar. Perhaps the conservation of mass is the easiest concept to understand. If we have a quantity of matter, mass m, we cannot destroy it. We may convert it chemically, change its state (to liquid or gas, for example), disperse it widely by burying it or blowing it up, but, at least theoretically, we can restore it to its former glory. This idea is expressed as the conservation of matter. We will meet the conservation of momentum formally in the next chapter. In this section, we are concerned with the conservation of energy. Einstein showed the equivalence of mass and energy in his now-famous equation $E = mc^2$, but we use this only as an indication to show that, if mass is conserved, so should energy be conserved – we steer clear of relativistic effects!

Energy, however, can take many forms. So, although energy as a whole is always conserved, it is often converted to different forms. When plants grow, they convert the Sun's radiative energy into chemical energy. This energy is absorbed by us when we eat. If we then push a wheelbarrow, the chemical energy in our muscles is converted to heat and mechanical energy. There are plenty of other examples. In this chapter, we are concerned only with mechanical energy. Mechanical energy will be conserved only if it is not converted into another form of energy, which is usually heat. Therefore, air resistance, friction between bodies, inelastic impacts, non-perfect springs, which all convert mechanical energy to heat, stop mechanical energy being conserved.

In the introduction, the two forms of mechanical energy, kinetic energy and potential energy, were defined verbally. We now define them mathematically.

The kinetic energy of a particle, abbreviated to KE, is the energy derived from the motion of the particle. Energy is the capacity for doing work, and work is defined as:

$$\int_c \mathbf{F} \cdot \mathrm{d}\mathbf{r} = \int_{x_0}^{x_1} F \, \mathrm{d}x$$

in one dimension, with $\mathbf{F} = F\mathbf{i}$, $\mathbf{r} = x\mathbf{i}$, and the curve C is the straight line (portion of the x-axis) between $x = x_0$ and $x = x_1$. Now, Newton's second law states that:

$$F = mv \, \frac{\mathrm{d}v}{\mathrm{d}x}$$

using the expression $v \, \mathrm{d}v/\mathrm{d}x$ for acceleration. Hence, the work done is:

$$\int_{x_0}^{x_1} F \, \mathrm{d}x = \int_{x_0}^{x_1} mv \, \frac{\mathrm{d}v}{\mathrm{d}x} \, \mathrm{d}x = \left[\frac{mv^2}{2} \right]_{x = x_0}^{x = x_1}$$

If the mass m is stationary at $x = x_0$, the work done would be the value of $mv^2/2$ at $x = x_1$. The expression $mv^2/2$ is called the kinetic energy of the particle moving with speed v.

(For those well versed in vector calculus, the systematic vector treatment proceeds as follows:

$$\int_c \mathbf{F} \cdot d\mathbf{r} = \int_c m\ddot{\mathbf{r}} \cdot d\mathbf{r}$$

from Newton's second law ($\mathbf{F} = m\ddot{\mathbf{r}}$). Hence:

$$\int_c \mathbf{F} \cdot d\mathbf{r} = \int_c m\ddot{\mathbf{r}} \cdot \frac{d\mathbf{r}}{dt}\, dt$$

$$= \int_c m\ddot{\mathbf{r}} \cdot \dot{\mathbf{r}}\, dt$$

$$= \int_c \frac{m}{2}\, d(\dot{\mathbf{r}})^2$$

since $\dfrac{d(\dot{\mathbf{r}})^2}{dt} = 2\ddot{\mathbf{r}} \cdot \dot{\mathbf{r}}$:

$$= \left[\frac{m\dot{\mathbf{r}}^2}{2} \right]_c = \left[\frac{mv^2}{2} \right]_c$$

That is, the change is $mv^2/2$ as C is traversed.)

In general, therefore, the kinetic energy of a particle of mass m and moving with velocity $\mathbf{v}$ is $mv^2/2$, which can be written in any of the following equivalent forms:

$$\frac{m}{2}\, \mathbf{v} \cdot \mathbf{v}, \qquad \frac{m}{2}\, |\mathbf{v}|^2 \quad \text{or} \quad \frac{mv^2}{2}$$

The potential energy of a particle, abbreviated to PE, is defined by:

$$\text{PE} = -\int_c \mathbf{F} \cdot d\mathbf{r}$$

where, once more, $\mathbf{F}$ is the force acting on the particle and C is the curve along which the particle moves. The presence of the minus sign will become clearer later. In the case of a force acting in a straight line, those who dislike line integrals can breathe more easily because:

$$PE = -\int_{x_0}^{x} \mathbf{F} \cdot \mathbf{a}\, dx \tag{1}$$

where $x = x_0$ is the level of zero potential and $\mathbf{a}$ is the direction along which the particle moves. (We have used x both as a point of the path and as the dummy variable. We think this is the least confusing.)

To be even more specific, let us calculate the general form for potential energy of the two types of force we have considered in detail. In Chapter 6, we will be concerned with the force of gravity:

$$\mathbf{F} = -mg\mathbf{k} \tag{2}$$

If we take equation (1) with $x_0 = 0$ and $\mathbf{a} = \mathbf{k}$, then

$$PE = -\int_{0}^{x} -mg\, dx$$
$$= +mgx \tag{3}$$

That is, the potential energy in the gravitational force field is mg, the weight of the particle, multiplied by the distance of the particle from the origin (the level of zero potential). Of course, this level of zero potential is arbitrary, but like the origin and direction of axes, once decided upon it is fixed and must not change. The minus sign in equation (1) is at least now seen as reasonable, since it means that potential energy increases with increasing x (height). In general, it is felt desirable to define potential energy as being positive when a particle moves against the force (the particle goes up, the force of gravity acts downwards). This is why there is a negative sign in equation (1): it counteracts a minus sign inherent in $\mathbf{F} \cdot \mathbf{a}$. Exercise 5.3.1 also justifies its presence.

In Chapter 9, we will be concerned with the restoring force of a spring. Once again, we can calculate the potential energy that is stored in a stretched spring by inserting the expression for force in equation (1). For a stretched spring:

$$\mathbf{F} = -kx\mathbf{i} \tag{4}$$

if the spring lies along the x-axis as shown in Figure 4.3, and the origin is at its natural length, l. Evaluating equation (1) with $x_0 = 0$, $\mathbf{a} = \mathbf{i}$ and $\mathbf{F}$ given by equation (4) gives:

$$PE = -\int_{0}^{x} -kx\, dx$$
$$= \frac{kx^2}{2} \tag{5}$$

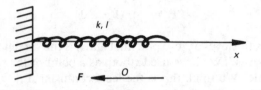

Fig. 4.3

Equation (5) is the equation for the stored potential energy of a stretched perfect spring of stiffness k and extension x. In both of these cases, we are in one dimension and the use of vectors is not appropriate. If mechanical energy is conserved, then at any time during the motion, the total mechanical energy is constant. This is usually expressed as:

$$KE + PE = constant$$

Mathematically, for a single particle:

$$\frac{m}{2}|v|^2 - \int_c F \cdot dr = constant \tag{6}$$

For one-dimensional, vertical, motion under gravity:

$$\frac{mv^2}{2} + mgx = constant \tag{7}$$

For the horizontal motion of a mass m attached to a perfect spring:

$$\frac{mv^2}{2} + \frac{kx^2}{2} = constant = C \tag{8}$$

We know from Chapter 1 that $v = dx/dt$, hence equation (8) can be written:

$$\frac{dx}{dt} = \left(\frac{2C}{m} - \frac{kx^2}{m}\right)^{1/2}$$

What we have, therefore, is a first-order differential equation but with an unknown constant. If we differentiate either equation (7) or equation (8) with respect to t, then we obtain Newton's second law for the problem. Conservation of energy is a *first integration* of the equation of motion. It can, therefore, save a considerable amount of time when solving problems to use energy. Some examples will make this clear.

Examples 4.3.1

1. A boy throws a ball vertically upwards with a speed of 15 ms^{-1}. What is the maximum height reached by the ball? (Take $g = 10$ ms^{-2}.)

Solution If $x = 0$ is the ground, with x pointing upwards, equation (7) holds. Dividing by m gives:

$$\frac{v^2}{2} + gx = A$$

We are given that $x = 0$ and $v = 15$ at the start of the motion. This enables us to find A as follows:

$$\frac{15^2}{2} + 0 = A$$

$$A = \frac{225}{2}$$

so that:

$$v^2 + 2gx = 225 \tag{9}$$

At the maximum height, the velocity of the ball is instantaneously zero, so equation (9) gives x_m, the maximum height, as:

$$x_m = \frac{225}{2g} \approx 11.25 \text{ m}$$

At the start of the motion, all the energy is kinetic. At the maximum height, $x = x_m$, all the energy is potential. As the ball travels, there is a continuous transfer of energy between kinetic and potential in such a way that the sum of the two remains a constant.

2. A perfect spring, natural length l and stiffness $mg/2l$, hangs vertically with a mass m at the end. It is pulled a distance l down from its equilibrium position and released. Calculate the distances of the extreme points of the oscillation below the point of attachment of the spring, and the maximum speed of the mass.

Solution In this problem, we have both gravitational force and the force of the spring. First of all, we need to find the equilibrium position, E, in Figure 4.4.

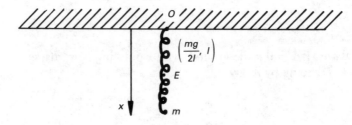

Fig. 4.4

At equilibrium, the force of the spring is equal to the force exerted by gravity on the mass m. Hence, at E, where $x = x_E$ say, we have:

$$mg = \frac{mg}{2l}(x_E - l)$$

which immediately implies:

$$x_E = 3l$$

The potential energy due to gravity is $-mgx$, where the minus sign is present because we are *below* O, our level of zero gravitational potential. The potential energy due to the stretched spring is:

$$\frac{1}{2}\,(\text{stiffness}) \times (\text{extension})^2 = \frac{1}{2}\left(\frac{mg}{2l}\right)(x - 1)^2$$

and is always positive. The energy equation is thus:

$$KE + PE = \text{constant}$$

or:

$$\frac{mv^2}{2} + \frac{mg}{4l}(x - 1)^2 - mgx = A \tag{10}$$

When the mass m is pulled down a distance l, $x = 4l$ and $v = 0$.
These values inserted into equation (10) gives:

$$0 + \frac{mg}{4l}(4l - l)^2 - mg \cdot 4l = A$$

$$A = -\frac{7mgl}{4}$$

As we will see in Chapter 9, the mass m will oscillate between two levels, with an amplitude dictated by how far the mass is pulled down. Hence, the mass oscillates between $x = 3l + l$ and $x = 3l - l$, or $x = 4l$ and $x = 2l$. The peak velocity (speed) occurs when the mass passes through its equilibrium position. Inserting $x = x_E = 3l$ (and $A = -7mgl/4$) into equation (10) will give v_m, the maximum speed, as follows:

$$\frac{mv_m^2}{2} + \frac{mg}{4l}(3l - l)^2 - mg \cdot 3l = -\frac{7mgl}{4}$$

Hence:

$$\frac{v_m^2}{2} = -\frac{7gl}{4} + 3gl - gl$$

$$= \frac{gl}{4}$$

$$v_m = \frac{1}{2}\sqrt{(2gl)} \text{ ms}^{-1}$$

To solve this using Newton's second law would take considerably more effort.

3. A child sits on a swing that rocks to and fro. Use energy arguments to find (a) the maximum velocity of the child and (b) the motion for large angle of swing.

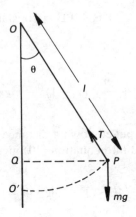

Fig. 4.5

Solution The swing is considered as a simple pendulum, as shown in Figure 4.5. The child plus swing, mass m, is at P, the length of the chain is l and the angle the swing makes with the vertical, at a general position, is labelled θ. Of course, we cannot consider any form of resistance, since this would mean that the conservation of mechanical energy was violated.

The most straightforward way to progress is to consider O, the equilibrium point of the child plus swing, as the level of zero potential. Therefore, at a general point P, the potential energy gained by the child and swing will be $mg \times OQ$. Since:

$$O'Q = OO' - OQ$$

$$= l - l \cos \theta$$

this is $mgl(1 - \cos \theta)$ and the energy equation is thus:

$$\frac{mv^2}{2} + mgl(1 - \cos \theta) = A \tag{11}$$

where $A = mv_0^2/2$ (v_0 = speed of child and swing at O'). Inserting this value for A in equation (11) and cancelling the $m/2$ gives:

$$v^2 + 2gl(1 - \cos \theta) = v_0^2 \quad \text{or} \quad v^2 = v_0^2 - 2gl(1 - \cos \theta)$$

which can be written as:

$$v^2 = v_0^2 - 4gl \sin^2 \tfrac{1}{2}\theta \tag{12}$$

In Chapter 8, we will introduce the notion of angular velocity, $d\theta/dt$; however, all we need here is that $v = l \, d\theta/dt$. If $\theta = \theta_0$ at maximum amplitude, then v is instantaneously zero. Inserting $v = 0$ when $\theta = \theta_0$ in equation (12) gives:

$$0 = v_0^2 - 4gl \sin^2 \tfrac{1}{2}\theta_0 \tag{13}$$

which enables equation (12) to be rewritten as:

$$v^2 = 4gl(\sin^2 \tfrac{1}{2}\theta_0 - \sin^2 \tfrac{1}{2}\theta) \tag{14}$$

Equation (13) is an exact expression for v_0, the maximum speed of the child in terms of θ_0, which is the greatest angle of the chain from the vertical. Recall that we said θ_0 need not be small. However, if we assume it was, then $\sin \tfrac{1}{2}\theta_0 \approx \tfrac{1}{2}\theta_0$ and $\sin \tfrac{1}{2}\theta \approx \tfrac{1}{2}\theta$ (since $\theta \leqslant \theta_0$), whence equations (13) and (14) become:

$$v_0^2 = gl \, \theta_0^2 \quad \text{and} \quad v^2 = gl(\theta_0^2 - \theta^2)$$

respectively. The second of these equations is precisely equation (24) of Chapter 9, which will be obtained by integrating Newton's second law once assuming a small angle θ. For large angles of swing, equations (12) or (14) must be used.

In fact, energy can be used very successfully in analysing the generalisation of this problem: motion in a vertical circle. Full consideration of this takes place in Chapter 8.

Before trying some exercises, here is an example involving *loss* of mechanical energy.

Example 4.3.2

A food parcel is dropping from a helicopter. Calculate the loss of energy if the resistance is such that it restricts the speed of the food parcel (mass 10 kg) to 20 ms^{-1} at the ground. The helicopter remains at 200 m. (Take $g = 10$ ms^{-2}.)

Solution   Initially, all the (mechanical) energy is potential:

$$\text{PE} = mgx = 10 \times 10 \times 200 = 20\ 000 \text{ W} = 20 \text{ kW}$$

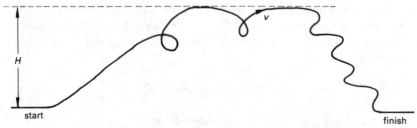

Fig. 4.6

As the parcel hits the ground with a speed of 20 ms⁻¹, it has lost all of its potential energy, since it is now at zero height. The amount of kinetic energy it has gained is:

$$KE = \frac{mv^2}{2} = \frac{10}{2} \times 20^2 = 2000 \text{ W} = 2 \text{ kW}$$

The parcel has only 10% of its initial energy in the form of mechanical energy. The other 90% (= 18 kW) has been dissipated in the form of heat (etc.). Of course, once the parcel hits the ground, all of its mechanical energy has gone. It is better to convert it gradually through the descent rather than lose 20 kW of mechanical energy on impact; hence, the existence of parachutes!

We finish this section with a look at practical, everyday examples of situations where the conservation of energy can be used. We have all seen roller-coasters in seaside fairgrounds and theme parks. The track cork-screws and loops around in shapes that defy precise geometrical description. Let us assume that, at the highest point of the roller-coaster, the speed of the car is v_0, and that, after the initial acceleration, no further power or significant brake is applied to the car. If the highest point, H in Figure 4.6, is a distance h above the ground, then the total mechanical energy at H is:

$$PE + KE = \frac{mv_0^2}{2} + mgh$$

where m is the mass of the car. At any other point of the track, all we need is the height above the ground (x, say), then the speed, v, is given by the conservation of energy as:

$$\frac{mv^2}{2} + mgx = \frac{mv_0^2}{2} + mgh$$

or:

$$v^2 = v_0^2 + g(h - x) \tag{15}$$

cancelling the mass m.

For example, for a roller-coaster 30 m high, on which v_0 is 5 ms^{-1} and taking $g = 10$ ms^{-2} when $x = 10$ m, equation (15) gives the velocity of the car as $v(10)$ where:

$$v(10) = 5 + 10(30 - 10) = 225$$

$$= 15 \text{ ms}^{-1}$$

There are three points to be made here. First, you may argue with some conviction that equation (15) is not accurate because friction has been ignored. However, the designers of fairground roller-coasters are concerned with the *maximum* speed when designing safe corners and corkscrews (etc.). Any friction would reduce the speed, v, calculated using equation (15), hence the calculated speed could be used as a design criterion. If it was safe for this speed, it would certainly be safe for the real speed which, due to resistance, would be less than v. Second, the thrill of a roller-coaster is due to its acceleration or rate of change of speed, rather than the speed itself. This is most easily calculated directly from the local slope of the track (this acceleration is $g \sin \alpha$ where α is the local slope). Third, the shape of roller-coasters is usually significantly three dimensional, which leads to sideways accelerations. We have not considered these yet, but will do so in Chapter 8.

Finally, we hope that the reader now realises that many of the problems of previous chapters could have been tackled more simply using energy considerations. Newton's cradle (example 2.2.1) can be analysed in terms of kinetic and potential energy, as can the apple problems of Section 7.2 (no resistance) and the mass–spring problems (no damping) of Chapter 9. In general, it is best to use the equation of conservation of mechanical energy when possible. However, problems involving time are more easily dealt with from Newton's second law.

We have only looked at power, work and energy, and have not yet addressed impulse. This is best considered in the context of collisions – balls hitting walls in snooker, for example – and this is the subject of the next chapter. We therefore leave consideration of impulse until then. We will also meet impulse in Chapter 10 when we consider variable mass problems.

EXERCISES 4.3

1 By considering the energy equation in the form:

$$\frac{mv^2}{2} + PE = \text{constant}$$

and differentiating with respect to x, show that:

$$PE = -\int^x F \, dx$$

where F is the force. All motion may be assumed to take place in a straight line.

2 Two masses $3m$ and $6m$ are connected by a light inextensible string of length l. They are suspended around a small frictionless pulley such that each mass is held at the same level, distance $l/2$ below the pulley. If the masses are released, find their speed when they are a distance $l/3$ apart.

3 A uniform heavy chain is dropped over a smooth peg. It is held with one-third of its length on one side and two-thirds of its length on the other side, and then released. If the chain has length l, show that its speed, when the end just leaves the peg, is $10\sqrt{(gl)}/9$ ms^{-1}. (*Hint*: The centre of mass of a chain of length x is half-way along its length, and the mass of this length is x where ρ is the uniform density.)

4 A mass m is attached by two springs of stiffness $mg/2$ and $mg/3$, both of natural length 1 m, to supports 4 m apart. If the mass is displaced 0.8 m and released, find the maximum speed of the mass. (Take $g = 10$ ms^{-2}.)

5 Example 6.5 considers a parachutist. Find the loss of mechanical energy when (a) the parachute opens after 5 s and (b) the parachute opens after 13.5 s.

6 Indicate which of the following problems can be conveniently dealt with using conservation of mechanical energy, and briefly explain why:

(a) The motion of a planet around the Sun.
(b) The motion of a smooth truck down a hill.
(c) A cable car for skiers.
(d) A mass suspended on a piece of light elastic string.
(e) A hydraulic door stop.
(f) The motion of a ball bouncing down the stairs.

4.4 CONNECTED PARTICLES

In the context of this section, connected particles are point masses connected by light strings or springs. Situations that can be modelled using
connected particles include a bucket joined to a counterweight over a
pulley, or a ball connected to a bat by a piece of elastic.

m

M

Fig. 4.7

Problems involving connected particles are readily solved using energy
methods in the following way. If a mass M is connected over a pulley to a
smaller mass m by a light inextensible string as shown in Figure 4.7, then
mass M will fall. If at time t, mass m is distance x below the pulley and mass
M is distance y below the pulley and both have speed v, then:

$$\frac{mv^2}{2} + \frac{Mv^2}{2} - mgx - Mgy = \text{constant}$$

using the energy equation. Let us do a specific example.

Example 4.4.1

A bucket is connected by a light rope over a pulley to a counterweight that
is half the weight of the bucket. Initially, the bucket is held at the pulley
with the counterweight 10 m below, just touching the ground. What is the
speed of the bucket when (a) the bucket passes the counterweight and (b)
the bucket hits the ground? (Take $g = 10$ ms^{-2}.)

Solution   Initially, there is zero kinetic energy, and the potential energy of
the counterweight is zero if we take the ground as the level of potential.
Therefore, the only energy in the system is the potential energy of the
bucket, 10 m above the ground.

Let the bucket have mass M, then the potential energy is $100M$. Figure
4.8 shows the two situations where the speed of the bucket is required. If

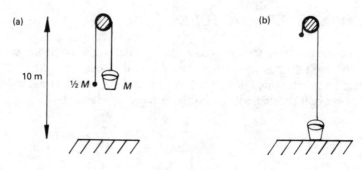

Fig. 4.8

the speed of each mass is v_1, then the expression:

$$\frac{1}{2}\left(\tfrac{1}{2}M\right) v_1^2 + \frac{1}{2} Mv_1^2 + 50x\frac{1}{2} M + 50xM$$

is the total energy of the masses in Figure 4.8(a). By the energy equation, this equals $100M$. Solving this equation gives:

$$v_1 = 5.7 \text{ ms}^{-1}$$

In Figure 4.8(b), given that the speed of the bucket and counterweight is now v_2, the energy equation yields:

$$\frac{1}{2}\left(\tfrac{1}{2}M\right) v_2^2 + \frac{1}{2} v_2^2 + 100x\frac{1}{2} M = 100M$$

Solving this equation for v_2 gives:

$$v_2 = 8.2 \text{ ms}^{-1}$$

The following example involves a spring.

Example 4.4.2

Two identical masses A and B of mass m lie on a horizontal table and are connected by a light spring of natural length l and stiffness mg/l. The two masses are held a distance $2l$ apart. The mass at A is then released. What is its speed when, once again, it is a distance l from B? If both masses were released, what would be the new speed of A?

Solution The energy stored in a stretched spring is given by the expression $\frac{1}{2}$ (stiffness) $\times$ (extension)^2. This is the only energy present initially, hence when A and B are held, the energy of the system is:

$$\frac{mg}{2l} (2l - l)^2 = mgl$$

When A and B are distance l apart, the spring is at zero extension, hence all the energy is kinetic. Since only A is moving, this is $\frac{1}{2}mv^2$ where v is A's speed.

By the conservation of energy:

$$\frac{mv^2}{2} = \frac{mgl}{2}$$

$$v = \sqrt{(gl)}$$

If A and B were both released, by symmetry they would both have the same speeds (Figure 4.9). Hence, the speed of each would be $1/2\sqrt{(gl)}$ relative to the table.

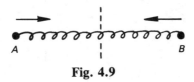

Fig. 4.9

EXERCISES 4.4

1 A bucket of cement has mass 10 kg and is winched to a height of 5 m by a man pulling on a (light) rope attached to the bucket and passed over a pulley. He ties a rock to the rope he is holding. Unfortunately, the rock is not heavy enough to support the cement and the bucket hits the ground at a speed of 4 ms⁻¹. Assuming that the pulley is frictionless and that the rock has climbed 5 m, estimate the mass of the rock. A man on a platform 5 m up now adds a mass of 3 kg to the rock. Will the bucket of cement now rise?

2 A man of mass 75 kg stands on the ground holding a (light) rope which is connected over a pulley to a bucket containing bricks, of combined mass 80 kg. Initially, the bricks are stationary at a height of 8 m. The man (of course) is lifted off the ground. What is the relative velocity of man and bucket at impact? On collision, the bucket sheds 60 kg of bricks. At

what speed does the man reach the ground? (Acknowledgements and apologies to Gerard Hoffnung!)

3 A catapult is modelled using a mass attached to a linear spring. If the mass is 0.5 kg and the spring has a stiffness of 5×10^3 Nm^{-1}, calculate the speed of the mass if the stretching of the catapult's elastic is simulated by an extension of 0.2 m and the mass is released when the spring returns to its natural length.

5 COLLISIONS

5.1 INTRODUCTION

In Chapter 3, the term momentum was defined as the product of mass and velocity. It has particular significance when we study collisions. Let us demonstrate this with a simple example. A heavy lorry and a car are travelling side by side at the same speed and need to stop at a red light. Common experience leads us to expect that the braking force required to bring the lorry to a stop must be greater than that required to stop the lighter car. Newton's second law states that:

$$\text{force} = \text{mass} \times \frac{\text{d(velocity)}}{\text{d}t}$$

or, for constant mass:

$$\text{force} = \frac{\text{d(mass} \times \text{velocity)}}{\text{d}t}$$

The right-hand side of this equation represents the rate of change of momentum. Hence, the lorry, which has the larger momentum, needs a greater force to make it stop than does the car.

5.2 IMPULSE AND MOMENTUM FROM NEWTON'S LAWS

Let us, at a gentle pace, derive some simple expressions directly from Newton's second law as stated in Chapter 2. If a constant force of F N acts on a body of mass M kg, it will produce a constant acceleration of a ms^{-2},

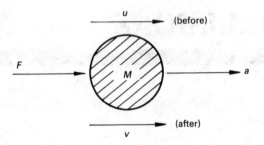

Fig. 5.1

regardless of the state of the motion before the force was applied. According to the relationship:

$$F = Ma \tag{1}$$

the force and acceleration are in the same direction, as shown in Figure 5.1. If the velocity of the mass was u ms^{-1} directly before the force was applied and v ms^{-1} t seconds after its application, the constant acceleration formulae can be applied to the motion to give:

$$a = \frac{v - u}{t}$$

Substituting this in equation (1) gives:

$$F = \frac{Mv - Mu}{t} \tag{2}$$

In this equation, we can identify Mv as the final momentum and Mu as the initial momentum of the body, so that the right-hand side of equation (2) represents the rate of change of momentum of the body, which is constant.

As already stated, an alternative statement of Newton's second law could then be that the impressed force is directly proportional to the rate of change of momentum. If we consider equation (2) written in the form:

$$Ft = Mv - Mu$$

then Ft, defined as the impulse, would be the change of momentum. For a constant force acting for t seconds, the quantity $I = Ft$ Ns is the impulse of the force and is a vector quantity in the same direction as F.

Forces are usually applied only for a finite time, so impulse is a very important quantity. From Newton's second law, non-constant acceleration is the result of a non-constant force. If the redefined definition of Newton's law is still to apply, we can write that, if a variable force of F N acts between the times $t = t_1$ and $t = t_2$ seconds, so that at time $t_1 \leqslant t \leqslant t_2$ its velocity is V ms^{-1}, then:

$$F = \frac{d(MV)}{dt} \tag{3}$$

Although we have only considered mass as a constant, this expression takes account of any possible variation in mass that can occur. Here, the rate of change of momentum can be found by integrating with respect to t, to give:

$$\int_{t_1}^{t_2} F \, dt = \left[MV\right]_{t_1}^{t_2} = Mv - Mu$$

The impulse, I, of a variable force can then be written as:

$$I = \int_{t_1}^{t_2} F \, dt$$

Examples 5.2.1

1. A force of 25 N acts for 2 s, in the direction of motion, on a body of mass 10 kg travelling with a velocity of 5 ms^{-1}. Calculate (a) the impulse and (b) the final velocity of the body.

   Solution

   (a) The force is constant, so:

   $$\text{impulse} = 25 \times 2 = 50 \text{ Ns}$$

   (b) The velocity after the impulse has been applied is shown as V in Figure 5.2. Using impulse = change in momentum gives:

   $$50 = 10V - 10 \times 5$$

   so that V, the final velocity, is 10 ms^{-1}.

2. If a force $F(t) = 10 \sin(\pi t)$ N at time t seconds, find the impulse applied by this force to the body in the previous example moving with the same initial velocity, and find the new final velocity.

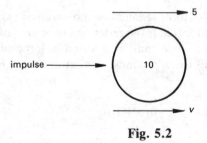

Fig. 5.2

Solution The force is variable, so:

$$\text{impulse} = \int_0^1 10 \sin (\pi t) \, \mathrm{d}t = \left[\frac{-10 \cos (\pi t)}{\pi} \right]_0^1 = \frac{20}{\pi} \text{ Ns}$$

Again, using impulse = change in momentum gives, for the final velocity V:

$$\frac{20}{\pi} = 10V - 10 \times 5$$

where the final velocity is 5.64 ms⁻¹.

The directional qualities of impulse and momentum should not be forgotten. The following example is intended to highlight the variety of effects that an impulse can have.

Example 5.2.2

In Figure 5.3, a body of mass 5 kg has been struck by an impulse of I Ns. Three different cases are shown in the figure: for each case, the direction

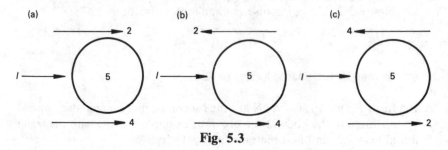

Fig. 5.3

and magnitude of the velocity before and after the application of the impulse are shown. Calculate the impulse required to produce the effect in each case.

Solution   In each case, the relationship impulse = change in momentum is used:

(a) gives:

$$I = 5 \times 4 - 5 \times 2 = 10 \text{ Ns}$$

(b) gives:

$$I = 5 \times 4 - 5 \times (-2) = 30 \text{ Ns}$$

(c) gives:

$$I = 5 \times (-2) - 5 \times (-4) = 10 \text{ Ns}$$

So far, we have discussed impulse and momentum in one dimension. The extension to two and three dimensions can easily be made. Consider a body with mass M kg that is travelling with velocity vector $\mathbf{V}$ at time t. If an impulse vector $\mathbf{I}$ acts from $t = t_1$ to $t = t_2$ with its velocity vector changing from $\mathbf{u}$ to $\mathbf{v}$, then the equivalent vector equation is:

$$\mathbf{I} = M\mathbf{v} - M\mathbf{u} \qquad (4)$$

and the force $\mathbf{F}$ at time t seconds satisfies the relationship:

$$\mathbf{F} = \frac{\mathrm{d}(M\mathbf{V})}{\mathrm{d}t}$$

Example 5.2.3

A particle of mass 2 kg is moving in a flat horizontal plane so that it is travelling at 3 ms^{-1} in a direction with bearing 120°. If an impulse of magnitude 2 Ns is applied to the particle towards the north, find the new direction of the particle and its speed.

Solution   The motion is illustrated in Figure 5.4. If the analysis is carried out using unit vectors $\mathbf{i}$ and $\mathbf{j}$ in the east and north directions respectively,

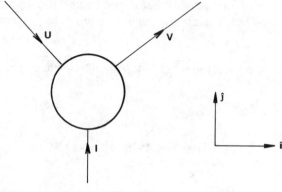

Fig. 5.4

then the initial velocity vector can be written as:

$$U = 3 \cos 60°i - 3 \sin 60°j = 1.50i - 2.60j$$

and the final velocity vector as:

$$V = ui + vj$$

The impulse vector is:

$$I = 2j$$

Equation (4) gives:

$$2j = 2 \times (ui + vj) - 2 \times (1.5i - 2.6j)$$

From which, on equating components:

$$u = 1.5 \quad \text{and} \quad v = 5$$

The new velocity of the particle has vector $V = 1.5i + 5j$ or magnitude 5.22 ms^{-1} in a direction 16.7°.

EXERCISES 5.2

1 For each of the following forces, calculate the impulse for the time t (in seconds) given and the final velocity if the impulse is applied to a body of mass 3 kg that is moving with speed 2 ms^{-1} in the direction of its

motion:

(a) $F = 25$ N; $t = 0$ to $t = 5$;
(b) $F = \sin^2 (2\pi t)$; $t = 0$ to $t = 1$;
(c) $F = \begin{cases} 5t, & 0 \leqslant t \leqslant 5 \\ 25, & 5 < t \leqslant 10. \end{cases}$

2 A particle of mass 5 kg is moving in a straight line towards the east with velocity 3 ms^{-1}. Calculate the magnitude of the impulse acting towards the north that is required to change its direction towards 45°.

3 Two particles A and B, both of mass m, are fastened to the ends of a piece of inextensible string and placed on a horizontal table. Particle A is then projected with speed v in a direction of 45° to the string, so that the string slackens. Calculate the impulse in the string when the string next tightens, and find the magnitude and direction of the velocity of A and B immediately afterwards.

4 A small ball of mass m is dropped into a bucket of mass M, striking the bucket with speed v. The bucket is attached to a counterbalance by an inextensible string which hangs over a pulley, as shown in Figure 5.5. If the pulley system begins to move with speed V, calculate:

(a) the impulse in the string at impact;
(b) the speed of the ball immediately after impact.

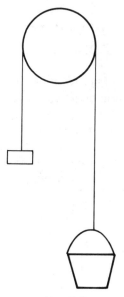

Fig. 5.5

5.3 COLLISIONS IN THE REAL WORLD

Collisions of freely moving bodies, or of a body with some fixed object, are important everyday occurrences. Perhaps sport gives the most obvious applications. For example, snooker or pool involves collisions of freely moving bodies as well as collisions with a fixed body (the cushions at the edge of the table). Brownian motion, which is molecular activity in a liquid, is an example of free collisions between bodies. A shunt in a traffic column is an example of two bodies that may become one after the impact.

The interaction experienced in collisions involves Newton's third law: '. . . *action and reaction are equal and opposite*'. It is from this point that we begin our analysis of collisions.

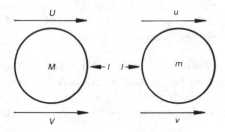

Fig. 5.6

5.4 CONSERVATION OF MOMENTUM VIA IMPULSE FOR COLLIDING BODIES

In Figure 5.6, two bodies of mass M and m are shown travelling in a straight line so that they are in direct collision. Velocities before and after the impact are also shown. When in collision, the body of mass m has its velocity changed by the action of an impulse, I, acting as shown. Newton's third law says that there is an impulse of equal magnitude but in the opposite direction acting on the body of mass M, which is also shown. Using the impulse momentum relationship for M gives:

$$-I = MV - MU$$

and for m:

$$I = mv - mu$$

The addition of these two equations gives:

$$MU + mu = MV + mv$$

where the momentum before the collision is the same as the momentum after. This is the *law of conservation of momentum for the linear motion for two particles in direct collision*.

This can be extended to motion in three dimensions by using vectors to give:

$$MU + mu = MV + mv$$

where the notation remains as before. This is the law of conservation of linear momentum for two particles. More generally, in any collision, the total momentum before the collision will be equal to the total momentum after.

Examples 5.4

1. A bullet of mass 10 g is fired horizontally into a block of wood of mass 1 kg which rests on a smooth horizontal plane. If the bullet's velocity is 1000 ms^{-1}, find the final velocity of the block, if the bullet becomes embedded in the block.

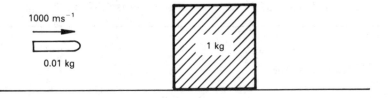

Fig. 5.7

Solution Figure 5.7 shows the block and bullet with the combined velocity when the bullet is at rest relative to the block. Conservation of momentum gives:

$$0.0001 \times 1000 = 1.001 \times V$$

This gives the combined velocity as 0.999 ms^{-1}.

2. A man of mass 50 kg throws a medicine ball of mass 10 kg with a speed of 5 ms^{-1}. The man is standing on a trolley of mass 20 kg, which is at rest and can travel on smooth tracks. He throws the ball along the tracks.

101

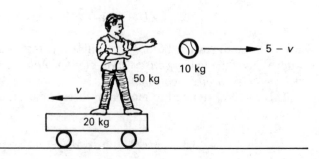

Fig. 5.8

What will be the true speed of the ball as seen by an observer standing on the ground?

Solution   In Figure 5.8, the man is shown on the trolley after the ball has been thrown. The velocity of the trolley is v ms^{-1} in the direction indicated. The true velocity of the ball will be $5 - v$ ms^{-1}. This means that $v > 5$. Applying the law of conservation of momentum to the man and trolley gives:

$$0 = 10 \times (5 - v) + 70 \times (-v)$$

Solving this for v gives that the trolley moves with a velocity of 0.625 ms^{-1}. Hence, the velocity of the ball is 4.375 ms^{-1}.

EXERCISES 5.4

1   A woman climbs on to a light trolley standing at one end. She then moves quickly to the other end, stopping when she arrives there. She then jumps off the trolley. Describe the motion of the trolley during the woman's movements, assuming no friction between the trolley and the ground.

2   Two putty-like masses m and $2m$ are travelling in the same straight line but in opposite directions, with speed u, when they collide and unite. Find the magnitude and direction of the velocity of the combined masses and determine the loss in energy.

3   A cannon of mass M is free to move on a smooth horizontal track. If the cannon fires a shell, with muzzle speed v, horizontally along the track,

find the resulting recoil velocity of the cannon and calculate the energy generated in the firing.

4 A bullet of mass 10 g is fired horizontally into a block of wood of mass 1 kg, which rests on a smooth horizontal plane. If the bullet's velocity is 1000 ms⁻¹, find the velocity of the block, if the bullet emerges from the block with a speed of 500 ms⁻¹.

5.5 NEWTON'S EXPERIMENTAL LAW

Consider the example of two bodies of masses 2 kg and 3 kg moving in a collision course on a smooth surface: they hit each other and move independently after the collision. In Figure 5.9, the motion is illustrated. The speeds before the collision are 4 ms⁻¹ and 1 ms⁻¹, their direction being as indicated. It is our aim to calculate their respective speeds, v and V, after the collision.

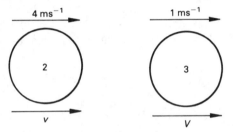

Fig. 5.9

Conservation of momentum at the collision gives:

$$2 \times 4 + 3 \times 1 = 2v + 3V$$

which simplifies to give:

$$11 = 2v + 3V \tag{5}$$

This equation gives a relationship between the two velocities but not a solution. We seek a second relationship between v and V so that values for v and V can be obtained.

There is a second law governing the collision of such bodies, Newton's experimental law of restitution. It takes account of energy losses at collision. It can be stated as: If two bodies collide, their relative velocity before impact is $-e$ times their relative velocity after impact. The constant e is called the *coefficient of restitution* for the two bodies concerned. The case $e = 1$, which is unattainable in practice, is called a perfectly elastic collision, and there is no energy loss. If $e = 0$, the collision is termed inelastic and the bodies unite or coalesce. This was the case in the bullet and block problem (example 5.4.1).

For the velocities as shown in Figure 5.6, the restitution law would give:

$$-e(U - u) = (V - v)$$

Returning to the problem in this section, if we know that $e = 1/2$, then we have:

$$-\frac{1}{2}(4 - 1) = V - v$$

$$-1.5 = V - v \qquad (6)$$

Equations (5) and (6) can be solved by simple algebra to give:

$$v = 1.6 \text{ ms}^{-1} \quad \text{and} \quad V = 0.1 \text{ ms}^{-1}$$

Clearly, the energy loss and its dependence on e does warrant further study. In Figure 5.10, the graph of energy loss for the two bodies we have

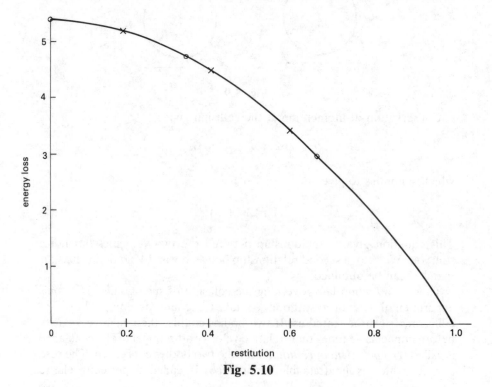

Fig. 5.10

just considered is shown for values of e from 0 to 1. Note that when $e = 0$, an inelastic collision, the energy loss, measured as the difference in the kinetic energy before and after the collision, is greatest. When $e = 1$, the elastic case, it is zero.

Example 5.5

Three small spheres A, B and C lie in a straight line on a smooth table. Their masses are m, $2m$ and $4m$ respectively. Sphere A is projected towards sphere B with a speed of 8 ms⁻¹. If the coefficient of restitution is 1/4, find the velocities of the three spheres after three collisions and show that there can be no more collisions.

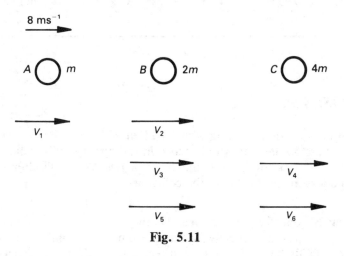

Fig. 5.11

Solution In Figure 5.11, the speeds of the spheres before and after each collision are shown. If the motion of the spheres is modelled as particles, then for the first collision we have:

$$\text{conservation of momentum: } 8 = V_1 + 2V_2$$

Restitution gives:

$$-2 = V_1 - V_2$$

This gives $V_1 = 1.33$ ms⁻¹ and $V_2 = 3.33$ ms⁻¹.
   For the second collision:

$$\text{conservation of momentum: } 6.67 = 2V_3 + 4V_4$$

Restitution gives:

$$-0.83 = V_3 - V_4$$

This gives $V_3 = 0.56$ ms^{-1} and $V_4 = 1.39$ ms^{-1}.
    For the third collision:

conservation of momentum: $2.44 = V_5 + 2V_6$

Restitution gives:

$$-0.05 = V_5 - V_6$$

This gives $V_5 = 0.69$ ms^{-1} and $V_6 = 0.88$ ms^{-1}. As $V_5 < V_6 < V_4$ there can be
no more collisions.

EXERCISES 5.5

1 A ball of mass $4m$ is moving with speed $2u$ and collides with a second
   ball of mass $5m$ moving with speed u in the opposite direction. If the
   coefficient of restitution is 1/2, find the velocities of the balls after impact
   and the loss in energy due to the collision.

2 A ball falls from a height of 20 m and at the same time a ball of the same
   mass is projected vertically upwards from the ground with speed
   40 ms^{-1}, so that they meet in a direct impact. If the coefficient of
   restitution between the two balls is 1/2, find the time that elapses before
   the two balls reach the ground.

3 Three spheres of masses m, $3m$ and $6m$ whose speeds are $6u$, $2u$ and u
   respectively are moving in the same direction in the same straight line in
   the order given. If the collisions that take place are perfectly elastic,
   show that the first two spheres will be brought to rest.

4 Three particles of masses m_1, m_2 and m_3 are at rest on a smooth
   horizontal table. The first sphere is given a speed u towards the second.
   The coefficients of restitution are e and e' between m_1 and m_2, and m_2
   and m_3 respectively. Determine how the values of m_1, m_2, m_3, u, e and e'
   may be allotted so that the total number of collisions is a maximum.

5.6 DIRECT COLLISION BETWEEN A PARTICLE AND A FIXED BARRIER

In Figure 5.12, a particle of mass m is shown in collision with a fixed barrier. Its velocity before the collision is U and after is V. The barrier supplies an impulse I to the particle, which has its motion reversed by the collision. This is not a case in which conservation of momentum can apply, as the momentum supplied to the barrier through the impact is lost (this system resembles that in Figure 5.3(b)).

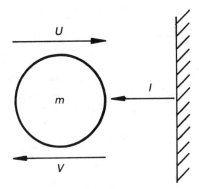

Fig. 5.12

The impulse momentum relationship applied to the particle only gives:

$$I = mV - m(-U) = m(V + U)$$

The loss in energy can still be analysed using the restitution law. Applying the law to the impact gives:

$$-e(-U - 0) = V - 0$$

to give the reduced relationship in this case of:

$$eU = V$$

Example 5.6

A ball m is dropped from a height h on to a horizontal floor and it rebounds to a height $(1/2)h$. Calculate (a) the value of the coefficient of restitution, e, between the ball and the floor, (b) the impulse applied by the floor to the ball and (c) the time until bouncing ceases.

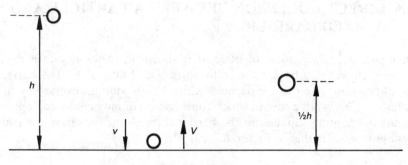

Fig. 5.13

Solution   In Figure 5.13, the ball is shown at the point of impact. The velocities immediately before and after the impact are also shown. If the velocity just before the impact is v, we have:

$$v^2 = 0 + 2gh$$

$$v = \sqrt{(2gh)}$$

If the velocity after impact is V, we can also say:

$$0 = V^2 - 2g \times \frac{1}{2}h$$

$$V = \sqrt{(gh)}$$

(a) Applying the law of restitution to the ball at impact gives:

$$e\sqrt{(2gh)} = \sqrt{(gh)}$$

$$e = \frac{1}{\sqrt{2}}$$

(b) The impulse momentum relationship gives for the impulse I:

$$I = m\sqrt{(gh)} - m(-\sqrt{(2gh)}) = m\sqrt{(gh)}(\sqrt{2} + 1)$$

(c) When the velocity immediately after impact with the floor is V, then the time to the next bounce is given by:

$$0 = Vt - \frac{1}{2}gt^2$$

which gives the time as $2V/g$.

In theory, there will be an infinite number of bounces. As the velocity at each bounce is multiplied by a factor e, we have that the total time of bouncing is:

$$\frac{2v}{g} + \frac{2ev}{g} + \frac{2e^2v}{g} + \frac{2e^3v}{g} + \ldots$$

where $v = \sqrt{(2gh)}$. Note that the time to the first impact is, in effect, half of a complete bounce. This series can be rewritten as:

$$\frac{2v}{g}(1 + e + e^2 + e^3 + \ldots)$$

The geometric progression can be summed to infinity, as $e < 1$, to give:

$$\frac{2v}{g}(1 - e)^{-1} = (1 + \sqrt{2})\frac{4}{3}\sqrt{\left(\frac{h}{g}\right)}$$

EXERCISES 5.6

1 A small body slides over a smooth horizontal floor hitting a wall along its normal. If the time taken for the body to return from the wall to its point of projection is twice the journey to the wall, find the coefficient of restitution between the body and the wall.

2 A ball is projected vertically upwards with a speed U from the floor of a room of height h. It hits the ceiling and then returns to the floor, from which it rebounds, managing to just hit the ceiling a second time. Calculate the coefficient of restitution between the floor and the ball, and the ceiling and the ball, if they are equal.

3 A ball is dropped on to a horizontal plane. If the coefficient of restitution between the ball and the plane is e, show that the average speed for each bounce decreases at a rate of e per bounce.

4 Two smooth spheres A and B of equal radii and masses $2m$ and $3m$ respectively lie on a smooth horizontal table. A is given a velocity so that it hits B, at rest, directly, which then goes on to strike the wall normally. If the coefficient of restitution between the spheres is 1/2 and

that between B and the wall is 1/4, show that there is a total of three collisions only.

5 Two particles A and B of masses m and M are placed so that they are in a line perpendicular to a wall. The coefficient of restitution between A and B is e, and between B and the wall is e'. If A is projected towards the wall with speed u, so that it strikes particle B first, find how the total number of collisions can be maximised by suitable choice of m, M, e, e' and u.

5.7 OBLIQUE COLLISION BETWEEN A PARTICLE AND A FIXED BARRIER

In Figure 5.14, a particle of mass M is shown at the point of impact with a smooth barrier. Although this type of problem appears three dimensional, the motion can always be considered to take place in a plane containing the normal to the barrier and the particle's initial velocity, provided that the barrier is smooth.

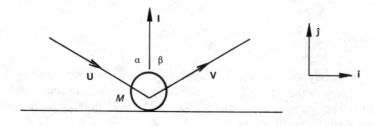

Fig. 5.14

In Figure 5.14, the particle is shown to have a speed U before its impact with the barrier, at an angle α with the normal, that is, velocity vector **U**. Its speed after impact is V at an angle β with the normal, that is, velocity vector **V**. As the plane is smooth, the impulse I applied to the particle will be normal to the plane. If the impulse vector is **I**, then the vector equation for the impulse momentum relationship gives:

$$\mathbf{I} = M\mathbf{V} - M\mathbf{U}$$

If unit vectors **i** and **j** are taken as shown in Figure 5.14, then the relationship becomes:

$$I\mathbf{j} = M(V \sin \beta \mathbf{i} + V \cos \beta \mathbf{j}) - M(U \sin \alpha \mathbf{i} - U \cos \alpha \mathbf{j})$$

Solving gives a decoupling of the components as:

$$I = MV \cos \beta + MU \cos \alpha$$

which is the impulse momentum equation applied along the normal to the plane, and $MV \sin \beta = MU \sin \alpha$, which is the conservation of momentum along the plane.

The restitution law supplies the second governing equation for the motion, applied normal to the plane where energy loss occurs, to give:

$$eU \cos \alpha = V \cos \beta$$

Given the direction α and the magnitude U of the incoming velocity, it is possible to find the direction β from:

$$\tan \beta = \frac{\tan \alpha}{e}$$

and magnitude:

$$V = U\sqrt{(e^2 \cos^2 \alpha + \sin^2 \alpha)}$$

of the outgoing velocity.

Examples 5.7

1. A ball of mass m is dropped from a height h on to a plane inclined at α to the horizontal. If the ball rebounds so that its motion is initially horizontal, calculate (a) the coefficient of restitution, e, between the ball and the plane, and (b) the loss in kinetic energy due to the impact.

Solution Figure 5.15 shows the motion of the ball just before and just after impact. The speeds just before and after impact are v and V. The information given allows the angles before and after impact to be determined in terms of α.

The ball falls vertically a height h to give:

$$v^2 = 0 + 2gh$$

$$v = \sqrt{(2gh)}$$

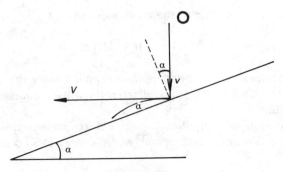

Fig. 5.15

Conservation of momentum along the plane at impact gives:

$$mv \sin \alpha = mV \cos \alpha$$

and the law of restitution gives:

$$ev \cos \alpha = V \sin \alpha$$

(a) Dividing these two expressions leads to:

$$e = \tan^2 \alpha$$

(b) Loss in kinetic energy at impact is:

$$\frac{1}{2} mv^2 - \frac{1}{2} mV^2$$

which can be rewritten to give:

$$\frac{1}{2} v^2 (1 - (\sin^2 \alpha + e^2 \cos \alpha))$$

which simplifies to give:

$$\frac{1}{2} mv^2 \cos^2 \alpha (1 - e^2) = mgh(1 - \tan^2 \alpha)$$

2. A large smooth horizontal circular table has a vertical rim around its edge. Show that, if a small body is projected from a point P at the edge of the table, in a direction making an angle α with the radius to P, so that after two impacts the body returns to P, then:

$$\cot^2 \alpha = \frac{1 + e + e^2}{e^3}$$

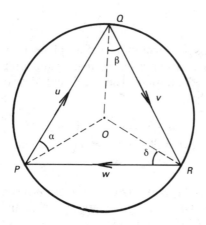

Fig. 5.16

Solution In Figure 5.16, the possible path of the particle from P is shown. The angles made by the direction of motion after the first and second impacts, at Q and R, are shown as β and δ. The speeds u, v and w represent the speeds between the impacts shown.

The geometry of the circle allows the incident angle at Q to be identified as α and at R as β, while $\alpha + \beta + \delta = (1/2)\pi$. For the point Q:

$$e \tan \alpha = \tan \beta \qquad (7)$$

For the point R:

$$e \tan \beta = \tan \delta \qquad (8)$$

Removing δ from equation (8) gives:

$$e \tan \beta = \tan \left(\frac{1}{2} \pi - (\alpha + \beta) \right) = \cot (\alpha + \beta)$$

The expansion formula for $\tan (\alpha + \beta)$ then gives:

$$e \tan \beta = \frac{1 - \tan \alpha \tan \beta}{\tan \alpha + \tan \beta}$$

Eliminating $\tan \beta$ using equation (7) and rearranging gives the required result.

EXERCISES 5.7

1 A particle of mass m moves on a smooth plane so that its speed before impact with a fixed barrier is u at an angle α and afterwards its speed is v at an angle β with the normal. The coefficient of restitution between the particle and the barrier is e.

 (a) If $u = 2$ ms^{-1}, $\alpha = 60°$ and $e = 1/4$, find v and β.
 (b) If $u = 5$ ms^{-1}, $\alpha = 30°$ and $\beta = 45°$, find e and the loss in kinetic energy.

2 A smooth rectangular table $ABCD$ of width d has a vertical rim along each of the edges AB and CD of length $21d$. A small sphere is projected from the point A with speed u at an angle of $\tan^{-1}(3/4)$ with the side AB down the table. The coefficient of restitution between the sphere and the rim is $1/2$. Show that the particle makes four collisions with the rim before leaving the table.

3 A ball is projected with speed u at an inclination α to the horizontal from a point P a distance d from a smooth vertical wall. After striking the wall, it again strikes the point P for a second time. If e is the coefficient of restitution between the wall and the ball, show that:

$$eu^2 \sin 2\alpha = ga(1 + e)$$

4 A ball is projected from the bottom of a smooth plane of angle α up the line of greatest slope at an angle θ to the horizontal. The coefficient of restitution between the plane and the ball is e. Show that, if $e > (\cot (\theta - \alpha) - 2 \tan \alpha)$, the ball will bounce down the plane after its first collision.

5.8 OBLIQUE COLLISION BETWEEN TWO PARTICLES

Oblique collisions between two particles represent the most demanding analysis that we shall carry out in the case of collisions. It is here that the advantages of vector notation become apparent. In fact, using the impulse momentum equation for each particle separately, and the law of restitution to consider energy losses along the normal at impact, allows us to solve any such problem.

The method of analysis can be summarised as follows, with reference to Figure 5.17, where two smooth bodies of masses m and M are shown at impact. The velocity vectors before impact are **u** and **U**, and after impact **v** and **V** respectively. The mutually opposite impulse vectors are $-\mathbf{I}$ and $\mathbf{I}$.

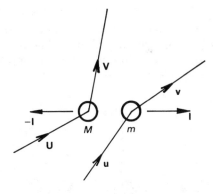

Fig. 5.17

The governing equations for the motion are as follows. (Note that the motion of the two particles need not be solely in the same plane.) From the impulse momentum relationship for M:

$$-\mathbf{I} = M\mathbf{V} - M\mathbf{U}$$

and for m:

$$\mathbf{I} = m\mathbf{v} - m\mathbf{u}$$

From the law of restitution:

$$-e(\mathbf{u} - \mathbf{U}) \cdot \mathbf{n} = (\mathbf{v} - \mathbf{V}) \cdot \mathbf{n}$$

where $\mathbf{n}$ is the unit vector in the direction of $\mathbf{I}$.

Clearly, the compactness of vector notation is a great advantage in expressing the general equations. The same equations, when written in component form, are extremely lengthy. As an example, if we wish to model the motion of snooker balls as particles on a smooth table, we will only need to consider motion in two dimensions. It is also the case that the image ball is usually, but not always, stationary. The example that follows demonstrates some of the simplifications.

Example 5.8

A snooker ball A travels on a smooth table and impinges on a second snooker ball B, which is at rest. If ball A is travelling with speed U in a direction θ to the line of centres at impact, find the velocity of B after impact and the value of θ in order that A's path suffers the greatest deflection.

Solution In this special case, the motion of B is such that it is at rest before impact and during impact the ball, which we assume to be smooth, is subject to an impulse of magnitude I along its line of centres. This means that momentum can only change along the line of centres and, as a result, B must start to move in this direction.

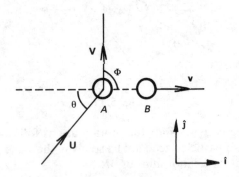

Fig. 5.18

In Figure 5.18, the motion of the balls before and after the impact is shown. The unit vectors **i** and **j** are also defined. The governing equations for the motion, assuming that the spheres can be modelled as particles, are as follows. From the impulse momentum relationship for A:

$$-I\mathbf{i} = M(V \cos \Phi \mathbf{i} + V \sin \Phi \mathbf{j}) - M(U \cos \theta \mathbf{i} + U \sin \theta \mathbf{j})$$

For B:

$$I\mathbf{i} = mv\mathbf{i}$$

These give:

$$U \sin \theta = V \sin \Phi \tag{9}$$

$$U \cos \theta = V \cos \Phi + v \tag{10}$$

The restitution law gives:

$$-eU \cos \theta = V \cos \Phi - v \tag{11}$$

Subtracting equation (11) from equation (10) gives:

$$v = \frac{1}{2} U \cos \theta \, (1 + e)$$

the velocity of B as required.

We now need to maximise the deflection $\Phi - \theta$ for variation in θ. Adding equations (10) and (11) gives:

$$\frac{1}{2} U \cos \theta \, (1 - e) = V \cos \Phi \qquad (12)$$

and dividing equation (9) by equation (11) gives:

$$\tan \Phi = \frac{2 \tan \theta}{1 - e}$$

This allows the deflection to be analysed using the expansion formula for $\tan (\Phi - \theta)$ to give:

$$\tan (\Phi - \theta) = \frac{\tan \Phi - \tan \theta}{2 \tan^2 \theta + 1 - e}$$

As $0 \leqslant \theta \leqslant (1/2)\pi$, then $\tan \theta$ is an increasing function for all values of θ in this range. We shall look here for the maximum value by differentiating with respect to $\tan \theta$.

Differentiation gives:

$$\frac{d(\tan (\Phi - \theta))}{d(\tan \theta)} = \frac{(1 + e)(1 - e - 2 \tan^2 \theta)}{(2 \tan^2 \theta - e)^2}$$

The stationary value occurs for:

$$\tan^2 \theta = \frac{1}{2} (1 - e)$$

and by considering values greater than and less than $\tan \theta$ in the given range, this can be seen to be a maximum. So, the angle θ is given by:

$$\tan \theta = \sqrt{\left(\frac{1}{2} (1 - e) \right)}$$

EXERCISES 5.8

1 A small sphere of mass m is travelling with speed u along a straight line. It is met by a second similar sphere travelling at an angle of 30° to the

first sphere's motion with speed u. They collide. If the coefficient of restitution is 1/2, determine the new direction of travel of each of the spheres.

2 A sphere A of mass m, travelling with speed u, is in collision with a similar stationary sphere B of mass $2m$. The direction of motion makes an angle of θ with the line connecting their centres. If after the collision sphere A is travelling in a direction at right angles to its original motion, find the value of the coefficient of restitution between the two spheres.

3 The assumptions that have been made regarding the motion of a snooker ball are that it should be modelled as a particle travelling on a smooth table. Discuss the effects of removing the assumptions.

6 MOTION UNDER GRAVITY IN ONE DIMENSION

6.1 INTRODUCTION

In this chapter, we shall examine one-dimensional motion under gravity. By their very nature, the problems are restricted to those involving bodies moving vertically under the influence of the Earth's gravity, with or without resistance. Nevertheless, falling raindrops, parachutists, balls and so on, and upwardly projected bullets, missiles and balls comprise a very important class of problems. Because of their limited scope, we can solve virtually all such problems by examining just five types. First, there is motion without resistance. There are then upwards and downwards motions, each under the action of two different types of resistance.

This chapter is very much a prelude to two others. Chapter 10 takes into account that some masses either lose material (for example, rockets) or gain material (for example, raindrops) as they move under gravity, while Chapter 7 generalises the analysis to apply it to two dimensions by considering projectiles.

We will continue to emphasise the importance of the set procedure for solving mechanics problems: drawing a diagram, deciding on an origin, deciding on a direction for the x-axis, drawing in the forces and then, and only then, writing down Newton's second law of motion.

6.2 MOTION WITH NO RESISTANCE

Tradition has it that Newton first had the idea for his laws of motion by observing a falling apple. We have already discussed the appropriateness of modelling large masses as particles (see Chapter 2); therefore, we know that to model a falling apple as a particle is perfectly valid, provided it is not spinning (and, even then, it models linear motion).

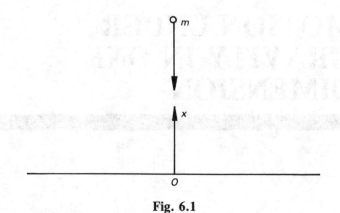

Fig. 6.1

Figure 6.1 shows a particle in motion under gravity. For now, we neglect air resistance, so that the only force acting is gravity itself. Gravity is assumed to be constant, hence this is a special case of motion under constant acceleration, which was dealt with in Chapter 1. Let us derive the equation of motion for the simple system shown in Figure 6.1. Note that we have chosen the x-axis to point in the opposite direction to the force due to gravity; therefore:

$$-mg = m \times \text{acceleration} \qquad (1)$$

We recall that acceleration can be expressed in a number of different forms, so we need to select one that is convenient for our particular problem. You should use dv/dt if you are interested in obtaining velocity as a function of time, and $v\,dv/dx$ if you are interested in obtaining velocity as a function of distance. Finally, you should use d^2x/dt^2 and integrate twice if you want displacement (distance above ground) as a function of time. Our equation of motion, after cancelling the mass m from both sides, is thus one of the following:

$$\frac{dv}{dt} = -g$$

$$v\,\frac{dv}{dx} = -g$$

$$\frac{d^2x}{dt^2} = -g \qquad (2)$$

In order to become adept at choosing which of these equations to apply, we need to solve particular problems. Here are some examples that will help to focus these ideas.

Example 6.2.1

An apple of mass 0.3 kg falls from a tree. Find (a) its velocity after 2 s, ignoring air resistance and assuming it has not hit the ground, and (b) the distance it travels.

Solution

(a) We wish to find v as a function of time, hence we use the first of the equations (2):

$$\frac{dv}{dt} = -g$$

Integrating this with respect to time gives:

$$v = -gt + A$$

where A is an arbitrary constant. We determine the value of A by using the condition that at time $t = 0$, $v = 0$. Hence, $A = 0$. Taking $g = 9.81$ ms^{-2}, we obtain:

$$v = -gt = -9.81t \tag{3}$$

Hence, for a particular time, v is completely determined. In particular, when $t = 2$, $v = -19.62$ ms^{-1}. The velocity is negative since the apple is travelling downwards, that is, in the negative x direction. Also note that the mass does not enter into this problem. This fact was foreseen by Galileo when he dropped stones from the leaning tower of Pisa in the early seventeenth century. They all hit the ground at the same time despite being of different masses. (Rather more spectacularly, a feather and a rock were, more recently, dropped on the Moon with similar results. The latter experiment would not work on Earth owing to air resistance, which affects the velocity of falling bodies, especially that of the feather.)

(b) We now need information connecting distance and time. Therefore, we integrate equation (3) by substituting dx/dt for v. The equation:

$$\frac{dx}{dt} = -gt$$

thus becomes:

$$x = -\frac{1}{2}gt^2 + B \tag{4}$$

where B is an arbitrary constant. The evaluation of B requires the use of a boundary condition. However, to solve the problem we do not actually need to know B. To see this, we note that from equation (4) at time $t = 0$ (when the apple was still on the tree):

$$x(0) = B \tag{5}$$

Here, $x(0)$ denotes the value of x at $t = 0$, the standard functional notation. We now put $t = 2$ into equation (4), with $g = 9.81$ ms^{-2} as before, to obtain:

$$x(2) = -19.62 + B \tag{6}$$

The total distance travelled is the difference between $x(0)$ and $x(2)$, and performing the subtraction eliminates B:

$$x(2) - x(0) = -19.62 \text{ m}$$

This value is negative because the apple is heading towards the origin, so that $x(2)$ is smaller than $x(0)$. The distance travelled, in absolute terms, is 19.62 m. That answers the problem, but 19.62 m is very large – far larger than the height of an average apple tree! In normal circumstances, the apple hits the ground in far less than 2 s.

The foregoing rather silly example applies only to apples that fall down holes or from apple trees adjacent to cliffs. It is important always to question your results. In a more serious example, such questioning could result in modifying some of the underlying assumptions, after, of course, checking all calculations very carefully.

Example 6.2.2

A boy throws an apple with a speed of 10 ms^{-1} vertically upwards. How high does it rise?

Solution   Since here we wish to find velocity as a function of distance, this time we choose $v \, dv/dx$ to represent acceleration. As in the previous example, Figure 6.1 will apply. So will equation (2), namely:

$$v \frac{dv}{dx} = -g$$

Integrating this equation with respect to x gives:

$$\frac{v^2}{2} = -gx + C \qquad (7)$$

where C is a constant of integration. This time, at the start of the motion, $x = 0$ and $v = 10 \text{ ms}^{-1}$. We note that v is now positive since it is travelling in the direction of Ox. Substituting these values into equation (7) with $g = 9.81 \text{ ms}^{-2}$, we obtain:

$$C = 50$$

The equation for v is thus:

$$v = 100 - 2gx \qquad (8)$$

The maximum height is attained when the velocity is instantaneously zero. This, from equation (8), occurs at the height x given by:

$$x = \frac{50}{g} = \frac{50}{9.81} = 5.10 \text{ m}$$

We are now ready to include air resistance in our modelling. First, however, try these exercises.

EXERCISES 6.2

1 A boy drops a stone down 'the bottomless pit'. He hears a splash 5 s later. How far has the stone fallen before hitting the water? (You may assume that the sound arrives instantaneously.)

2 A ball is dropped from a tower 20 m high. If its speed is halved on impact, how high does it bounce?

3 A stone is thrown vertically upwards from the ground with speed 20 ms^{-1}. A second stone is thrown upwards from exactly the same spot with exactly the same speed but after a time of 3 s has elapsed. How long does it take for the stones to collide? How far above the ground does the collision take place?

4 A girl leans out of an upstairs window and drops a ball to her brother who is standing on the ground a distance H m vertically below her. At precisely the same moment as the girl releases the ball, the boy throws another ball with speed u ms^{-1} vertically up at her. When and where do they collide?

5 A train travelling with a constant speed of 100 ms^{-1} is approaching a bridge which is 30 m high. Some naughty children want to drop a tomato on to the cab. How far must the train be from the bridge when they release the tomato if they are to succeed?

6.3 MOTION WITH RESISTANCE PROPORTIONAL TO SPEED

At all times, it is important to distinguish between velocity and its magnitude, the speed. This is never more so than when relating force to speed, as is done in this section and in Section 9.3. In both of these sections, we are concerned with one-dimensional motion, so the use of vectors is more confusing than helpful. However, to emphasise that we mean the absolute value of velocity, the speed, we use the notation $|\mathbf{v}|$.

In Chapter 2, we discussed the modelling of resistance. We showed that, on dimensional grounds, we might expect resistance to motion through air, called drag, to be proportional to the square of the speed. Observations confirmed this for spheres, at least over a certain size range, and the same observations showed a linear relationship between resistance and speed for small masses. Therefore, although it is possible mathematically to propose other laws, for example, resistance proportional to the inverse of speed or to displacement, such laws have no experimental back-up. We thus restrict attention to resistance proportional to speed and resistance proportional to the square of speed. In this section, we discuss resistance proportional to speed only.

Resistance, as the name implies, always opposes motion. Thus, the upwards and downwards motions are best treated separately. (This is not essential here, as $-mkv$ changes sign as v changes sign. However, it is essential for more complex resistance laws.) These motions are shown in Figure 6.2. The equations of motion are:

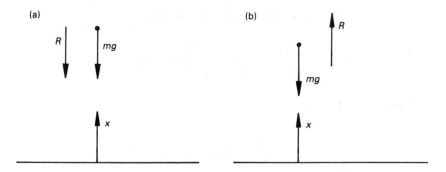

Fig. 6.2

$$-R - mg = m\frac{d^2x}{dt^2} \qquad \text{(going up)} \tag{9}$$

$$R - mg = m\frac{d^2x}{dt^2} \qquad \text{(going down)} \tag{10}$$

and in each case $R = mk|\mathbf{v}|$, where m is the mass and k is a constant dependent only on the size and shape of the 'particle'. The following examples will help to establish these ideas.

Examples 6.3

1. An apple is thrown vertically upwards with a velocity v. If resistance is proportional to speed, calculate the maximum height reached.

   Solution   Once again, we use $v\,dv/dx$ for acceleration. Equation (9) applies, as does Figure 6.2; hence:

   $$-mk|\mathbf{v}| - mg = mv\frac{dv}{dx}$$

   As the apple is going up, v is in the same direction as x and so is positive, that is, $|\mathbf{v}| = v$; k is the drag constant, which was explained in Chapter 2. Cancelling m and rearranging gives:

   $$-\frac{v\,dv}{kv + g} = dx$$

125

Some manipulation of the left-hand side leads to:

$$\left[-\frac{1}{k} + \frac{g}{k(kv + g)} \right] dv = dx$$

Integrating this gives:

$$-\frac{v}{k} + \frac{g}{k^2} \ln (kv + g) = x + A \tag{11}$$

where A is a constant of integration, evaluated by setting $v = v_0$ when $x = 0$. This gives:

$$A = -\frac{v_0}{k} + \frac{g}{k^2} \ln (kv_0 + g)$$

Hence:

$$x = \frac{v_0 - v}{k} + \frac{g}{k^2} \ln \left(\frac{kv + g}{kv_0 + g} \right) \tag{12}$$

As in the example with zero resistance, the maximum height is reached when v is instantaneously zero. Thus, the maximum height, x_m, is given by:

$$x_m = \frac{v_0}{k} - \frac{g}{k} \ln \left(1 + \frac{kv_0}{g} \right) \tag{13}$$

Typically, the constant k lies between 10^{-3} and 10^{-6} (see Chapter 2), so some of the terms in equation (13) are either very large (for example, g/k^2) or very small (for example, kv_0/g). Much care is thus required in carrying out the calculations, otherwise there will be considerable round-off error. You may recall that:

$$\ln (1 + x) = x - \frac{1}{2}x^2 + \frac{1}{3}x^3 - \ldots \qquad \text{for } |x| < 1$$

is the Maclaurin expansion of $\ln (1 + x)$. If we use this in equation (13) to expand the logarithm term, we obtain:

$$\ln\left(1 + \frac{kv_0}{g}\right) = \frac{kv_0}{g} - \frac{1}{2}\left(\frac{kv_0}{g}\right)^2 + \frac{1}{3}\left(\frac{kv_0}{g}\right)^3 - \cdots$$

for $k|v_0| < g$

So equation (13) becomes:

$$x_m = \frac{v_0}{k} - \frac{g}{k^2}\left[\frac{kv_0}{g} - \frac{1}{2}\left(\frac{kv_0}{g}\right)^2 + \frac{1}{3}\left(\frac{kv_0}{g}\right)^3 - \cdots\right]$$

$$x_m \approx \frac{v_0^2}{2g} - \frac{kv_0^3}{3g^2} \tag{14}$$

It is comforting to see that, when $k = 0$, equation (14) reverts to $v^2/2 = -gx + C$ (with $C = |v_0|/2$). Equation (13) is the exact answer to the problem. However, for numerical calculation the approximation in equation (14) is more useful. If we let $v_0 = 10$, the leading term of equation (14) gives the solution to example 6.2.2, $x = 5.10$ m. The second term is $-3.464k$, which is not very significant. If $k = 10^{-3}$, just about the largest value permitted where resistance proportional to speed remains valid, then:

$$x = 5.09 \text{ m}$$

The approximation is a good one, since $k|v_0| = 0.01$, which is certainly much less than g. If we consider much faster missiles and let $v_0 = 100$, then the first term of equation (14) is 509.7 m. The second term is, however, -3.5 m (with $k = 10^{-3}$ again). The approximation in equation (14) thus gives:

$$x_m = 506.2 \text{ m}$$

The difference between this and the *exact* value is less than 10 cm, which is not significant. However, neglecting resistance would lead to $x_m = 509.7$ m, which is 3.5 m greater than the exact value. This could be significant in military applications.

2. Rework example 6.2.1 with air resistance proportional to $mk|v|$, where $k = 10^{-3}$.

Solution We are wiser now, in that we disregard the mass, knowing that it cancels out from our calculations. This time we take acceleration as dv/dt. We are dealing with a falling object so equation (9) is appropriate; that is:

$$R - mg = m \frac{dv}{dt}$$

So $R = mk|\mathbf{v}| = -mkv$ ($|\mathbf{v}| = -v$ since $v < 0$). This gives:

$$-kv - g = \frac{dv}{dt}$$

which has solution:

$$-t + B = \frac{1}{k} \ln (kv + g)$$

When $t = 0$, $v = 0$, so:

$$B = \frac{1}{k} \ln g$$

which gives:

$$-t = \frac{1}{k} \ln \left(1 + \frac{kv}{g}\right)$$

or making v the subject:

$$v = - \frac{g}{k} (1 - e^{-kt}) \tag{15}$$

Now it is possible to expand the exponential term in much the same way as was done to transform equation (13) into equation (14); however, it is not necessary here. Using the values $k = 10^{-3}$, $g = 9.81$ ms^{-2}, the velocity after 2 s is:

$$v = -19.60 \text{ ms}^{-1}$$

(compared to -19.62 ms^{-1} with zero resistance). This may be thought an insignificant difference. However, if we let time increase without limit in equation (4), then velocity tends to (minus) infinity. If we let time tend to infinity in equation (15), then v gets closer and closer to $-g/k$. This concept, which involves terminal velocity, will be explored later.

3. Find the distance travelled by the apple in example 6.2.2 after 2 s.

Solution Integrating equation (15) gives:

$$x = -\frac{gt}{k} - \frac{ge^{-kt}}{k^2} + C$$

Evaluating this at $t = 0$ gives:

$$x(0) = -\frac{g}{k^2} + C$$

Evaluating at $t = 2$ gives:

$$x(2) = -\frac{2g}{k} - \frac{ge^{-2k}}{k} + C$$

The distance travelled is $x(2) - x(0)$ which, by subtraction, is:

$$x(2) - x(0) = -\frac{2g}{k} + \frac{g}{k}(1 - e^{-2k})$$

With $k = 10^{-3}$ and $g = 9.81$ ms^{-2}, there are some very small and very large terms here, so care is required in evaluation. It is more instructive to use expansion methods:

$$e^{-2k} = 1 - 2k + \frac{4k^2}{2!} - \frac{8k^3}{3!} + \ldots$$

which when inserted into the expression above gives:

$$x(2) - x(0) = -2g + \frac{4}{3}gk - \ldots$$

$$\approx -19.62 + 0.013$$

$$= -19.61 \text{ m}$$

The difference between the results here and those obtained neglecting resistance have been, in most cases, minimal. Obviously, concepts like terminal velocity are important. In the next section, we examine the model of resistance proportional to the square of speed with its potentially greater drag effects.

EXERCISES 6.3

1 A glider of mass 250 kg needs to travel at 40 ms⁻¹ before it can take off. It starts from rest, and a constant force of 500 N pulls it along. If air resistance is $10|\mathbf{v}|$ N, where $\mathbf{v}$ is the velocity of the glider, how long does the glider take to get airborne? If the runway needs to be at least 100 m longer than the required take-off distance, what should its minimum length be?

2 A stone of unit mass is dropped over a high cliff and hits the bottom of the cliff 10 s later. What are your estimates of the cliff's height:

(a) neglecting air resistance;
(b) assuming a resistance of $0.1|\mathbf{v}|$, where $\mathbf{v}$ is the velocity of the stone;
(c) assuming a resistance of $0.01|\mathbf{v}|$, where $\mathbf{v}$ is the velocity of the stone?

3 You have a small stone and a large stone. The resistance of the large stone is $0.1v$ per unit mass, whereas that of the small stone is $0.01v$ per unit mass (v being the speed of the stone). Show that, if the large stone is dropped over the cliff and the small stone is dropped from exactly the same place 1.3 s later, they will collide 10 s after the first stone leaves your hand. How far down the cliff does the collision take place and what are the speeds of the two stones at collision?

6.4 MOTION WITH RESISTANCE PROPORTIONAL TO THE SQUARE OF SPEED

The equations of motion with resistance included are not dependent on how we decide to model the resistance. Hence, equations (9) (going up) and (10) (going down) remain valid. Let us examine, for the third time, our 'apple' problems, though of course apples are merely representative of all vertically moving particles.

Examples 6.4

1. An apple is thrown vertically upwards with velocity v. If the resistance is

proportional to the square of the speed, calculate the maximum height it reaches.

Solution Again, we use $v \, dv/dx$ for acceleration. Then equation (9), the going-up equation, with $R = -mDv^2$ is:

$$-mDv^2 - mg = mv \frac{dv}{dx} \qquad (16)$$

where m is the mass and D is a constant called the drag. We are spared the use of modulus signs, since v^2 is always positive. Cancelling m and rearranging gives:

$$dx = - \frac{v \, dv}{Dv^2 + g}$$

which integrates directly to:

$$-2Dx + K = \ln (Dv^2 + g)$$

where K is a constant of integration. Since $v_0 = v$ when $x = 0$:

$$K = \ln (Dv_0^2 + g)$$

Hence:

$$2Dx = \ln \left(\frac{Dv_0^2 + g}{Dv^2 + g} \right)$$

At the maximum height, $v = 0$ and $x = x_m$ so that:

$$x_m = \frac{1}{2D} \ln \left(1 + \frac{Dv_0^2}{g} \right) \qquad (17)$$

In order to compare this solution with that evaluated in the previous sections, we let $v = 10$ ms^{-1}. $D = 0.1$ is a typical value (see Chapter 2). These values may be inserted into equation (17), this time without the numerical difficulties that were associated with equation (13), and we obtain:

$$x_m = 3.51 \text{ m}$$

This is significantly less than 5.09 m, the previous answer. More surprising is the result we get if we let $v_0 = 100$ ms^{-1} in equation (17). This leads to:

$$x_m = 23.17 \text{ m}$$

Compare this with $x_m = 506$ m, which is 20 times larger. Resistance is obviously a major factor in this example.

2. Rework example 6.2.1 with air resistance proportional to mDv^2, where $D = 0.1$.

Solution As in example 6.2.1, we use dv/dt for acceleration. Equation (10), the equation of motion for falling objects, is appropriate for the plummeting apple, so:

$$mDv^2 - mg = m \frac{dv}{dt} \qquad (18)$$

Rearranging this equation, after cancellation of m, gives:

$$\int dt = \int \frac{dv}{Dv^2 - g}$$

The integral on the right-hand side is a standard form for the inverse hyperbolic tangent:

$$\int \frac{dx}{x^2 - a^2} = \frac{1}{2a} \operatorname{arctanh} \frac{x}{a} + C$$

For those not familiar with inverse hyperbolic functions, we can also use:

$$\int \frac{dx}{x^2 - a^2} = \frac{1}{2a} \ln \left| \frac{1 + x}{1 - x} \right| + C$$

The choice is up to us, so let us stick with logarithms, to give:

$$t = \frac{1}{2\sqrt{(gD)}} \ln \left| \frac{1 + v\sqrt{(D/g)}}{1 - v\sqrt{(D/g)}} \right| + C$$

At time $t = 0$, $v = 0$, so $C = 0$. To find the value of v after 2 s, we need to make v the subject of this formula. Doing this yields:

$$v = -\frac{g}{D} \left(\frac{e^{2t\sqrt{(gD)}} - 1}{e^{2t\sqrt{(gD)}} + 1} \right) \qquad (19)$$

where the minus sign has been taken because v is negative for all values of time. Inserting the values $D = 0.1$, $g = 9.81$ ms^{-2} and $t = 2$ s, we obtain:

$$v = -9.53 \text{ ms}^{-1}$$

Indeed, as t tends to infinity, v tends to $-\sqrt{(g/D)}$, which has the value -9.90 ms^{-1}. This is the terminal velocity, which is the subject of the next section.

3. Find the distance travelled by the apple in the previous example (see example 6.2.1).

Solution To get x in terms of t we should integrate equation (19), which amounts to solving:

$$\frac{dx}{dt} = -\sqrt{\frac{g}{D}} \left(\frac{e^{2t\sqrt{(gD)}} - 1}{e^{2t\sqrt{(gD)}} + 1} \right)$$

However, this is difficult. An easier route is to use $v \, dv/dx$ for acceleration to give the following alternative version of equation (18):

$$Dv^2 - g = v \frac{dv}{dx}$$

or, rearranging:

$$\int dx = \int \frac{v \, dv}{Dv^2 - g}$$

which integrates directly to give:

$$x + E = \frac{1}{2D} \ln |Dv^2 - g|$$

where E is a constant. At time $t = 0$, $v = 0$, so that:

$$x(0) + E = \frac{1}{2D} \ln g = \frac{1}{0.2} \ln (9.81) = 11.42$$

At time $t = 2$, $v = -9.53$ (from the previous example) giving:

$$x(2) + E = \frac{1}{0.2} \ln |0.1 \times (9.53)^2 - 9.81|$$

$$= \frac{1}{0.2} \ln (0.728) = -1.59$$

Subtracting gives the distance travelled as:

$$x(2) - x(0) = -13.01 \text{ m}$$

This is 6.6 m less than the apple which fell when no resistance or resistance proportional to speed acted. What we have here, therefore, is a much more realistic model for the drag of everyday objects moving at reasonable speeds. The simpler, linear resistance law is applicable to small, fast moving objects such as bullets. This is in agreement with the experimental evidence outlined in Chapter 2.

EXERCISES 6.4

1 A stone is falling through a cloud 100 m thick. It starts from rest and is subject to a resistance of $0.01v^2$ per unit mass, where v is its velocity.

   (a) Calculate its velocity when it emerges from the cloud.
   (b) Calculate the time the stone takes to fall through the cloud.

   (You may assume that the mass of the stone remains constant.)

2 A food parcel is dropped from a helicopter, which is hovering at a height of 200 m. Assuming a resistance law $mv^2/100$, at what speed does the food parcel hit the ground and how long does it take to reach the ground?

3 In exercise 6.4.2, the food parcel was found to be damaged. In order for it not to be damaged, it is necessary to attach a parachute to the food parcel to restrict the speed on contact to be less than 20 ms^{-1}. What value of k in the resistance model mkv^2 ensures this? What is the new time the food parcel takes to reach the ground?

6.5 TERMINAL VELOCITY

If a mass is falling under gravity, then equation (10) will apply, assuming the set-up in Figure 6.2(b). In general:

$$R - mg = ma \qquad (20)$$

where a denotes acceleration. We have solved many versions of this equation. For example, with $R = mkv$ and choosing $a = dv/dt$ leads to equation (15):

$$v = -\frac{g}{k}(1 - e^{-kt})$$

Equation (20) with $R = mDv^2$ is given by equation (19):

$$v = -\sqrt{\frac{g}{D}}\left(\frac{e^{2t\sqrt{(gD)}} - 1}{e^{2t\sqrt{(gD)}} + 1}\right) = \sqrt{\frac{g}{D}}\left(\frac{1 - e^{2t\sqrt{(gD)}}}{1 + e^{2t\sqrt{(gD)}}}\right)$$

As $t \to \infty$, under each of these laws, the velocity tends to a constant value. These values are $-g/k$ for R α speed and $-\sqrt{(g/D)}$ for R α (speed)^2. Each of these values is called the *terminal velocity*, for obvious reasons. As this velocity is approached, the acceleration gets smaller and smaller. Ultimately, acceleration becomes negligible, and so, according to Newton's *first* law, the net external force on the particle will also be negligible. The terminal velocity must, therefore, be given by putting $a = 0$ in equation (20); thus:

$$R = mg$$

With $R = mk|\mathbf{v}|$, this implies $|\mathbf{v}| = g/k$, and with $R = mDv^2$, this implies $v^2 = g/D$, which is consistent with previous results. Also, if initially the speed of the particle *exceeds* the terminal speed, $R - mg > 0$, whereas if initially the speed of the particle is less than the terminal speed (the case considered above), $R - mg < 0$. In each case, the sign of a, the acceleration, ensures that the speed approaches the terminal speed for large t. Figure 6.3 summarises these findings. Note that the arguments leading to the results in Figure 6.3 are independent of the form of R.

This completes what we want to say about one-dimensional motion under gravity. Here is an extended example which may be considered a case study.

Example 6.5

A helicopter is stationary at a height of 1000 m above the ground when a parachutist jumps out. When the parachute is *not* open, air resistance can be assumed to be negligible. After the parachute is open, resistance is assumed to be proportional to the square of speed through the formula $R = mv^2/100$, where m is the mass of the parachutist and her parachute.

(a) If all is well, the parachutist will count 5 s, then pull the rip-cord.

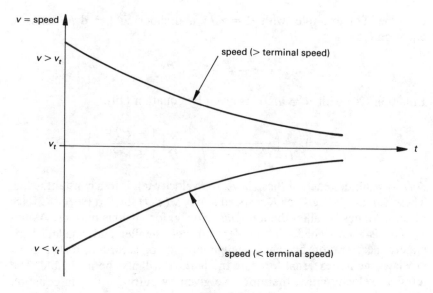

Fig. 6.3

Assuming that the parachute opens instantaneously, calculate the parachutist's velocity as a function of time and draw a graph of v against t. Calculate the terminal velocity and mark this on the graph. (Take $g = 9.81$ ms^{-2}.)

(b) All is not well, and the parachute only opens after a struggle at 13.5 s after the initial jump. How far from the ground is she before the parachute opens? What is her speed on reaching the ground? Will she survive? (Assume that at no time must her speed exceed 150 ms^{-1}, and that her speed on impact must be less than 60 ms^{-1}.)

(c) Compare the total travel times for (a) and (b).

Solution It is instructive to solve this problem with the axis pointing towards Earth. All velocities are then positive. As origin, the helicopter is the obvious choice. Figure 6.4 displays the set-up.

The motion is in two parts: without resistance and with resistance.

No resistance Newton's second law gives:

$$mg = m\frac{d^2x}{dt^2} = m\frac{dv}{dt} = mv\frac{dv}{dx}$$

To calculate v as a function of time, obviously we choose acceleration in the form dv/dt:

136

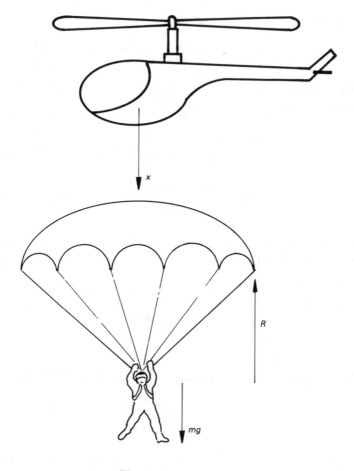

Fig. 6.4

$$g = \frac{dv}{dt}$$

$$gt = v + A$$

and, since $v = 0$ when $t = 0$, we have:

$$v = gt \tag{21}$$

In part (a), her fall with zero resistance lasts for only 5 s. Therefore, when the parachute opens:

$$v = 9.81 \times 5 = 49.05 \text{ ms}^{-1}$$

137

With resistance Newton's second law gives:

$$mg - R = m\frac{dv}{dt} \quad \text{or} \quad g - \frac{v^2}{100} = \frac{dv}{dt}$$

again using acceleration = dv/dt. The details of integration of this equation are not given here but the result is:

$$t + B = \frac{10}{2\sqrt{g}} \ln \left| \frac{1 + v/\sqrt{(100g)}}{1 - v/\sqrt{(100g)}} \right| = \frac{10}{g} \text{arctanh} \left(\frac{v}{\sqrt{(100g)}} \right)$$

$$= 1.596 \ln \left| \frac{1 + 0.0319v}{1 - 0.0319v} \right| = 3.193 \text{ arctanh } (0.0319v) \quad (22)$$

For part (a), when $t = 5$, $v = 49.05$. These values can be substituted in equation (22) to find B; thus:

$$5 + B = 1.596 \ln (1.513)$$

$$= 2.415$$

$$B = -2.585$$

Making v the subject of equation (22) with $B = -2.585$ gives:

$$v = \frac{0.198 + e^{-0.627t}}{0.00632 - 0.0319e^{-0.627t}} \quad (23)$$

(Note that $|1 - 0.0319v| = 0.0319v - 1$ for this problem, since v tends to $1/0.0319$ *from above*, so $1 - 0.0319v$ is always negative.)

To complete the graph of v against t, we must know how long the parachutist remains aloft. Thus, we must solve for x against t. However, this is impractical for this problem, and integrating equation (23) leads to an intrinsic equation for t which can only be solved numerically.

A more rewarding approach is to solve the whole problem again for v against x, that is, using $v\, dv/dx$ for acceleration.

No resistance This time we integrate:

$$g = v\frac{dv}{dx}$$

so that $gx + C = v^2/2$, where $C = 0$ since $v = 0$ when $x = 0$. When the parachute opens, we have already calculated that $v = 49.05$, so:

$$x(5) = \frac{49.05}{2 \times 9.81} = 122.625$$

With resistance   With the addition of $-R$ on the left-hand side we get:

$$g - \frac{v^2}{100} = v\frac{dv}{dx}$$

which integrates to:

$$-50 \ln \left| g - \frac{v^2}{100} \right| = x + D$$

With $x = 122.625$ when $v = 49.05$, this gives $D = -255.459$. Making v the subject of the expression gives:

$$v^2 = 981 + 16553e^{-0.02x} \tag{24}$$

As a check, we see that, as $x \to \infty$, $v \to \sqrt{981} = 31.321$, the terminal velocity, and with $x = 122.625$, $v = 49.05$, regaining the initial condition (for this part of the motion). It is clear that we can eliminate v between equations (23) and (24) to get x in terms of t, so all the information is contained in these equations. The problem is that, when $x = 1000$ m, v is so close to its terminal velocity that round-off error makes calculation imprecise. However, judicious use of logarithms gives $t = 26.7$ s as the total time taken for the drop. Using equation (23) for $t \geq 5$ and $v = gt$ for $0 \leq t \leq 5$ leads to the graph shown in Figure 6.5.

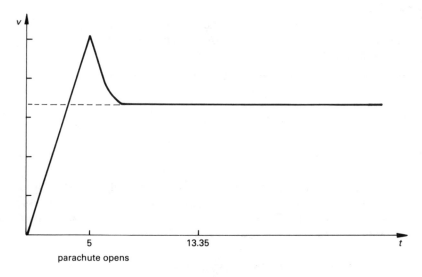

Fig. 6.5

139

If the parachute does not open until $t = 13.5$ s, then $v = gt$ applies until this time; that is, v is given by:

$$v(13.5) = 9.81 \times 13.5 = 132.435$$

This is the maximum velocity, since the parachute slows woman and parachute down. With resistance, the equation preceding (22) is valid, but the boundary condition is no longer $v = 49.05$ when $t = 5$, but $v = 132.435$ when $t = 13.5$. This gives:

$$t - 12.73 = 1.596 \ln \left| \frac{1 + 0.0319v^2}{1 - 0.0319v} \right| \tag{25}$$

Again, $v^2 = 2gx$ is also valid until $v = 132.435$, so:

$$x(13.5) = \frac{132.435}{2 \times 9.81} = 893.94$$

The equation preceding (24) is valid, but with conditions $x = 893.94$ when $v = 132.435$, which gives:

$$v = 981 + 9.63 \times 10^{11} e^{-0.02x}$$

When $x = 1000$ this leads to $v = 54.46$. Since the speed never exceeds 150 ms^{-1}, and the speed on impact is less than 60 ms^{-1}, we deduce that the parachutist survives.

For (a), the total time is 26.7 s. For (b), the total time is 14.8 s ($v = 54.46$ in equation (25)). Under the conditions prevailing in (b), the parachutist gets there faster than in (a), but they are far more risky!

EXERCISES 6.5

1 Galileo II stands at the top of a 100 m tower. He notices that an object dropped from the top has reached a constant speed by the time it has travelled half-way to the ground. Galileo II times the last half of the drop at 3 s. Calculate the resistance law if:

(a) resistance is proportional to speed;
(b) resistance is proportional to the square of speed.

2 Find the terminal velocities of falling bodies under the following resistance laws:

   (a) mkv^3;

   (b) $ma \ln (v/v_0)$;

   (c) mk (a constant).

7 PROJECTILES

7.1 PROJECTILES, MOTION IN THE REAL WORLD

Projectile motion is the free motion under gravity of a body projected in some direction which is not vertical. Examples of projectile motion are the flight of a golf ball, a high jumper or the motion of a jet of water from a hose pipe. The analysis of projectile motion is one of the most common uses of kinematics in the real world. The number of occasions in any one day that you will encounter examples of projectile motion are many. If you are involved in field events in athletics or ball games, then the motion involved is likely to be that of a projectile. Sports scientists are particularly interested in the use of projectile motion when attempting to analyse and improve the performances of competing sports men and women. In fact, a major proportion of the problems in this chapter are based on sporting applications. If, at some later stage, you perform an in-depth analysis of a particular event such as tennis, shot-put, football or long jump, you will find that the material of this chapter will be of considerable use.

The theory of projectile motion is not only important in sport, but also anywhere that the free motion of a body is involved. In films, stunt men and women are required to analyse very accurately their expected motion when they perform daring leaps. Originally, the theory became important when the use of cannons in battles made it necessary to understand the flight of cannon balls, and many ancient technical manuals for gunners existed on the subject. Perhaps it was then that a greater scientific understanding of this area was considered to be necessary.

7.2 INDEPENDENCE OF HORIZONTAL AND VERTICAL MOTIONS

The use of velocity and acceleration in vector form is an important factor in the analysis of projectile motion. The motion of any body which travels

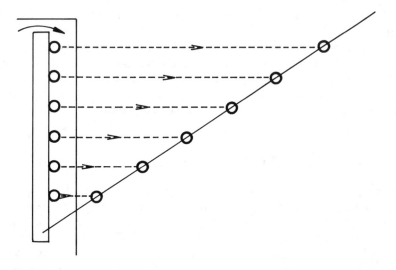

Fig. 7.1

freely, so that it is subject only to the vertical acceleration due to gravity, can be analysed simply in terms of its horizontal and vertical motion. The law of vector addition, which allows us to resolve components, is a key method in the analysis of projectile motion.

The independence of the two perpendicular motions is perhaps not obvious. We shall now describe an experiment which illustrates practically the independence of the horizontal and vertical motions of a projectile.

Collect six identical small, heavy objects: coins are ideal. Fix a one metre rule at one end to a horizontal table, so that it can pivot freely about that end. Rest the six coins at 15 cm intervals, touching the rule's edge and at equal distances from the edge of the table, as shown in Figure 7.1. Draw the rule back and project it horizontally along the table, so that it rotates about the pivot, coming into contact with all the coins simultaneously. Their positions when they strike the horizontal floor are shown in Figure 7.1. Note that:

(a) all six coins strike the floor at the same time;
(b) their positions are in a straight line which passes through the axis at the pivot.

What do these results tells us?

The rule supplies different horizontal velocities to each of the coins. These velocities are proportional to the distance of each coin from the pivot. They all start with zero vertical velocity and, as all six coins strike the

143

floor at the same time, we can conclude that their vertical motions must be identical.

The time of each coin's horizontal motion is the same so we can assume that the horizontal motion of each is uniform, as the horizontal distance travelled is directly proportional to its velocity at the rule.

Clearly, in this case then, we can conclude that the different horizontal motions are independent of their equal vertical motions.

7.3 VELOCITY AS A VECTOR

The properties of the motion described in Section 7.2 confirm that a vector approach can be used in the analysis of projectile motion. We have already considered examples of velocity as a vector – see for example the relative velocity problems of Chapter 1. Here we will need to use vector concepts of displacement, velocity and acceleration. As with any vector quantity in two dimensions, we can resolve the motions so that they can be analysed independently in any two mutually perpendicular directions. This independence was illustrated in the coin experiment and will be used in the examples that follow.

7.4 ASSUMPTIONS FOR MODELLING PROJECTILE MOTION

If you have attempted the experiment in Section 7.2, then it is unlikely that your results will have been entirely conclusive. Such experiments highlight the shortcomings of idealised mathematical models. The term 'ideal conditions' will often be used. These conditions embody the following assumptions:

(a) The particle model: Projectiles are particles and, as a result, are subject to no resistance forces which depend upon their size. All resulting motion will be translational.

For real problems, modelling a body as a particle is a major assumption. A long-jumper's jump may be considered as the path of a projectile, but are we justified in using the particle model in such a case? Any body of finite size will rotate, and that rotational motion may appear to have an effect on the projectile path.

In addition, air resistance will always act as the jumper has size, and those forces of resistance usually depend upon the velocity and size of the body. The effects of resistance can be large, but will be minimised if the time of flight is kept short, the velocity is not large and the body's dimensions are small. Analysing these assumptions carefully can supply important feedback to the projectile problem.

(b) The acceleration due to gravity is a constant. This is a reasonable assumption. Clearly, launching satellites from the Earth's surface cannot be modelled as a projectile.

(c) The motion will be confined to two dimensions. This is not always the case in real examples of projectile motion, as any golfer or footballer will know. There can be considerable sideways movement (swerve) created by what is known as the *Magnus effect* (the description of which is outside the scope of this book, but see for example texts on fluid mechanics, or S. Townend, *The Mathematics of Sport*, Ellis Horwood, 1987).

(d) The space in which the projectile travels is a vacuum. The inclusion of this assumption removes many of the problems of resistance already mentioned. The effects of wind and air currents would not be experienced in a vacuum, which is a prospect that would be relished by many sports men and women.

In real problems, these assumptions may not be explicitly stated. It is always advisable to list any assumptions that you feel you are making in modelling a real problem and consider the significance of each in your final solution. In this way, you will become aware of which assumptions are justifiable and which are not.

Example 7.4

A woman is standing on a horizontally moving airport walkway which moves at a uniform speed of 2 ms^{-1}. She notices that the walkway passes under a fixed barrier some distance ahead of her and decides she will jump the barrier when at some strategic position. She remembers that she can jump, from a standing position, a vertical height of only 1.25 m, and realises that this is exactly the height of the barrier. If she jumps vertically in order to just clear the barrier, by considering her motion to be 'ideal' as described, determine:

(a) the vertical velocity with which she leaves the ground;
(b) the time she will be airborne;
(c) the distance from her take-off position, on the walkway, that she touches down;
(d) the distance her touch-down position has moved horizontally during the motion.

(We will assume that the acceleration due to gravity is 10 ms^{-2}.)

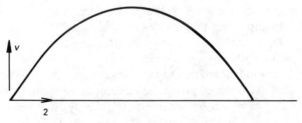

Fig. 7.2

Solution   Figure 7.2 defines the relevant quantities.

(a) Consider the vertical motion: At her greatest height, the woman will have zero vertical velocity; thus:

$$0 = v^2 - 2 \times 10 \times 1.25$$

where v is her initial vertical velocity. It follows that $v = 5$ ms⁻¹.

(b) Consider vertical motion: The woman will be airborne for t seconds until she is again at zero vertical height; thus:

$$0 = 5t - 0.5 \times 10 \times t^2$$

The two solutions here give $t = 0$ at take-off and $t = 1$ at landing. The time airborne is thus 1 s.

(c) Consider horizontal motion: Both the woman and the walkway have the same horizontal velocity; she will, as a result, touch down at the same place on the belt that she takes off.

(d) Consider horizontal motion: Horizontal distance = horizontal velocity × time airborne. The distance moved horizontally is thus $2 \times 1 = 2$ m.

EXERCISES 7.4

(In all cases, take $g = 10$ ms⁻¹, unless otherwise stated.)

1 A car drives off a horizontal pier with a speed of 45 kmh⁻¹ and crashes into the sea 2 s after leaving the pier. Find (a) the height of the pier and (b) the horizontal distance the car travels before entering the sea.

2 A high jumper makes his jump by first running directly towards the bar with speed U and then, without stopping, jumps vertically with speed U.

Find (a) the greatest height he can jump and (b) the distance he needs to be from the bar at take-off.

3 A coin is dropped from a height of 3 m in a railway carriage travelling with a uniform speed of 50 ms⁻¹.

(a) Why does the coin appear to fall vertically in the carriage?
(b) What is the time taken for the coin to strike the floor?

7.5 MAGNITUDE AND DIRECTION OF THE VELOCITY OF A PROJECTILE AT A GIVEN INSTANCE

The facility to resolve vectors in any two mutually perpendicular directions is common to all vector quantities. At any instant, in projectile motion, the velocity of the projectile is made up of two parts: its constant horizontal part u and its variable vertical part v, which usually needs to be determined. Completing the vector triangle for these two components, as illustrated in Figure 7.3, gives the magnitude of the velocity as $\sqrt{(u^2 + v^2)}$ in a direction $\tan^{-1}(v/u)$ with the horizontal.

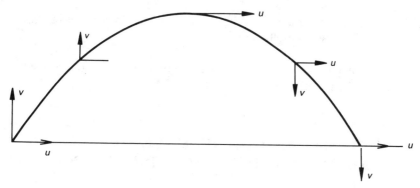

Fig. 7.3

It is also possible to apply the process in reverse, so that, at any instant when the projectile has a velocity of magnitude V travelling in a direction θ above the horizontal, the velocity can be resolved into horizontal and vertical components, as shown in Figure 7.4. Here, the horizontal component is $V \cos \theta$ and the vertical component is $V \sin \theta$, which we will write as the vector:

$$V \cos \theta \mathbf{i} + V \sin \theta \mathbf{j}$$

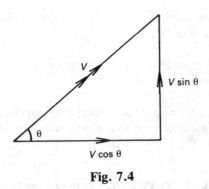

Fig. 7.4

Hence, if we return to example 7.4, then the woman's velocity at take-off is $2\mathbf{i} + 5\mathbf{j}$, or a velocity of magnitude $\sqrt{29}$ ms^{-1} in a direction $\tan^{-1}(5/2)$ above the horizontal.

EXERCISES 7.5

1 Find the magnitude and direction of the velocity with which the car in exercise 7.4.1 strikes the sea.

2 Find the magnitude and direction of the velocity of the high jumper in exercise 7.4.2 at take-off.

3 Find the magnitude and direction of the actual velocity of the coin when it strikes the carriage floor in exercise 8.4.3.

7.6 DISCUSSING MOTION RELATIVE TO HORIZONTAL AND VERTICAL DIRECTIONS

The motion of a projectile is often analysed in terms of (a) the greatest height it reaches above the horizontal plane and (b) the range it achieves on the horizontal plane through the point of projection. Let us determine these by considering the motion of a particle projected with velocity V at an angle θ above the horizontal, as illustrated in Figure 7.5

Consider the vertical motion, with a view to determining the greatest height reached. At time $t = 0$, the vertical velocity is $V \sin \theta$. The upwards acceleration is $-g$, where g is the acceleration due to gravity. At the greatest height h, the vertical velocity is 0. Using constant acceleration formulae, this gives:

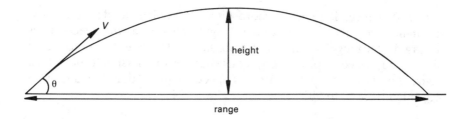

Fig. 7.5

$$0 = (V \sin \theta)^2 - 2gh$$

$$h = \frac{V^2 \sin^2 \theta}{2g}$$

Interpreting this function, we see that the vertical height attained by the particle can be increased by increasing either (a) the speed of projection or (b) the angle of projection in the range 0° to 90°. For a given speed of projection, the height increases with θ until it achieves its maximum value when $\theta = 90°$.

Consider vertical motion once more, this time with a view to determining the particle's range. When the particle returns to the horizontal plane, then the vertical distance above the plane is 0. This gives:

$$0 = V \sin \theta t - \frac{1}{2}gt^2$$

and the time taken to achieve the range is:

$$t = \frac{2V \sin \theta}{g}$$

Consider horizontal motion: The horizontal velocity is constant and its magnitude is $V \cos \theta$. The range is thus given by:

$$V \cos \theta \times \frac{2V \sin \theta}{g}$$

This equation for the range is usually written in one of the following forms:

$$\frac{2V^2 \sin \theta \cos \theta}{g} \qquad \text{or} \qquad \frac{V^2}{g} \sin 2\theta$$

At first glance, it seems a more difficult problem to determine the maximum range than the maximum height. Clearly, as the speed, V, is increased, the range will increase accordingly. To study the range for a given, fixed, speed of projection, let us consider the possible trajectories. Figure 7.6 shows the paths, for this speed of projection, for angles of projection from 0° to 90°.

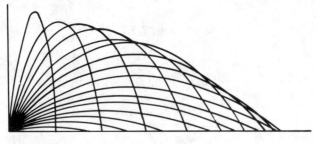

Fig. 7.6

The trajectories show that there is a maximum range that appears to be at an angle of projection of 45°. It is also apparent that all ranges less than the maximum range can be reached using two possible angles of projection.

Examination of the function:

$$\text{range} = \frac{V^2 \sin 2\theta}{g}$$

reveals that its maximum value occurs when $\sin 2\theta = 1$ (i.e. when $\theta = 45°$) and is V^2/g. For any range less than this maximum value, we will be required to solve an equation in terms of $\sin 2\theta$, to find the necessary angle of projection. Solving the equation $\sin 2\theta$ equal to a positive value less than unity gives two solutions for 2θ in the range 0° to 180°, which in turn gives two values of θ, the angle of projection, in the range of 0° to 90°. The following example illustrates these ideas.

Example 7.6

A fielder wishes to return the ball to a catcher. The greatest distance from the catcher to any point on the boundary of the play area is 80 m. If the fielder can throw the ball with a maximum speed of 25 ms⁻¹, can he reach the catcher from any point in the field?

(a) Throwing the ball with its maximum speed, what are the possible angles of projection for the ball to reach the catcher without bouncing, if the distance from the fielder is 40 m?

(b) In order to return the ball as quickly as possible, which angle of projection should be chosen?

(Take the acceleration due to gravity to be 10 ms^{-2}.)

Solution The maximum range will be:

$$\frac{25^2}{10} = 62.5 \text{ m}$$

This means that the fielder can return the ball anywhere within a circle of radius 62.5 m of the catcher. Hence, the catcher cannot be reached from all points in the field.

(a) For a range of 40 m, we have:

$$\frac{25^2 \sin 2\theta}{10} = 40$$

to give $\sin 2\theta = 0.64$. Solving this equation gives two values for the angle of projection in the range 0° to 90°. They are 19.9° and 70.1°.

(b) The horizontal velocity for an angle of projection of 19.9° is 25 cos 19.9° = 23.51 ms^{-1}, and that for an angle of projection of 70.1° is similarly 8.509 ms^{-1}. This gives the times of the ball's travel as 40/23.51 = 1.701 s and 40/8.509 = 4.701 s. Clearly, the lesser angle of projection, 19.9°, gives the faster return time.

EXERCISES 7.6

1 What is the smallest speed of projection required to obtain a horizontal range of 40 m and what will be the time of flight in that case?

2 When projected at an angle of elevation of tan^{-1} (3/4), a projectile falls 40 m short of a target in a horizontal plane through the point of projection. When the elevation is 45°, the projectile overshoots the target by 50 m. Show that the target is at a horizontal distance of 2200 m from the point of projection and find the correct elevations of projection so that the projectile hits the target.

151

3 If a particle is projected from the horizontal floor of a large room whose ceiling is at a height of 5 m, what will its greatest possible range be, if its speed of projection is (a) 20 ms⁻¹ and (b) 12 ms⁻¹?

7.7 THE PATH OF A PROJECTILE: THE TRAJECTORY

To study the path of a projectile (the trajectory), it is convenient to refer to horizontal and vertical axes Ox and Oy through the point of projection O, as shown in Figure 7.7

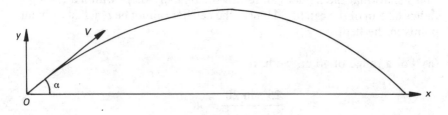

Fig. 7.7

If the velocity of projection is V at an angle α to Ox, as illustrated in Figure 7.7, then the velocity of projection can be written as the vector:

$$\mathbf{u} = V \cos \alpha \mathbf{i} + V \sin \alpha \mathbf{j}$$

The horizontal motion is unaffected by the acceleration and the component of velocity in that direction is constant. The upwards vertical motion is subject to an acceleration of $-g$. The acceleration vector is written in the form:

$$\mathbf{a} = -g\mathbf{j}$$

For a given point $\mathbf{r}$, relative to O at time t, on the trajectory, we can write:

$$\mathbf{r} = \mathbf{u}t + \frac{1}{2}\mathbf{a}t^2$$

The vector diagram in Figure 7.8 shows the dependence of the position vector $\mathbf{r}$ on the vectors $\mathbf{u}$ and $\mathbf{a}$. This gives, for a given point on the path with coordinates (x, y):

$$x\mathbf{i} + y\mathbf{j} = ((V \cos \alpha)t\mathbf{i} + (V \sin \alpha)t\mathbf{j}) + \frac{1}{2}(-g\mathbf{j})t^2$$

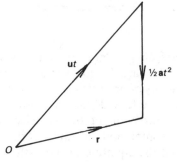

Fig. 7.8

The set of equations:

$$x = (V \cos \alpha)t \qquad \text{and} \qquad y = (V \sin \alpha)t - \frac{1}{2}gt^2$$

represent the parametric equations of the trajectory.

Making t the subject of the first of these formulae, we obtain:

$$t = \frac{x}{V \cos \alpha}$$

This enables us to derive:

$$y = x \tan \alpha - \frac{gx^2 \sec^2 \alpha}{2V^2} \tag{1}$$

as the Cartesian equation for the trajectory. From this equation, we can see that, for a given V and α, the trajectory is a parabola. Having once determined this, we can use any of the properties of a parabola to discuss projectile motion. The most important of these is the symmetry of the curve about a vertical line through its maximum value, its greatest height. Using this symmetry property, we can make the following observations about projectile motion:

(a) The greatest height is the maximum value of y.
(b) The range is the value of x for which $y = 0$.
(c) The range is twice the x value to the greatest height. (The time to the range is twice the time to the greatest height, which follows directly.)
(d) All heights are symmetrical about the greatest height's horizontal position.
(e) The direction of the particle's motion is anti-symmetric about the greatest height's horizontal position.

Example 7.7

A particle P is projected from a point O at the top of a cliff, 52 m vertically above the sea-level, and the particle moves under gravity until it strikes the sea at a point S. The velocity of projection of P has horizontal and upwards vertical components of magnitude 24 ms^{-1} and 7 ms^{-1} respectively. Calculate the magnitude and direction of the velocity of P at the point of projection. Define horizontal and upwards vertical axes Ox and Oy through O and show that the equation of the path can be written as:

$$y = \frac{7x}{24} - \frac{5x^2}{576}$$

Find the horizontal distance of S from O.

Solution   At O, the magnitude of the velocity is:

$$\sqrt{(7^2 + 24^2)} = 25 \text{ ms}^{-1}$$

The direction of the velocity is $\tan^{-1}(7/24)$ above the horizontal. This gives the trajectory as:

$$y = x \cdot \frac{7}{24} - \frac{10x^2}{(2.25)^2} \cdot \frac{25}{24}$$

which reduces to:

$$y = \frac{7x}{24} - \frac{5x^2}{576}$$

as required.

Figure 7.9 shows the trajectory of the particle, and that at S, $y = -52$, to give:

$$5x^2 - 168x + 29952 = 0$$

Factorising gives:

$$(x - 96)(5x + 312) = 0$$

This gives $x = -62.4$ or 96. As x is positive at S, then the horizontal distance from O to S is 96 m.

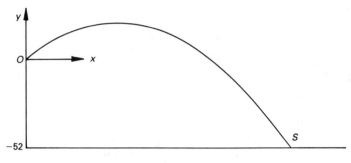

Fig. 7.9

7.8 DIRECTION OF TRAVEL AND MAGNITUDE OF VELOCITY

The tangent of the angle of travel θ at the point (x, y) at time t is given by:

$$\tan \theta = \left(\frac{dy}{dt} \middle/ \frac{dx}{dt}\right) = \frac{dy}{dx}$$

This corresponds to a direction of travel being along the tangent at that point. From the Cartesian equation, we have:

$$\tan \theta = \frac{dy}{dx} = \tan \alpha - \frac{gx \sec^2 \alpha}{V^2}$$

or, from the parametric equations:

$$\frac{dy}{dx} = \frac{dy}{dt} \middle/ \frac{dx}{dt} = \frac{V \sin \alpha - gt}{V \cos \alpha}$$

Example 7.8

Find the magnitude and direction of the velocity of a projectile, which is projected with speed 30 ms⁻¹ at an angle of 45° with the horizontal, when it has travelled a horizontal distance of (a) 30 m and (b) 50 m.

Solution The equation of the trajectory is, from equation (1):

$$y = x - \frac{x^2}{90}$$

155

Differentiating gives:

$$\frac{dy}{dx} = 1 - \frac{x}{45}$$

The horizontal velocity component is:

$$30 \sin 45° = 15\sqrt{2} \text{ ms}^{-1}$$

(a) If $x = 30$, then:

$$\frac{dy}{dx} = 1 - \frac{30}{45} = \frac{1}{3} = \tan \theta$$

The direction of travel is thus at an angle $\tan^{-1} (1/3)$ above the horizontal.

The magnitude of velocity is:

$$\frac{15\sqrt{2}}{\cos \theta} = 10\sqrt{5} \text{ ms}^{-1}$$

(since $\cos \theta = 3/\sqrt{10}$).

(b) If $x = 50$, then:

$$\frac{dy}{dx} = -\frac{1}{9} = \tan \theta$$

The direction of travel is thus $\tan^{-1} (1/9)$ below the horizontal.
The magnitude of velocity is:

$$\frac{5\sqrt{164}}{3} \text{ ms}^{-1}$$

7.9 TWO TRAJECTORIES

For a given point (a, b) on the trajectory of a projectile, whose speed of projection is V, we can use the Cartesian equation for the trajectory, equation (1), to give:

$$b = a \tan \alpha - \frac{ga^2 \sec^2 \alpha}{2V^2}$$

Using the trigonometric identity $\sec^2 \alpha = 1 + \tan^2 \alpha$, we can rearrange this to give:

$$2bV^2 = 2aV^2 \tan \alpha - ga^2(1 + \tan^2 \alpha)$$

or:

$$ga^2 \tan^2 \alpha - 2aV^2 \tan \alpha + (2bV^2 + ga^2) = 0$$

This quadratic equation for $\tan \alpha$ can be solved to give two solutions. As a result, there are two possible angles of projection for any reachable point (a, b); that is, we are able to determine two trajectories through such a point. This is consistent with the two angles of projection for a given range (less than the maximum) on the horizontal. Figure 7.10 illustrates the two

(a)

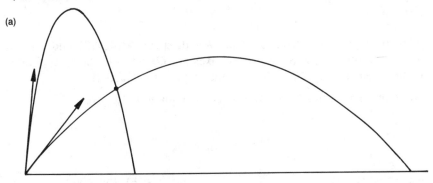

(b)

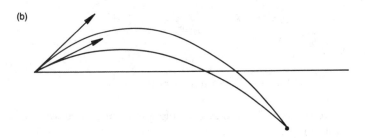

(c)

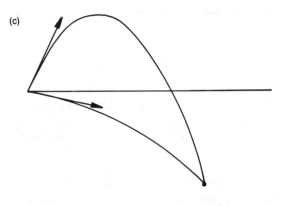

Fig. 7.10

paths, in three different cases, which can be used to reach the points shown. They are:

(a) both angles above the horizontal for a point above the horizontal;
(b) both angles above the horizontal for a point below the horizontal;
(c) one angle above the horizontal and one below, for a point below the horizontal.

Example 7.9

A body is projected from a point O with speed $\sqrt{(4gh/3)}$ and passes through a point $(h, h/8)$ where the axes are Ox and Oy, horizontal and vertical respectively. Find the possible angles of projection.

Solution The equation of the trajectory, equation (1), gives:

$$y = x \tan \alpha - \frac{3x^2}{8h} (1 + \tan^2 \alpha)$$

using that $\sec^2 \alpha = 1 + \tan^2 \alpha$. At the point $(h, h/8)$, this gives:

$$3 \tan^2 \alpha - 8 \tan \alpha + 4 - 0$$

Factorising gives:

$$(3 \tan \alpha - 2)(\tan \alpha - 2) = 0$$

and the solutions are $\tan \alpha = 2/3$ and 2. Possible angles of projection are then $\tan^{-1} (2/3)$ and $\tan^{-1} 2$.

EXERCISES 7.9

1 A particle is projected with speed $\sqrt{(4gh/3)}$ from a point O on a table of height h, standing on a horizontal floor. The particle reaches the floor at a point a horizontal distance $2h$ from O. Find the two possible angles of projection.

2 Find the range of values of the angle of projection of a ball which is projected with speed $\sqrt{(2gh)}$ in a plane perpendicular to a vertical wall of height h and a distance $2h$ away, so as to pass over it.

3 A particle is projected with speed V ms^{-1} at an angle of elevation θ from a point O on horizontal ground. The particle moves freely under gravity and strikes the plane again at a point A. When the particle is at horizontal distances 30 m and 60 m from O, its vertical heights are 8 m and 12 m respectively. Calculate:

(a) the value of tan θ;
(b) the value of V;
(c) the time taken by the particle to reach A from O;
(d) the distance OA;
(e) the speed of the particle when it is 8 m above the ground.

(Take the acceleration due to gravity to be 10 ms^{-2}.)

4 A particle is projected at an angle θ above the horizontal. At a subsequent time, its horizontal and vertical displacements are equal, and its direction of motion is then inclined at 45° to the downwards vertical. Prove that tan $\theta = 3$.

5 A particle is projected at an angle α above the horizontal from a point on the edge of a table of height h, standing on a horizontal floor. The particle reaches the floor at a point whose horizontal distance from the point of projection is $2h$. Show that, when it strikes the floor, the inclination θ below the horizontal of its direction of motion is given by:

$$\tan \theta = \tan \alpha + 1$$

Find the speed of projection and the time of flight of the particle in terms of g, α and h.

7.10 ENVELOPE OF TRAJECTORIES

For a given projection speed then, as the angles of projection are varied, a projectile can only pass through points in a finite region. Figure 7.11 shows 17 trajectories for the same speed of projection in a plane. The angles of projection are 10°, 20°, . . . , 160°, 170°. If we consider the envelope, that is, the equation of the boundary of the region, of all trajectories, then we can see some of the properties it possesses. It has a vertical axis of symmetry. Its greatest value is the greatest possible height that a projectile can reach (that is, when the angle of projection is 90°). Its range on the horizontal is the maximum range in each direction.

The envelope is in fact a three-dimensional surface and the envelope

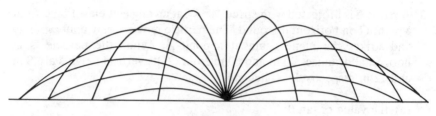

Fig. 7.11

shown in Figure 7.11 is a plane section through that surface. For a given point (x, y) in a plane, the equation that gives the possible angles of projection is:

$$gx^2 \tan^2 \alpha - 2xV^2 \tan \alpha + (2yV^2 + gx^2) = 0$$

Points (x, y) contained within the envelope will give two solutions for $\tan \alpha$ from the above equation. The condition for this quadratic equation to have two solutions is that:

$$(2xV^2)^2 - 4gx^2(2yV^2 + gx^2) > 0$$

This gives the region:

$$y < \frac{1}{2gV^2} (V^4 - g^2x^2)$$

The bounding equation (equation of the envelope) is:

$$y = \frac{1}{2gV^2} (V^4 - g^2x^2)$$

This envelope corresponds to points with two equal solutions; that is, two equal angles of projection. Points on the envelope can be reached by just the one angle of projection.

EXERCISE 7.10

1 A footballer, when attempting a conversion kick, has to kick the stationary ball from horizontal ground over a bar. The greatest horizontal distance a player can kick the ball before it first bounces is 55 m.

Determine whether or not the player could kick the ball over the bar, which is 3 m high, when the horizontal distance to the bar is 50 m.

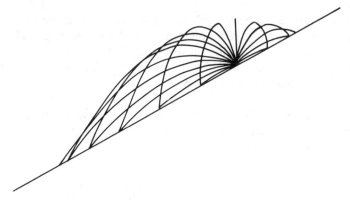

Fig. 7.12

7.11 THE MOTION OF A PROJECTILE RELATIVE TO AN INCLINED PLANE

Consider a particle projected from a point on an inclined plane up or down it, where the motion is in the vertical plane containing the line of greatest slope. If we compare the trajectories illustrated in Figure 7.12, which are for the same projection speed, with those for trajectories over a horizontal plane, as illustrated in Figure 7.11, then we can note some significant differences; for example:

(a) Symmetry is no longer apparent for any of the angles of projection of a particle over the inclined plane.
(b) The greatest height no longer seems important. The greatest perpendicular distance from the plane is perhaps more relevant.
(c) The motions up and down the plane show major differences in their trajectories. Ranges up and down the plane are not equal. Of course, we would expect the range to be greatest when the projection is down the plane.

With the velocity component along the plane no longer constant, it may be thought that the analysis of such a problem is different as well as significantly more difficult. However, inclined plane problems involving projectile motion can still be tackled with respect to *horizontal* and *vertical* directions. Including an inclined plane in such problems does nothing more than interrupt the projectile's motion. The following example illustrates this.

161

Example 7.11

A particle is projected with a velocity of 40 ms⁻¹ at an angle of 30° to an inclined plane in a plane containing the line of greatest slope. The plane makes an angle of 30° with the horizontal. Calculate (a) the range of the particle along the plane and (b) the angle that the projectile's motion makes with the plane just before impact.

Solution Removing the plane from our considerations would give a projectile with a trajectory whose equation relative to the horizontal and vertical axes Ox and Oy is:

$$y = x \tan 60° - \frac{gx^2}{(2.40)^2} \sec^2 60°$$

$$= \sqrt{3}x - \frac{x^2}{80}$$

We can analyse the effect of the inclined plane in this projectile's motion by considering only those points for which:

$$y > x \tan 30° = \frac{x}{\sqrt{3}}$$

For the range, consider the point of intersection between the trajectory and the plane to be at (a, b). Then:

$$\frac{a}{\sqrt{3}} = a\sqrt{3} - \frac{a^2}{80}$$

The solution of this equation gives $a = 160/\sqrt{3}$. The range can then be found by simple trigonometry using the right-angled triangle in Figure 7.13:

$$\text{range} = \frac{a}{\cos 30°} = \frac{212}{3} \text{ m}$$

For the direction of travel at the plane, consider:

$$\frac{dy}{dx} = \sqrt{3} - \frac{x}{40}$$

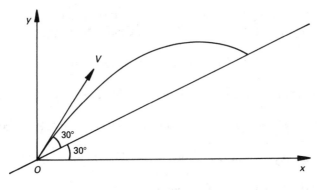

Fig. 7.13

at $x = a$, which gives $dy/dx = -1/\sqrt{3}$ and the direction of the velocity at impact as 30° below the horizontal. Again, from the geometry of Figure 7.13, this is seen to give motion at the plane in a direction of 60° with the plane.

7.12 MOTION ON AN INCLINED PLANE REFERRED TO AXES ALONG AND PERPENDICULAR TO THE PLANE

In the first instance, we will look at the motion when projection is up the plane, in the plane containing the line of greatest slope. The axes OX and OY, up and perpendicular to the plane of inclination α, are defined as shown in Figure 7.14.

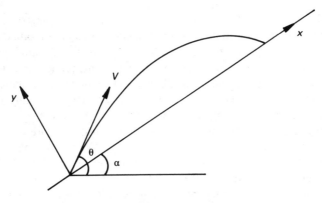

Fig. 7.14

If we define **i** and **j** up and along the plane as shown, then the motion of a projectile relative to the axes OX and OY is defined by:

$$\ddot{X}\mathbf{i} + \ddot{Y}\mathbf{j} = -g \sin \alpha \mathbf{i} + g \cos \alpha \mathbf{j}$$

Integrating with respect to t gives the velocity as:

$$\dot{X}\mathbf{i} + \dot{Y}\mathbf{j} = (V \cos (\theta - \alpha)\mathbf{i} + V \sin (\theta - \alpha)\mathbf{j}) - (g \sin \alpha \mathbf{i} + g \cos \alpha \mathbf{j})t$$

where the projectile is at O at time $t = 0$ and has velocity V at an angle θ to the horizontal.

A second integration with respect to t gives:

$$X\mathbf{i} + Y\mathbf{j} = (V \cos (\theta - \alpha)\mathbf{i} + V \sin (\theta - \alpha)\mathbf{j})t - \frac{1}{2} (g \sin \alpha \mathbf{i} + g \cos \alpha \mathbf{j})t^2$$

If X is equal to the range up the inclined plane, $Y = 0$, which gives:

$$t = \frac{2V \sin (\theta - \alpha)}{g \cos \alpha} \tag{2}$$

The range is given by:

$$\frac{V^2 \sin (\theta - \alpha)}{g \cos^2 \alpha} (\cos (\theta - \alpha) \cos \alpha - \sin (\theta - \alpha) \sin \alpha)$$

which reduces to:

$$\frac{2V^2 \sin (\theta - \alpha) \cos \theta}{g \cos^2 \alpha}$$

This leads to a possible investigation problem using a microcomputer. Consider the ranges obtained for a given speed of projection on an inclined plane of given inclination. From the tabulated results, it should be possible to suggest a relationship between the angles of projection that have the same range. If this is repeated for different values of angle of plane, then a generalised result can be derived. It is then necessary to attempt to verify the result algebraically using the relationship for the range.

The results of such an investigation should also indicate a maximum range for some angle of projection both up and down the plane. If you have not performed this investigation, you should note Figure 7.12, which shows the envelope of trajectories.

The problem of maximising the range is again important, and as θ varies with V constant, the range varies. Increasing only the speed of projection,

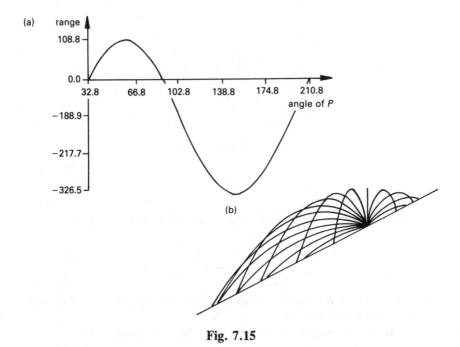

Fig. 7.15

V, will always increase the range. The graph in Figure 7.15(a) shows the range as the angle of projection θ varies for a plane inclined at an angle of 30° to the horizontal. This also arises from the trajectories shown in Figure 7.15(b).

To consider the changes in range for projection up the plane as θ increases from α to 90°, with the speed of projection remaining constant, we write the function for the range as:

$$\frac{V^2}{g\cos^2\alpha}\,(\sin(2\theta - \alpha) - \sin\alpha)$$

The maximum value occurs when $\sin(2\theta - \alpha) = 1$ and then $2\theta - \alpha = 90°$. This gives the maximum range up the plane as:

$$\frac{V^2}{g\cos^2\alpha}\,(1 - \sin\alpha) \quad \text{or} \quad \frac{V^2}{g(1 + \sin\alpha)}$$

when $\theta = (90° + \alpha)/2$. As with the range on the horizontal plane, the angle of projection should bisect the angle between the horizontal and the perpendicular to the plane. This is illustrated in Figure 7.16 where the given value of θ is shown.

165

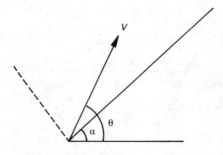

Fig. 7.16

At the greatest perpendicular distance from the inclined plane:

$$t = \frac{V \sin (\theta - \alpha)}{g \cos \alpha}$$

which is precisely half of the value of t given by equation (2), the time taken for the whole trajectory.

The greatest perpendicular distance from the plane is given as:

$$\frac{V^2 \sin^2 (\theta - \alpha)}{2g \cos \alpha}$$

The greatest perpendicular distance and range down an inclined plane can be derived as in the case for projection up the plane, an exercise you might like to attempt yourself. Here, we shall carry out the derivation using the results obtained for expressions up the plane.

It should be clear from Figure 7.17 that, if we exchange α for $-\alpha$ in the expressions already derived, then the results should follow.

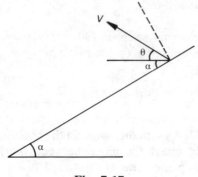

Fig. 7.17

The range down the inclined plane is:

$$\frac{2V^2 \sin \theta \cos (\theta + (-\alpha))}{g \cos^2 (-\alpha)} = \frac{2V^2 \sin \theta \cos (\theta - \alpha)}{g \cos^2 \alpha}$$

The maximum range again occurs when:

$$\theta = \frac{90° + (-\alpha)}{2} = \frac{90° - \alpha}{2}$$

and is given by:

$$\frac{V^2}{g(1 + \sin (-\alpha))} = \frac{V^2}{g(1 - \sin \alpha)}$$

Again, the angle of projection for the maximum range bisects the angle between the horizontal and the normal to the plane, in that direction.

The perpendicular distance from the plane, for a given angle of projection θ, follows as before and remains:

$$\frac{V^2 \sin^2 \theta}{2g \cos \alpha}$$

EXERCISES 7.12

1 A particle is projected down a plane inclined at 30° to the horizontal. The particle is projected from A on the plane with velocity 10 ms^{-1} at an angle θ to the horizontal in the plane of greatest slope. If the range is 15 m, find the possible angles of projection.

2 A point O is at the foot of a plane which is inclined at an angle α to the horizontal. A particle is projected with speed V from O at an angle of elevation θ to the horizontal, and moves in the vertical plane containing the line of greatest slope. It strikes the plane when travelling horizontally. Express tan θ in terms of tan α. Prove that the range in the inclined plane can be written as:

$$\frac{2V^2 \sec \alpha \tan \alpha}{g(1 + 4 \tan^2 \alpha)}$$

3 Identical particles are projected up and down a plane of inclination tan^{-1} (1/3) to the horizontal, the speed of projection being the same in each case. If the range up the plane is one-third that down the plane, find the angle of projection, which is the same for each case.

7.13 THE DIRECTION OF TRAVEL AT THE POINT OF IMPACT OF A PROJECTILE WITH AN INCLINED PLANE

In the case of motion relative to a horizontal plane, it proved an interesting exercise to calculate the direction of travel for varying t or x. This helped in viewing the symmetry properties of the projectile's flight. Here, we have already identified the lack of symmetry, so a similar analysis would not have the same value. However, the direction of velocity at the point of impact with the plane is important. It should be evident that any subsequent motion depends upon the direction of travel of the projectile immediately before impact with the plane.

Projection of particles down planes causes no problem, as the particle after impact will always continue to travel down the plane. If we project the particle up the plane then: (a) if the direction is below the normal to the plane before impact, the particle will continue to travel up the plane after impact; (b) if the direction is above the normal before impact, the particle will travel down the plane after impact (Figure 7.18).

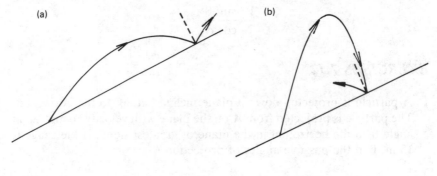

Fig. 7.18

Example 7.13

Consider a particle projected directly up a plane of inclination 30° to the horizontal. If θ is the angle of projection measured from the plane, find for which values of θ the particle will continue to travel up the plane after impact.

Solution The time to reach the plane is given by:

$$0 = (V \sin \theta)t - \left(\frac{1}{2}g \cos 30°\right)t^2$$

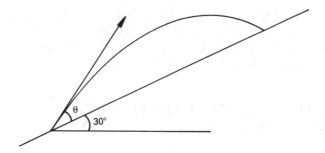

Fig. 7.19

which gives:

$$t = \frac{4V \sin \theta}{g\sqrt{3}}$$

The velocity at impact with the plane will then be:

$$\frac{V}{\sqrt{3}} (\sqrt{3} \cos \theta - 2 \sin \theta)\mathbf{i} - V \sin \theta\mathbf{j}$$

It should be noted that the magnitude of the velocity perpendicular to the plane, at impact, is equal to the magnitude of the velocity of projection perpendicular to the plane. This may seem a somewhat unusual result in the light of the lack of symmetry. (In fact, this can be shown to be true for all inclined planes.) If we write the velocity along the plane as:

$$V\sqrt{\left(\frac{7}{3}\right)} \cos (\theta + 49.1°)$$

then for the motion down the plane after impact we have:

$$\theta + 49.1° \geqslant 90° \quad \text{or} \quad \theta \geqslant 40.9°$$

EXERCISES 7.13

1 A particle is projected with speed V so that it strikes at right angles a plane through the point of projection inclined at 30° to the horizontal. Show that the range on the plane is $4V^2/7g$.

2 A shot is fired from a gun in a horizontal direction with a velocity of 300 ms^{-1}. The gun is on the side of a hill on inclination tan^{-1} (4/5) to the horizontal. Find how far along the hill the shot will strike, and determine the magnitude and direction of its velocity on impact.

7.14 REAL PROBLEMS WITH PROJECTILES AND INCLINED PLANES

Examples 7.14

1. A shell is fired with speed V from a point O on a cliff of height h above the sea. Find the greatest horizontal distance the shell can cover before landing in the sea.

Solution Method 1: Using range on an inclined plane. Let the point where the shell lands in the sea, which corresponds to the maximum distance, be S. Then the line OS can be considered to be an inclined plane, as indicated in Figure 7.20, the distance OS being the range in that inclined plane.

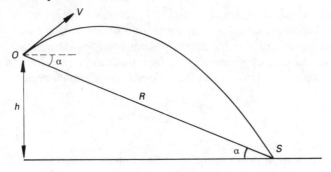

Fig. 7.20

Using an earlier result, the distance OS has a maximum value:

$$\frac{V^2}{g(1 - \sin \alpha)}$$

where $\sin \alpha = h/OS$. It follows that:

$$\sin \alpha = \frac{hg}{V^2 + hg}$$

and the corresponding value of:

$$\tan \alpha = \frac{\sqrt{(V^4 + 2V^2hg)}}{hg}$$

The resulting triangle in Figure 7.20 gives $h/\tan \alpha$ as the corresponding maximum horizontal distance covered by the shell. This simplifies to give:

$$\frac{V}{g}\sqrt{(V^2 + 2hg)}$$

Method 2: The same result can be obtained using calculus methods and considering motion relative to the horizontal and vertical axes. First, we define axes Ox and Oy horizontally and vertically through O. The equation of any trajectory when the angle of projection is θ is:

$$y = x \tan \theta - \frac{gx^2}{2V^2}\sec^2 \theta$$

Defining R as the distance horizontally out to sea, we have that the point $(R, -h)$ is a point on the trajectory, so that:

$$-h = R \tan \theta - \frac{gR^2}{2V^2}\sec^2 \theta$$

Differentiating with respect to θ gives:

$$0 = \frac{dR}{d\theta}\tan \theta + R\sec^2 \theta - \frac{gR\sec^2 \theta}{V^2}\frac{dR}{d\theta} - \frac{gR^2}{V^2}\sec^2 \theta \tan \theta$$

Maximum or minimum values of R will occur when $dR/d\theta = 0$. This gives two solutions: $R = 0$ corresponds to the minimum value and:

$$0 = 1 - \frac{gR \tan \theta}{V^2}$$

giving the maximum value for R by substituting in the original equation as:

$$\frac{V}{g}\sqrt{(V^2 + 2gh)}$$

which is the same result as before.

2. A rotary lawn sprinkler delivers water with constant speed V and at all angles. It is placed at a point O in a plane lawn, which is inclined at α to the horizontal. Defining axes Ox and Oy in the plane so that Ox is up the plane, find the equation of the edge of the area that is watered.

Solution For an inclined plane, inclined at an angle β to the horizontal, the maximum range R up the plane is given by:

$$R = \frac{V^2}{g(1 + \sin \beta)}$$

(Figure 7.21(a)). If we consider a direction at angle θ to the line of greatest slope up the plane, then from Figure 7.21(b), we have that:

$$\sin \beta = \sin \alpha \cos \theta$$

For a given point (x, y) on the edge of the watered area, we have:

$$x = R \cos \theta \quad \text{and} \quad y = R \sin \theta$$

or:

$$x = \frac{V^2 \cos \theta}{g(1 + \sin \alpha \cos \theta)} \quad \text{and} \quad y = \frac{V^2 \sin \theta}{g(1 + \sin \alpha \cos \theta)}$$

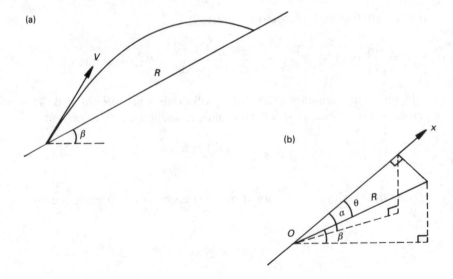

(a)

(b)

Fig. 7.21

These equations can be used as parametric equations for the watered regions, or the former equation for R allows us to study the region in polar form. The areas involved can be plotted simply using a micro. The results for $\alpha = 30°$, $60°$ and $90°$ are shown in Figure 7.22 – they should be compared with the expected result for the area on a horizontal plane. Note that any increase in V results in an enlargement of the figures.

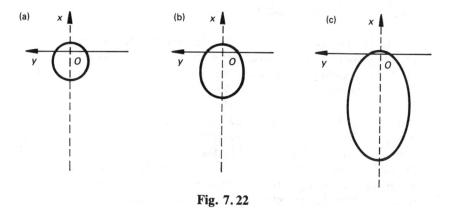

Fig. 7.22

The regions are elliptical and the position of the sprinkler is at the focus of the ellipse. We can see that the polar equation is in fact that for an ellipse with eccentricity $\sin \alpha$.

MISCELLANEOUS EXERCISES 7

1 A plane is inclined at an angle of $\tan^{-1}(3/4)$ to the horizontal. Unit vectors **i**, **j** and **k** are taken horizontal to the plane, up the line of greatest slope and perpendicular to the plane outwards respectively. Express g in terms of **i**, **j** and **k**.

A projectile is given a velocity of $20\mathbf{i} + 30\mathbf{j} + 60\mathbf{k}$ ms^{-1} from a point in the plane. Find its time of flight and the vector position of the point where it hits the plane again.

2 A small coin is projected along a smooth surface of a wedge with a velocity of 4 ms^{-1} so that its direction is at 60° to the line of greatest slope. If the wedge surface makes an angle of 30° with the horizontal, find:

(a) the greatest distance the coin travels up the wedge;

(b) the distance from the point of projection that the coin will next be at the same vertical height.

3 A tennis player volleys a ball from a point O a distance of 0.4 m below the level of the top of the net and a horizontal distance of 4 m from it. If the ball just clears the net, of height 1 m, when projected with speed 5 ms^{-1}, find the possible angles of projection. If we define axes Ox and Oy horizontally and vertically upwards, find:

(a) the equation of the path for the shortest time to the net;
(b) the distance from the net that the ball hits the ground;
(c) the magnitude and direction of the velocity with which the ball hits the ground.

4 Mud is thrown off the tyres of the wheels of a car travelling at constant speed V. Show that mud which leaves the ascending part of the tyre, at a point above the wheel hub, will be thrown clear of the wheel provided its height above the hub when it leaves the tyre is greater than $g(a/V)^2$, where a is the radius of the tyre. Also find the range of values of V for which mud will not travel above the level of the top of the wheel.

5 A ball P is projected from a point A with velocity U at an angle α to the horizontal; simultaneously, a ball Q is projected from a point B with velocity V at an angle β to the horizontal, where A and B are a distance a apart on the same horizontal level. Find the condition for them to meet and the magnitude of their relative velocity when they do.

6 A diver at an indoor pool can leave the springboard of height 10 m above the water at any velocity V and angle α above the horizontal. Owing to the height of the ceiling, she may not rise to more than 12.5 m above the water, or she would hit the roof. The diver turns a somersault in the air every 0.8 s, and must complete an odd number of half-somersaults so that she hits the water head first. Find the maximum number of half-somersaults she can complete in the dive. If, in such a dive, she may not travel a horizontal distance of more than 5 m before she enters the water, find the maximum value of her initial velocity and the corresponding value of her angle of projection. (Take $g = 10$ ms^{-2}.)

7 Show that the maximum range of a projectile on the horizontal plane through the point of projection is V^2/g, where V is the speed of projection, and state the angle of projection.

A long jumper at the instant of leaving the ground has a horizontal speed V due to his run-up, together with a speed V at an angle of θ to the horizontal due to the jump. Show that the longest jump is achieved when $\theta = \pi/3$ and find the distance achieved in the jump.

8 A hose pipe is used to water a horizontal flower bed. The water leaves the pipe at a height of 1 m above the flower bed and at an angle of 45° with the horizontal. If the speed that water leaves the hose can be adjusted, find the range of values of the speed required in order that the whole bed is watered, if the nearest and furthest points of the flower bed are at horizontal distances of 1 m and 5 m respectively.

8 CIRCULAR MOTION

8.1 INTRODUCTION

The effects of circular motion are a common daily experience. The motion of record players, the act of cornering in a car or on a bicycle, and the motion of washing in a spin dryer are common examples, and there are many more.

Circular motion is an example of *two-dimensional* motion. Previously, it has helped to analyse motion in two perpendicular directions, and a Cartesian coordinate system has proved ideal for this purpose. In Cartesians, the position of a body is represented parametrically, in terms of the time t, in the form $x = x(t)$, $y = y(t)$ – see for example the case of projectile motion in Chapter 7. For the analysis of motion in a circle, it is more convenient to use polar coordinates (r, θ). The advantages of using such a coordinate system will become obvious in the next section.

8.2 POLAR COORDINATES AND ANGULAR DISPLACEMENT

The particle P shown in Figure 8.1 is describing a circle with centre O in a plane. The radius of the circle is a metres. At a particular instant, the position of P is given in polar coordinates by $(r = a, \theta = 0$ radians$)$, and at some subsequent time, its position has moved to $(r = a, \theta = \pi/3$ radians$)$. The distance between the two positions is the most direct distance, which, using trigonometry, is $2a \sin(\pi/6)$. However, a more significant measure of the motion is the distance that P has travelled (that is, along the arc of the circle between the two points). This is given by the expression $a \times \pi/3$ metres.

More generally, if the angular coordinates of two points on a circle, of radius r metres, differ by an angle of θ radians, then the distance along the circular arc between them is $r\theta$ metres.

In Figure 8.2, a particle has travelled from a point A to point B, on a

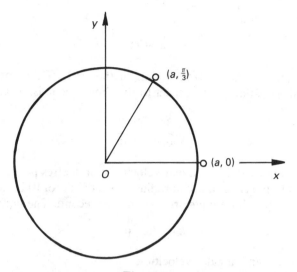

Fig. 8.1

circle of radius r. The angle subtended at the centre of the circle by the arc AB is θ radians. The angle θ radians is defined as the *angular displacement* experienced by the particle in moving from A to B. The distance s travelled along the arc AB is the *displacement* of the particle and is given by the expression $r\theta$. Note that equal angular displacements do not always result in equal displacements.

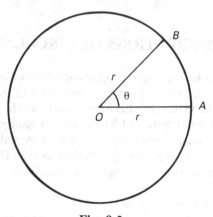

Fig. 8.2

8.3 ANGULAR VELOCITY AND ANGULAR ACCELERATION

From Section 8.2, the equation for a displacement of s metres of a particle

177

moving on a circle is:

$$s = r\theta$$

where r metres is the constant radius of the circle. Differentiating both sides of this equation, with respect to the time t seconds, gives:

$$\frac{ds}{dt} = r\frac{d\theta}{dt}$$

The expression ds/dt is the linear velocity, v, in metres per second, along the tangent to the circular arc of radius r, and $d\theta/dt$ (or $\dot{\theta}$) is its equivalent *angular velocity*, whose units are radians per second. The equation:

$$v = r\dot{\theta}$$

connects linear and angular velocities.

A second differentiation gives:

$$\frac{dv}{dt} = r\frac{d^2\theta}{dt^2}$$

Here, dv/dt ms^{-2} is the linear acceleration along the tangent to the arc of the circle and has an equivalent *angular acceleration* of θ radians per second^2 (rad s^{-2}).

8.4 SOME OBSERVATIONS OF CIRCULAR MOTION

A boy decides that he is going to project a small stone as far as possible. He knows that, if he throws it from his hand, he can only achieve a short distance and he looks for an alternative method. He has read in a book about the use of sling shots and he decides to improvise. He attaches a string to the stone and begins twirling it in a horizontal circle, holding one end of the string while the stone is attached to the other.

Here are a few questions we might ask ourselves:

(a) What forces act on the stone?
(b) Why is it impossible for the circle, described by the stone, to have as its centre the boy's hand?
(c) What happens if the string breaks?

The problem the boy has in projecting the stone is similar to that of hammer throwers in field athletics. If we perform an experiment of this type, we should notice that the motion in a circle is as illustrated in Figure

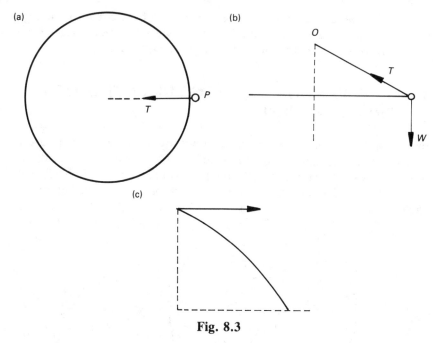

Fig. 8.3

8.3, where P is a particular point on the circular path. Also notice, in the side elevation shown in Figure 8.3(b), that the boy's hand has not been shown at the centre of the circle described by the stone.

In Figure 8.3, all the forces have been added to the diagram. The stone has no vertical motion, so upwards and downwards forces acting on the stone must balance. The weight of the stone has a fixed value W which acts vertically downwards. The weight must be balanced by an equal vertical force upwards, which can only be supplied by a component of the tension. It follows that the string cannot be horizontal if it is to have a non-zero vertical component. This answers (b).

What happens when the string breaks? Perhaps you would expect the stone to travel outwards along the direction of the string. Newton's first law tells us that, after the string is released, the motion of the stone will be unchanged in the horizontal direction, as the tension ceases to act and there will be no other horizontal force acting; hence, it will continue to travel along the *tangent* to the circle at release. Of course, the weight will continue to act vertically, so the stone travels as a projectile. The path of the stone is in the tangent plane at the point of release, as illustrated in Figure 8.3(c).

Returning to (a), it can be seen that a single force acts in the horizontal direction. This force is the component of tension there. Newton's second law tells us that the force will produce an acceleration in the same direction. This suggests that, in the case of non-uniform motion in a circle, there will be an acceleration towards the centre of the circle. In fact, the acceleration towards the centre of the circle is always present, even when a body performs circular motion with constant angular velocity.

8.5 ACCELERATION TOWARDS THE CENTRE OF A CIRCLE OF MOTION

In Section 8.3, we saw that, even when a body performs circular motion with constant angular speed, it experiences an acceleration towards the centre of the circle. Here, using the definition of acceleration from Chapter 1, we calculate the magnitude of the acceleration towards the centre of a circle.

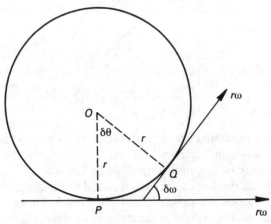

Fig. 8.4

In Figure 8.4, a body is moving in a circle of centre O and radius r metres with constant angular speed ω radians per second. The point P is the position of the body at some time t seconds and Q is its position at some subsequent time $t + \delta t$, where δt is small. The corresponding angular displacement in this time is $\delta\theta$ radians.

The linear tangential speed v is given by $r\omega$ ms^{-1} and it follows that the change in speed along the radius towards O, during the motion between positions P and Q, is:

$$\frac{r\omega \sin \delta\theta - 0}{\delta t}$$

In the limit, as δt tends towards zero, the point Q moves towards P and, as a result, $\delta\theta$ also becomes very small. The limit will represent the acceleration at P. This gives:

$$(\lim \delta t \to 0) \; \frac{r\omega \sin \delta\theta}{\delta t} = r\omega \times (\lim \delta\theta, \delta t \to 0) \frac{\sin \delta\theta}{\delta\theta} \times \frac{\delta\theta}{\delta t}$$

$$= r\omega \times 1 \times \frac{d\theta}{dt}$$

It is usual to adopt one of the following two forms for this expression:

$$r\omega^2 \quad \text{or} \quad \frac{v^2}{r}$$

the second being derived from the first using the relationship $v = r\omega$.

8.6 THE ANALYSIS OF PROBLEMS INVOLVING HORIZONTAL MOTION IN A CIRCLE

It has already been suggested that motion in a circle is common in the real world. Here, we analyse the circular motion in a number of real problems.

Examples 8.6

1. A body of mass m lies on a rough horizontal turntable so that its distance from the turntable's centre is r metres. If the turntable completes f revolutions every minute, show that the coefficient of friction, μ, between the body and the table must be $\geq mr\pi^2 f^2/900$, if the particle is to remain at rest relative to the turntable.

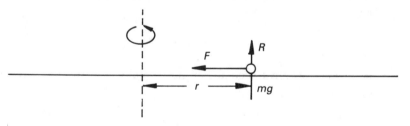

Fig. 8.5

Solution In Figure 8.5, the forces of friction and normal reaction have been added to the diagram. There is no motion in the vertical direction so that resolving in this direction gives:

$$R = mg$$

181

Applying Newton's second law to the body in the direction of the centre of the circle gives:

$$F = mr(2\pi f + 60)^2$$

For no slipping, we have $F \leqslant \mu R$ and this gives the required result:

$$\mu \geqslant \frac{mr\pi^2 f^2}{900}$$

Substituting values of 33 and 45 will give the coefficients of friction required for a typical record turntable.

2. A car of mass m kg travels on a horizontal carriage way so that, during cornering, its motion can be considered to be part of a circle of radius r metres.

   (a) If the coefficient of friction between the car's wheels and the carriage way is μ, find the greatest safe, steady cornering speed, v ms^{-1}, of the car.
   (b) If the distance between the car's wheels is d metres and the height of its centre of gravity is h metres above the carriage way, find the maximum speed of cornering in order that the car does not overturn.

Solution

   (a) In Figure 8.6, the car is shown cornering with speed v, where F and R represent the forces of friction and normal reaction between the carriage way and the car respectively. Again, resolving vertically we have:

$$R = mg$$

Applying Newton's second law horizontally towards the circle's centre gives:

$$F = \frac{mv^2}{r}$$

For no sliding, $F \leqslant \mu R$ and this leads to:

$$v^2 \leqslant \mu rg$$

The fastest cornering speed is then $\sqrt{(\mu rg)}$.

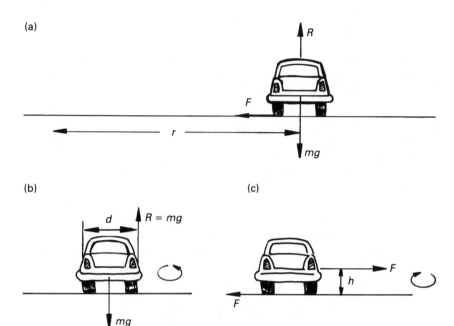

Fig. 8.6

(b) If the car overturns, it does so about its outer wheels (you may need to think about this). As a result, when it is at the point of overturning, the normal reaction and friction forces will act on the outside wheels only. From (a), we have that $F = mv^2/r$ and $R = mg$. The stability of the car is now controlled by a system of two couples. These couples have been illustrated separately in Figures 8.6(b) and (c). The couple in (b) has magnitude $mg \times (1/2)d$ and would cause an anti-clockwise rotation. The couple in (c) has magnitude $mv^2/r \times h$ and would cause a clockwise rotation. For no overturning, an anti-clockwise rotation must be encouraged, which gives:

$$\frac{1}{2}mgd \geqslant \frac{mv^2h}{r}$$

Provided there is no slipping, this gives the maximum cornering speed as $\sqrt{(rdg/2h)}$.

From this solution, it can be seen that the maximum speed will be increased if d increases and/or h decreases. These are both important considerations in high-speed car design: (a) the wheel base needs to be wide and (b) the centre of gravity of the car must be low. Both are noticeable characteristics of formula one racing cars.

EXERCISES 8.6

1 A car on a fairground roundabout has mass of 1000 kg and is connected
   to the roundabout's central spindle by an arm of length 4 m. If the car
   describes a horizontal circle every 2 s, find the tension in the arm.

2 A string of length $2a$ is connected to a point on a horizontal table. Two
   particles of mass m are fastened to the string, one at its middle point and
   the other at its end. If the string remains in the same straight line, while
   rotating with angular speed ω, find the tension in each portion of the
   string.

3 A car of mass 1000 kg travels on a rough circular track of radius 200 m.
   The track is banked at a constant angle of 30° to the horizontal, in order
   to reduce the possibility of the car skidding outwards. Find the value of
   the coefficient of friction between the car and the track if slipping occurs
   when the car is travelling at a speed of 80 kmh^{-1}.

4 A motor cyclist corners so that his motion can be considered to be on a
   circle of radius r. If the centre of gravity of the rider and his bike is at a
   height h when the bike is erect, find the angle that his bike makes with
   the vertical when cornering with speed v if he does not slip. If the motor
   cyclist rides on a wall of death, also of radius r with speed v, show that
   the angle made by his bike with the vertical is $\tan^{-1}(rg/v^2)$.

8.7 THE CONICAL PENDULUM

In our earlier discussion of circular motion, we considered hammer throwing and the sling shot. It is now possible to consider a more detailed
analysis of these problems.

The system consists of a small body P of mass m attached to a light
inextensible string of length a metres. The other end of the string is
attached to a fixed point A and the body describes a circle, about a vertical
axis through A, with constant angular speed ω radians per second. This
arrangement is that of a conical pendulum, which is illustrated in Figure
8.7, where the tension and weight acting on the body have also been
indicated. The string generates the curved surface of a cone during its
motion.

Again, the first stage in modelling the problem is to resolve vertically to
give:

$$mg = T \cos \theta \qquad (1)$$

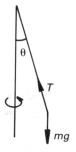

Fig. 8.7

where θ is the angle between the string and the vertical. If Newton's second law is applied to the body, in the direction of the centre of the circle, this gives:

$$ma \sin \theta \, \omega^2 = T \sin \theta$$

which reduces to:

$$ma\omega^2 = T \qquad (2)$$

Eliminating T between equations (1) and (2) gives:

$$\cos \theta = \frac{g}{a\omega^2}$$

Here, it can be seen that $\cos \theta$ can never be zero, although it becomes progressively smaller as ω increases. As the angular speed, ω, is increased, the cone generated becomes flatter, but never completely flat. This is a *conical pendulum*.

The development of this model has considerable potential. Here is a simple variation of the same problem.

Example 8.7

The ends of a light inextensible string of length $4a$ are attached to two fixed points A and B in the same vertical line, so that B is a distance $2a$ below A. A small smooth ring of mass m is tied to the string at its centre C. If the ring moves in a fixed horizontal circle, with angular speed ω, find the tension in the portion of the string BC and show that the motion is only possible if $\omega^2 \geq 4g/a$.

Solution In Figure 8.8, the arrangement has been illustrated and the weight mg and tensions T_1 and T_2, which act on the body, are indicated. As

185

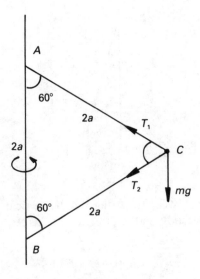

Fig. 8.8

$AB = BC = CA$, then the angles made by each of the strings AC and BC with the vertical are 60°. Resolving vertically for the body gives:

$$T_1 \cos 60° = T_2 \cos 60° + mg$$

Simplification of this expression leads to:

$$T_1 - T_2 = 2mg \qquad (3)$$

Applying Newton's second law to the body, in the direction of the circle's centre, gives:

$$T_1 \sin 60° + T_2 \sin 60° = 2ma\omega^2 \sin 60°$$

Again, simplification gives:

$$T_1 + T_2 = 2ma\omega^2 \qquad (4)$$

Eliminating T_1 from equations (3) and (4) enables the tension in the string BC to be written as:

$$T_2 = \frac{1}{2}m(a\omega^2 - 4g)$$

If this expression results in a negative value for the tension, then the string would be slack and the motion would not be possible. For the motion to be maintained, we must have that $T_2 \geqslant 0$, which gives $\omega^2 \geqslant 4g/a$.

EXERCISES 8.7

1 A particle of mass m is fastened by a string of length $2l$ to a point at a height l above a smooth table. If the particle describes a horizontal circle on the table, with angular speed ω, find the tension in the string and the reaction between the table and the particle. Determine the greatest angular speed possible for the particle to remain in contact with the table.

2 The ends of a light string of length $8a$ are attached to fixed points L and M, in the same vertical line, so that L is $4a$ below M. A small bead is threaded on the string and describes a circle of radius $3a$. Determine the tension in the string and calculate the speed of the bead.

3 Two particles of masses m and $2m$ are connected by a light inextensible string, which is threaded through a fixed smooth ring. If the lighter particle describes a horizontal circle of radius a, while the other particle remains stationary, find the lighter particle's speed.

4 A particle moving with a constant speed u inside a smooth spherical bowl of radius a describes a horizontal circle at a distance $(1/2)a$ below its centre. Find the value of u.

5 A circular cone of semi-vertical angle α is fixed with its axis vertical and its vertex downwards. A particle of mass m is fastened to one end of an inextensible string of length l, the other end of which is fixed to the vertex of the cone, so that the particle can move on the smooth inner surface of the cone, with constant angular speed ω. Find the least value of ω^2 in order that the string will remain in tension.

6 The mechanism shown in Figure 8.9 is designed to regulate the flow of steam from a boiler. It consists of four light rigid rods each of length $2a$, together with small spheres at A and B of mass m. AD and BD are smoothly hinged at D. A smooth ring of mass m is jointed to AC and BC at C and can slide on the vertical spindle below D. A, B and the spindle are all in the same vertical plane. When the valve is open, the ring rests on a horizontal ledge, fixed to the spindle at a distance $2a$ below D. The system rotates about the axis CD with angular speed ω.

(a) Find: (i) the tension or thrust in the rods;
　　　　　 (ii) the force exerted by the ledge on the ring.
(b) Show that if $a\omega^2 > 2g$, then the ring rises, opening the valve.

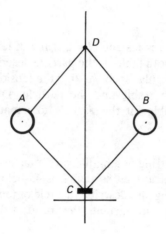

Fig. 8.9

8.8 MODELLING PROBLEMS OF MOTION IN A VERTICAL CIRCLE

Motion in a vertical circle is very different from motion in a horizontal circle. As we have seen, in the free motion in a horizontal circle, the speed is constant (although this does not always have to be the case). In contrast, motion in a vertical circle has variable speed.

To cause a body hanging in equilibrium by a string to move in a vertical circle, we might start the motion by giving the body a horizontal velocity. The result will be that the body rises in a circular arc. It may complete a circle, or just swing to and fro, or it may fall from the path at some point. One noticeable factor is that the speed of the freely moving body changes as it moves along the circular path. The analysis of motion in a vertical circle is of two types:

(a) Motion inside a circle, which occurs when a body is attached to the end of a string or travelling on the inner surface of a cylinder.
(b) Motion outside a circle, which occurs when a body slides on the outer surface of a cylinder.

First, we consider motion inside a vertical circle. Figure 8.10 illustrates two practical examples of motion inside a vertical circle of radius a: Figure 8.10(a) shows the motion of a body on the end of an inextensible string; Figure 8.10(b) shows the motion of a small body sliding on the smooth inner surface of a cylindrical drum. The analysis of these two problems is identical and in the diagrams we have labelled the tension in (a) and the

(a)

(b)

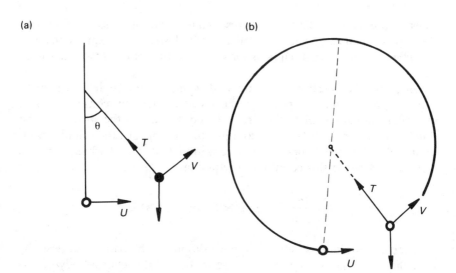

Fig. 8.10

reaction in (b) as T. This will result in the same governing equations for the motion.

The problem of the changing speed of the body must be considered first. If the body is projected horizontally with a speed U from its lowest position, then we need to derive an expression for the speed, V, at a position where the angle made by the radius to the particle and the downwards vertical is θ. Using conservation of energy (see Chapter 4) gives:

$$\tfrac{1}{2}mU^2 = \tfrac{1}{2}mV^2 + mga(1 - \cos \theta)$$

This gives V^2 in terms of θ as:

$$V^2 = U^2 + 2ga(\cos \theta - 1) \tag{5}$$

provided T is always positive (that is, the body remains on a circular arc).

The body has an acceleration towards the centre of the circle and again Newton's second law must be considered to give:

$$T - mg \cos \theta = \frac{mV^2}{a} \tag{6}$$

Eliminating V^2 between equations (5) and (6) gives the tension as:

$$T = \frac{mU^2}{a} + mg(3 \cos \theta - 2) \tag{7}$$

These expressions for V^2 and T represent a model of the possible motion of the body while it is moving in a vertical circle. Using these expressions, it is possible to identify what happens for various values of U, at various values of θ.

Let us ask the question: Does the body complete the circle? If the body can achieve the highest point of the motion, then, by conservation of energy, it should complete the circle. To do this, either the string must be taut, as in (a), or the body must continue to press against the cylinder wall, as in (b). This will happen if the condition that $T \geq 0$ when $\theta = \pi$ is satisfied. Applying this condition to equation (7) gives:

$$T = \frac{mU^2}{a} - 5mg \geq 0 \quad \text{or} \quad U^2 \geq 5ga$$

A second question is: What is the condition for the particle to describe only the lower half of the circle of the motion? Whenever a body has its motion confined to the lower half of a circle, then the need for the reaction or tension to be non-zero will always be satisfied. This time it is necessary to look at the equation for V^2 for a condition. For, provided $V^2 \geq 0$ when $\theta = (1/2)\pi$, then the particle can move on the lower half of the circle. Applying this condition to equation (5) gives:

$$V^2 = U^2 - 2ga \geq 0 \quad \text{or} \quad U^2 \geq 2ga$$

As a result, it would be expected that, in cases when $U^2 < 2ga$, the particle will oscillate on the lower circular arc.

Finally: What happens if $2ga < U^2 < 5ga$? In these cases, the contact or tension requirement will not be satisfied for some range of values of θ in the range $(1/2)\pi < \theta < \pi$. From the point when $T = 0$, the particle will begin to leave the vertical circle and will travel freely as a projectile, until it meets the circle once more. Obviously, many paths are possible, one of which is illustrated in Figure 8.11.

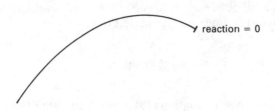

reaction = 0

Fig. 8.11

Next, let us look at motion *outside* a vertical circle. Examples of this type of motion can be analysed by considering the simple problem of a particle resting on the highest point of a fixed smooth sphere of radius a. In Figure 8.12, the position of the particle, whose mass is m, is shown when the radius to its position makes an angle θ with the upwards vertical. Its speed is then V. Forces of reaction, R, and the weight, mg, have also been indicated in the diagram. This motion can be started either by displacing the particle or by giving it a horizontal velocity. Certainly, we do not expect the particle to complete a circle.

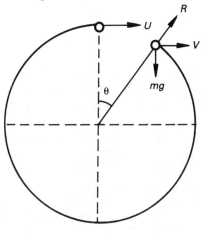

Fig. 8.12

Adopting a similar approach as before, if U is the initial speed, and when the angle the particle makes with the vertical is θ its speed is V, the conservation of energy gives:

$$\frac{1}{2}mU^2 = \frac{1}{2}mV^2 - mga(1 - \cos \theta)$$

and:

$$V^2 = U^2 + 2ga(1 - \cos \theta) \tag{8}$$

Newton's second law applied towards the centre of the circle gives:

$$mg \cos \theta - R = \frac{mV^2}{a} \tag{9}$$

Elimination of V^2 between equations (8) and (9) gives the reaction:

$$R = mg(3 \cos \theta - 2) - \frac{mU^2}{a}$$

It is clear that the particle will leave the circle at some point; in fact, it does so when $R = 0$. Solving this equation for $\cos \theta$ gives:

$$\cos \theta = \frac{1}{3}\left(\frac{U^2}{ga} + 2\right)$$

As would be expected, as U increases, θ decreases, which means that the particle leaves the circle at a higher position. When $U^2 \geqslant ga$, it leaves immediately and travels as a projectile.

EXERCISES 8.8

1 A bead lies inside a smooth narrow circular tube of radius a, whose plane is vertical. If the bead, which is initially stationary, is given a velocity U, show that it will complete circles if $U^2 \geqslant 4ga$.

2 A small mass m is attached to a point O by an inextensible string of length a. The mass is held with the string taut, at the same level as O, and released. Determine the angular velocity of the mass when the string makes an angle θ with the downwards vertical. From this relationship, determine the period of one complete swing. How does this time compare with the value of the period of a small pendulum of length a?

3 A small body of mass m is attached by an inextensible string of length $2a$ to a point O. The particle is released when the string is horizontal, and in its downwards motion it meets a peg A, a distance a vertically below O. Find how high the body will rise above A in its subsequent motion.

4 A particle rests at the top of a fixed smooth sphere of radius a, which is fastened to a horizontal plane. If the particle is disturbed, find the horizontal distance that it will have travelled when it strikes the plane.

8.9 MOTION IN A CIRCLE AND CONNECTED PARTICLES

To this point, we have examined the free motion of bodies describing horizontal and vertical circles. In this section, we look at motion of connected particles in which one or other of the particles is performing circular motion.

Example 8.9

Two beads P and Q of masses m and $2m$ respectively are attached to the ends of an inextensible string, whose length is greater than πa. The string, which is taut, passes over a smooth cylinder of radius a, so that the plane containing the string and the beads is perpendicular to the cylinder's axis. The plane through the axis of the cylinder and P is initially horizontal. If the system is released from rest, show that when the radius through P has turned through an angle θ and P is still in contact with the cylinder, then:

$$3a\left(\frac{d\theta}{dt}\right)^2 = 2g(2\theta - \sin\theta)$$

where θ is the angle made by the radius to P to the horizontal. Find the tension in the string and the reaction between the bead P and the cylinder. Hence, show that the bead loses contact with the cylinder before reaching the highest point.

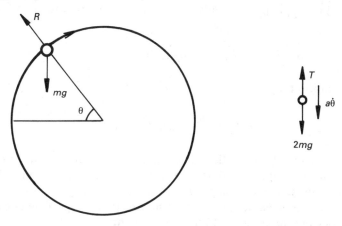

Fig. 8.13

Solution The particle's motion is illustrated in Figure 8.13. T is the tension in the string and R is the normal reaction between the particle P and the cylinder. The velocity of each particle is $a\dot\theta$ and the transverse acceleration of P and linear acceleration of Q are both $a\ddot\theta$. Conservation of energy gives:

$$\frac{1}{2}m(a\dot\theta)^2 + \frac{1}{2}2m(a\dot\theta)^2 + mga\sin\theta - 2mga\theta = 0$$

Simplification of this energy equation leads to the required equation as:

$$3a\dot\theta^2 = 2g(2\theta - \sin\theta) \qquad (10)$$

Differentiation of equation (10) gives:

$$6a\dot\theta\ddot\theta = 2ga(2\dot\theta - \cos\theta\dot\theta)$$
$$3a\ddot\theta = g(2 - \cos\theta) \qquad (11)$$

To find the tension, we apply Newton's second law to Q (or alternatively to P) along the tangent to give:

$$2ma\ddot\theta = 2mg - T$$

Using equation (10) now allows an expression for T to be found as:

$$T = \frac{2mg}{3}(1 + \cos\theta)$$

R is found by applying Newton's second law in a radial direction for P to give:

$$ma\dot\theta^2 = mg\sin\theta - R$$

Using equation (10) gives R as:

$$R = \frac{mg}{3}(5\sin\theta - 4\theta)$$

For the particle P to leave the circle, its value for some θ must be zero. Sketches of the graphs of 4θ and $5\sin\theta$, which are illustrated in Figure 8.14, show one zero in this range, and values of θ greater than that root will result in a negative value for R. This confirms that the particle does leave the cylinder before arriving at the highest point.

EXERCISES 8.9

1 Figure 8.15 shows a smooth narrow tube in the form of a circle, with centre O and radius a, which is fixed in a vertical plane. The tube contains two particles P, of mass m, and Q, of mass $3m$, which are connected by a light inextensible string of length $(1/2)\pi a$. The system is released from rest when P is at the level of O and Q is at the highest point of the tube. Show that, if after a time t, the line OP has turned through an angle θ, then:

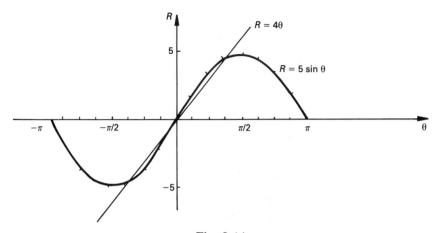

Fig. 8.14

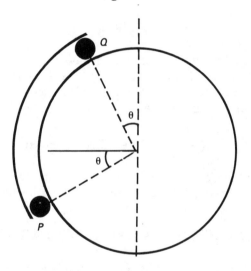

Fig. 8.15

$$2a\left(\frac{d\theta}{dt}\right)^2 = g(3 - 3\cos\theta + \sin\theta)$$

provided that the string remains taut. Find the reaction between P and the tube. Obtain the angular acceleration in terms of g and θ. Deduce that the string becomes slack when $\theta = (1/4)\pi$.

2 Figure 8.16 shows a smooth narrow tube in the form of a semi-circle of radius a which is fixed in a vertical plane with its diameter vertical. A particle of mass m is initially at rest inside the tube, at its lowest point A. The particle is attached to one end of a light inextensible string which

195

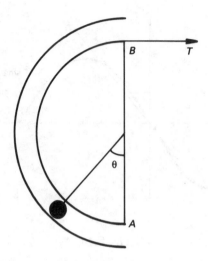

Fig. 8.16

passes through the tube and out at the highest point B. The string is taut and its other end is pulled with a constant force T. Show that, if at a time t after the particle has left A, the radius of the semi-circle through the particle makes an angle θ with BA, then:

$$ma\left(\frac{d\theta}{dt}\right)^2 = 2T\theta - 2mg(1 - \cos\theta)$$

Find the reaction of the tube on the particle and the angular acceleration. Show that, if $T = (1/2)mg$, then $d^2\theta/dt^2 = 0$ when $\theta = \pi/6$.

8.10 VECTOR METHODS AND CIRCULAR MOTION

In this section, the position vector of a body describing a circle is used and, from it, the definition of the velocity vector is derived for circular motion. The position P of a particle at time t is given by $\mathbf{r} = \mathbf{r}(t)$ and $|\mathbf{r}| = \mathbf{r}$, a constant. To use the definition of the velocity vector $\mathbf{v}$ in Chapter 1, $\mathbf{r}(t + \delta t)$ is taken to be the position vector of the point Q, as illustrated in Figure 8.17(a).

For the particle moving from P at time t to Q at time $t + \delta t$, the velocity vector $\mathbf{v}$ is written as:

$$\mathbf{v} = \lim_{\delta t \to 0}\left[\frac{\mathbf{r}(t + \delta t) - \mathbf{r}(t)}{\delta t}\right]$$

which may be reduced to:

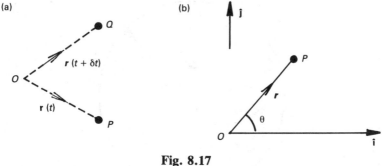

Fig. 8.17

$$\mathbf{v} = \frac{d\mathbf{r}}{dt}$$

It should be clear that the limit results in the velocity vector being along the tangent to the path at P, as was identified to be the case in Chapter 1.

Figure 8.17(b) shows the unit vectors $\mathbf{i}$ and $\mathbf{j}$ so that the position vector $\mathbf{r}$ of P, with respect to the centre of the circle O, can be written as:

$$\mathbf{r} = r \cos \theta \mathbf{i} + r \sin \theta \mathbf{j}$$

The velocity vector is then:

$$\mathbf{v} = \frac{d\mathbf{r}}{dt} = -r \sin \theta \cdot \dot{\theta}\mathbf{i} + r \cos \theta \cdot \dot{\theta}\mathbf{j}$$

It is usual, in the case of motion where the use of polar coordinates is preferred, to write $\mathbf{r}$ and $\mathbf{v}$ in terms of the radial unit vector:

$$\hat{\mathbf{r}} = \cos \theta \mathbf{i} + \sin \theta \mathbf{j}$$

and the transverse unit vector:

$$\hat{\boldsymbol{\theta}} = -\sin \theta \mathbf{i} + \cos \theta \mathbf{j}$$

This allows the position vector to be written as:

$$\mathbf{r} = r\hat{\mathbf{r}}$$

and the velocity vector as:

$$\mathbf{v} = r\dot{\theta}\hat{\boldsymbol{\theta}}$$

The more significant implications here are that, if any vector varying with t is differentiated with respect to t, the result is that its direction is rotated through $(1/2)\pi$ in an anti-clockwise direction and its magnitude multiplied

197

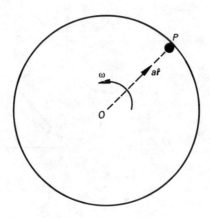

Fig. 8.18

by θ. This gives, in the case of $\mathbf{r}$ and θ:

$$\frac{d\hat{\mathbf{r}}}{dt} = \dot{\theta}\hat{\boldsymbol{\theta}} \quad \text{and} \quad \frac{d\hat{\boldsymbol{\theta}}}{dt} = -\dot{\theta}\hat{\mathbf{r}}$$

8.11 VECTOR FORMULATION FOR CONSTANT ANGULAR VELOCITY

In Figure 8.18, the particle P is describing a circle, of centre O and radius a, with constant angular speed ω. The position vector of P at any time t can be written as:

$$\mathbf{r} = a\hat{\mathbf{r}}$$

Differentiating this expression leads to:

$$\mathbf{v} = \frac{d\mathbf{r}}{dt} = a\omega\hat{\boldsymbol{\theta}}$$

where a is a constant. This gives, as in our earlier analysis, the velocity as along the tangent. A second differentiation gives the acceleration vector as:

$$\mathbf{f} = \frac{d\mathbf{v}}{dt} = a\omega(-\omega\hat{\mathbf{r}}) = -a\omega^2\hat{\mathbf{r}}$$

Here, as before, there is an acceleration along the radius, towards the centre of the circle $a\omega^2$.

The simplicity of this derivation should encourage the use of vectors in these problems.

198

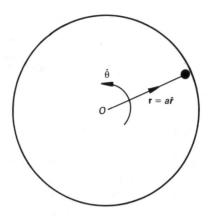

Fig. 8.19

8.12 VECTOR FORMULATION FOR NON-CONSTANT ANGULAR VELOCITY

Here, as in Section 8.10, the particle P is describing a circle of radius a and centre O, as illustrated in Figure 8.19. This time the angular velocity is not constant.

As before, the position vector is given by:

$$\mathbf{r} = a\hat{\mathbf{r}}$$

Differentiating to find the velocity vector gives:

$$\mathbf{v} = \frac{d\mathbf{r}}{dt} = a\dot{\theta}\hat{\boldsymbol{\theta}}$$

which is the result already derived in Section 8.10 and the same as would be expected for uniform speed. A second differentiation to find the acceleration vector gives:

$$\mathbf{f} = \frac{d\mathbf{v}}{dt} = a\ddot{\theta}\hat{\boldsymbol{\theta}} + a\dot{\theta}(-\dot{\theta}\hat{\mathbf{r}}) = a\ddot{\theta}\hat{\boldsymbol{\theta}} - a\dot{\theta}^2\hat{\mathbf{r}}$$

This acceleration vector consists of two parts: a transverse component $a\ddot{\theta}$ and a radial component $-a\dot{\theta}^2$. These acceleration components have already been found in Section 8.11, but the advantage of having them in this form is the ease with which they can be used.

8.13 CIRCULAR ORBITS

The value in using radial and transverse component vectors becomes increasingly apparent when the forces involved are central (directed along

199

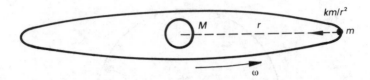

Fig. 8.20

the radius) or tangential. An important example of this is gravitational attraction.

Modelling planetary motion as a circle is often very useful. The gravitational force of attraction between two bodies of masses M and m kilograms at a distance r metres apart is expressed as:

$$\frac{GMm}{r^2}$$

In the case of a satellite of mass m, assuming a circular orbit around the Earth of $G = 6.64 \times 10^{-11}$ m^3 kg^{-1} s^{-2} and the mass of the Earth as $M = 6 \times 10^{21}$ kg, this allows the value of GM $(= k)$ to be set at 3.984×10^{14} m^3 s^{-1}.

In Figure 8.20, a satellite is in a circular orbit of radius r metres. Newton's second law applied to the satellite's motion towards the orbit's centre gives:

$$-mr\omega^2 = -\frac{km}{r^2}$$

which can be written as:

$$\omega^2 = \frac{k}{r^3}$$

Using this expression and the fact that the orbit is circular, so that r is constant, it follows that ω is also constant. Thus, the satellite has a constant angular speed, and its period is:

$$\frac{2\pi}{\omega} = 2\pi \sqrt{\left(\frac{r^3}{k}\right)}$$

8.14 ANGULAR VELOCITY AS A VECTOR

Having defined such vector quantities as displacement, linear velocity and linear acceleration, we now find vector representations for angular dis-

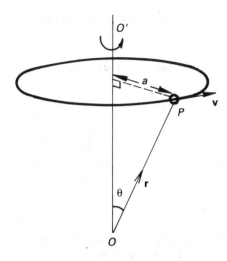

Fig. 8.21

placement, angular velocity and angular acceleration. Although the magnitude of these angular quantities is easily identified, the allocation of direction is not as obvious.

In Figure 8.21, a point P is rotating about the fixed axis OO' with angular speed ω. We shall use vector methods to determine the linear velocity of P at any point on its path. Clearly, the velocity vector changes continuously, as the rotation takes place, and the velocity will be directed along the tangent to the circle at any time. Its magnitude will be $a\omega$, where a is the radius of the circle described by P.

If the position vector of P is $\mathbf{r}$ at some time t and the angular speed is ω, then the linear velocity vector $\mathbf{v}$ has the direction illustrated in Figure 8.21 and its magnitude is:

$$\omega r \sin \theta$$

The velocity vector $\mathbf{v}$ can thus be identified as that of the vector product:

$$\mathbf{v} = \boldsymbol{\omega} \times \mathbf{r}$$

where the vector $\boldsymbol{\omega}$ is defined as the angular velocity vector. The angular velocity vector has a direction defined by its right-handed rotation along the axis of rotation. Similar representations can be found for angular displacement and acceleration. These ideas are developed more fully in Chapter 11.

If a point is rotating about OO', whose direction is defined by the unit vector $(\mathbf{i} + 2\mathbf{j} - 2\mathbf{k})/3$, with angular speed of 6 rad s^{-1}, its angular velocity vector is written as:

$$\boldsymbol{\omega} = 2\mathbf{i} + 4\mathbf{j} - 4\mathbf{k}$$

EXERCISES 8.14

1 Determine the velocity vector $\mathbf{v}$ for the following points with the position vector $\mathbf{r}$ and angular velocity vector $\boldsymbol{\omega}$ about an axis through the origin:

(a) $\mathbf{r} = 2\mathbf{i} - \mathbf{j} - 2\mathbf{k}$, $\boldsymbol{\omega} = \mathbf{i} - \mathbf{k}$;
(b) $\mathbf{r} = 3\mathbf{i}$, $\boldsymbol{\omega} = 3\mathbf{j}$.

2 A particle describes a circle about the line whose vector equation is $\mathbf{r} = (3 + \mu)\mathbf{i} + 2\mathbf{j} + (1 - \mu)\mathbf{k}$ with angular speed ω radians per second. If at time $t = 0$ the particle is at the point $2\mathbf{k}$, find its velocity vector.

3 The velocity vector $\mathbf{v}$ of a particle moving in a plane can be written as:

$$\mathbf{v} = \boldsymbol{\omega} \times \mathbf{r} + \dot{\mathbf{r}}$$

where $\mathbf{r}$ is the position vector of the particle with respect to a fixed point within the plane. Show that the acceleration vector can be written as:

$$\frac{1}{r}\frac{d(r^2\omega)\hat{\boldsymbol{\theta}}}{dr} + (r - r\omega^2)\hat{\mathbf{r}}$$

MISCELLANEOUS EXERCISES 8

1 A large space station is built in the form of a circular tube of radius 50 m. In order to combat the problem of weightlessness, the designers decide that the tube will rotate about its axis of symmetry with a constant angular speed ω radians per second.

(a) How will this work for the people who are on the space station?
(b) What value will ω have to take in order for the occupants of the space station to assume a 'weight' which is the same as that due to gravity on Earth?

2 A tumble dryer is made from a cylindrical drum whose axis is horizontal. If the radius of the drum is 30 cm, determine the best strategy for drying clothes and suggest suitable rotation speeds for the drum.

9 VIBRATIONS

9.1 INTRODUCTION

It is probably safe to assume that we all know what is meant by a vibration, whether we think of sitting on a bus, experiencing the rattles and bumps as it struggles uphill, or the twang of a guitar string. The essential ingredient common to all vibrations is the to-and-fro motion, without there being any overall movement in any direction. This chapter will enable us to understand more about all types of vibrations. Engineers need to understand many things that oscillate; a few examples are engines, buildings subject to high winds, offshore structures and output from electrical circuits (for example hi-fi systems). At first sight, all of these seem very different, and very difficult to model. However, if attention is focussed on the end product, they all exhibit a to-and-fro motion, and it is this that we will use Newton's laws to describe. We will restrict our attention to motion in one dimension, or, more strictly, to a single degree of freedom.

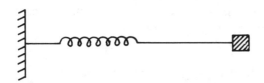

Fig. 9.1

Consider a mass attached to a spring on a smooth horizontal table as shown in Figure 9.1. If the spring is neither stretched nor compressed, the mass will not be subject to any force, and therefore it will be in equilibrium. If the mass is pulled (or pushed) in the line of the spring and then released, it will vibrate back and forth. The spring will always try to restore the mass to its equilibrium position, but it will overshoot and, in the absence of any damping or friction, never come to rest other than instantaneously. Perfect springs have no damping, and all the springs we consider will be perfect, so the simple spring system shown in Figure 9.1, once set in motion, will vibrate forever. This is the system that will be examined first.

Before starting on the mathematics, here are some terms with which we need to become acquainted. We have already met the phrase *equilibrium position* (where the mass is at rest). The distance between this position and the furthest point reached by the mass in either direction of its motion is called the *amplitude* of the vibration or oscillation. The words *vibration* and *oscillation* are used synonymously. The time the mass takes between leaving the left-most (say) extremity and returning there is called the *period*, and 2π divided by this number is called the *frequency* of the oscillation. In the last chapter, motion in a circle was discussed. If a particle is describing a horizontal circle with uniform speed, the time taken to describe the circle once is the period (one cycle). If the perpendicular from the particle to a diameter is drawn, the foot of this perpendicular will describe simple harmonic motion (SHM), that is, it will oscillate. The radius of the circle is the amplitude of the vibration. This provides an alternative view of vibration.

Finally, a few words about springs. In reality, springs can be tricky to understand, but once attention is restricted to perfect springs, most difficulties disappear. A perfect spring, if left lying on a smooth table, has a fixed length. If it is stretched or compressed, then freed once more to lie on the table, its length will be the same. This is called its *natural length*, and it is the length a spring has in the total absence of forces. There is, however, a second property of springs. Springs that have the same natural length can still be very different; for example, the spring found in the suspension system of a car may have the same natural length as the spring in an electric toaster, but they could not change roles. The car spring is stiffer (more difficult to stretch or compress) than the toaster spring, and this second property of springs is called their *stiffness*.

9.2 SIMPLE HARMONIC MOTION

The basic undamped vibration of Figure 9.1 is called *simple harmonic motion* (abbreviated to SHM). To derive an equation to describe it, we must use the second of Newton's laws of motion.

Figure 9.2 is the same as Figure 9.1 but with the addition of an origin, axis, force and some labels. It is most convenient to choose as origin the equilibrium position of the mass m. Figure 9.2 shows this, together with the decision to choose the positive x-axis to point to the right. The only force acting on m, the mass, is due to the spring and we assume it is stretched so

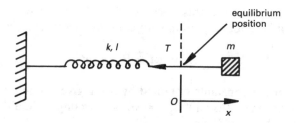

Fig. 9.2

that T, the tension in the spring, acts as shown. Note that these choices (origin, axis, whether the spring is stretched or compressed) are, by and large, arbitrary (origins have to be fixed, $x = 0$ at O etc.). However, once the choice is made, it does not change.

Applying Newton's second law (i.e. force = mass × acceleration) gives:

$$-T = m \frac{d^2x}{dt^2} \tag{1}$$

To solve this equation, we need to make some assumptions about T. Clearly, the larger x is the bigger T is. If you stretch a spring, the further it is stretched, the greater is the force it exerts. Also, the stiffer the spring, the greater will be the value of T. (Think again of car springs, large stiffness, as opposed to toaster springs, smaller stiffness.) The simplest model, therefore, is to assume that T is directly proportional to the extension of the spring x (this is Hooke's law) and that the constant of proportionality is the stiffness, k:

$$T = kx \tag{2}$$

Eliminating T between equations (1) and (2) gives:

$$m \frac{d^2x}{dt^2} = -kx \tag{3}$$

Dividing by m and writing $\omega^2 = k/m$ yields:

$$\frac{d^2x}{dt^2} = -\omega^2 x \tag{4}$$

where ω is a number with dimensions of (time)$^{-1}$ called the *natural frequency* of the mass and spring system. This name arises from the fact that it is the frequency at which the mass oscillates when pulled to one side and released. We can see this because the solution to equation (4), a second-order differential equation with constant coefficients, is:

$$x = A \sin \omega t + B \cos \omega t \tag{5}$$

where A and B are constants obtained by using given conditions on x or dx/dt at specific times (usually at $t = 0$). An example should make the determination of A and B clear.

Example 9.2.1

Calculate the displacement x in terms of ω and t if, at time $t = 0$, $x = 3$ and the velocity is zero.

Solution   The velocity of a particle that is displaced a distance x is its rate of change with respect to time, dx/dt (see Chapter 1), so if x is given by equation (5), then differentiating with respect to t gives:

$$\frac{dx}{dt} = \omega A \cos \omega t - \omega B \sin \omega t \tag{6}$$

At time $t = 0$, we obtain:

$$\left. \frac{dx}{dt} \right|_{t=0} = \omega A \tag{7}$$

If this is to be zero, we must have $A = 0$.
  Setting $A = 0$ results in the simplification of equation (5) to:

$$x = B \cos \omega t \tag{8}$$

and if $x = 3$ at $t = 0$:

$$B = 3 \tag{9}$$

We have thus determined the particular values of A and B that satisfy $x = 3$ and $dx/dt = 0$ at time $t = 0$. The solution is:

$$x = 3 \cos \omega t \tag{10}$$

Conditions like those in example 9.2.1 that enable us to find arbitrary constants are called boundary conditions – we have already met them in Chapter 6. Most of such conditions met in this chapter are given at time $t = 0$, and they are then termed *initial conditions* for obvious reasons. We see that the mass does indeed oscillate at the natural frequency ω (with amplitude 3 in the case of the last example).

For some problems, we know that it is more convenient to work in terms of velocity. We also know that acceleration can be described by one of the following alternative forms:

$$\frac{dv}{dt} \quad \text{or} \quad v\,\frac{dv}{dx}$$

Using the second of these, equation (3) becomes:

$$mv\,\frac{dv}{dx} = -kx$$

Or, rearranging:

$$\int v\,dv = -\int \frac{kx}{m}\,dx \tag{11}$$

Integrating equation (11) gives:

$$\frac{1}{2}\,v^2 = -\frac{kx^2}{2m} + C \tag{12}$$

where C is an arbitrary constant. We know that, at the extremity of an oscillation, velocity, v, is instantaneously zero. Hence, if we set $v = 0$ when $x = x_0$ (say), x_0 would then be the amplitude of the oscillation. Inserting this condition into equation (12) gives:

$$v^2 = \frac{k}{m}\,(x_0^2 - x^2) = \omega^2(x_0^2 - x^2) \tag{13}$$

There is a lot of information in equation (13). See examples 4.3.1 for an alternative approach using energy. The right-hand side must be positive or zero, because v^2 is, so:

$$x_0^2 \geqslant x^2$$

whence:

$$-x_0 \leqslant x \leqslant x_0 \tag{14}$$

that is, x lies in the range between $-x_0$ and x_0. We can also see from equation (13) that v is zero at the extremes ($x = \pm x_0$) and has its maximum value (x_0) at $x = 0$. All this is consistent with the oscillatory motion predicted by equation (5).

Returning to equation (5):

$$x = A \cos \omega t + B \sin \omega t$$

we can rewrite this as:

$$x = \sqrt{(A^2 + B^2)} \left[\frac{A \cos \omega t}{\sqrt{(A^2 + B^2)}} + \frac{B \sin \omega t}{\sqrt{(A^2 + B^2)}} \right] \tag{15}$$

or:

$$x = \sqrt{(A^2 + B^2)} \cos (\omega t - \Phi) \tag{16}$$

where:

$$\cos \Phi = \frac{A}{\sqrt{(A^2 + B^2)}} \quad \text{and} \quad \sin \Phi = \frac{B}{\sqrt{(A^2 + B^2)}} \quad \left(\tan \Phi = \frac{B}{A} \right)$$

The quantity $\sqrt{(A^2 + B^2)}$ is the amplitude (met earlier) and Φ is the *phase* (new concept) of the oscillation. Equation (16) is termed the amplitude–phase form of the solution and can be more easily related to what actually happens to the mass than can the solution in the form of equation (5). Twice the amplitude is the full extent of the oscillation, and the phase is linked to where we take the time origin. If we start a stop-watch when the particle in Figure 9.2 is furthest from the support (right-most extremity), then the phase is zero.

To complete this section, we can re-derive equation (13) from equation (16). Differentiating with respect to t gives:

$$v = \frac{dx}{dt} = -\omega \sqrt{(A^2 + B^2)} \sin (\omega t - \Phi) \tag{17}$$

Dividing equation (17) by $\omega \sqrt{(A^2 + B^2)}$ ($= \omega x_0$) and equation (16) by $\sqrt{(A^2 + B^2)}$ ($= x_0$), squaring and adding yields:

$$\left(\frac{v}{\omega x_0}\right)^2 + \left(\frac{x}{x_0}\right)^2 = \sin^2\left(\omega t - \Phi\right) + \cos^2\left(\omega t - \Phi\right) = 1$$

which, on rearrangement, regains equation (13). Let us now do a complete example.

Example 9.2.2

A particle P of mass m lies on a smooth horizontal table and is attached by two springs of natural lengths $3a$ and $2a$ and stiffness k and $3k$ to points A and B respectively. If $AB = 7a$, show that, when the particle is in equilibrium, $AP = 9a/2$. The particle is held at rest in the line AB with $AP = 5a$ and then released. Find the period of the motion and the particle's maximum speed.

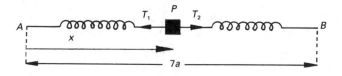

Fig. 9.3

Solution The tension in a spring = stiffness × extension and extension = actual length − natural length, so (Figure 9.3):

$$T_1 = k(x - 3a)$$
$$T_2 = 3k(7a - x - 2a) = 3k(5a - x)$$

Newton's second law applied to P gives:

$$m\ddot{x} = T_2 - T_1$$
$$= 3k(5a - x) - k(x - 3a)$$
$$= 18ak - 4kx$$

The equilibrium position is given when the net force on the particle is zero, so that:

$$18ak - 4kx = 0$$
$$x = \frac{9a}{2}$$

To solve the remainder of the problem, we find the solution to the equation:

$$m\ddot{x} = 18ak - 4kx$$

This is a second-order differential equation with constant coefficients. It is solved by finding a particular integral and the complementary function. The solution is:

$$x = A \cos \omega t + B \sin \omega t + \frac{9a}{2}$$

where A and B are arbitrary constants and $\omega^2 = 4k/m$. Without finding A and B, we can calculate the period of the oscillation. The period, $T = 2\pi/\omega$, so:

$$T = 2\pi \sqrt{\frac{m}{4k}}$$

$$= \pi \sqrt{\frac{m}{k}}$$

When $t = 0$, $x = 5a$ and the speed $= \dot{x} = 0$. Substituting these values for x in the solution gives two equations for A and B. Putting $t = 0$ and $x = 5a$ gives:

$$5a = A + \frac{9a}{2}$$

$$A = \frac{a}{2}$$

Differentiating the solution with respect to time gives:

$$\dot{x} = -\omega A \sin \omega t + \omega B \cos \omega t$$

so $B = 0$ if $x = 0$ at $t = 0$. The solution for x is thus:

$$x = 0.5a \cos \omega t + \frac{9a}{2} \quad \text{and} \quad \dot{x} = -0.5 \, a\omega \sin \omega t$$

The maximum speed occurs when $\sin \omega t = +1$ and is $a\omega/2$. Since

$\omega^2 = 4k/m$, this is:

$$\dot{x}_{\max} = a \sqrt{\frac{k}{m}}$$

Finally, in this section, we look at a real-life situation that involves oscillations in the form of simple harmonic motion. Figure 9.4(a) shows a child's swing. Technically, this is a two-dimensional (or even three-dimensional) problem, but the angle the swing makes with the vertical is the only variable; hence, it has only a single degree of freedom. We should, therefore, be able to tackle it. Rather than pose a mathematical question, here are three questions that a lay person may ask and which the mathematics of this section can answer:

(a) Does the length, l, of the chain of the swing affect the speed of the child? If so, how is it affected?
(b) Does the weight of the child affect the speed?
(c) Does the amplitude affect the period?

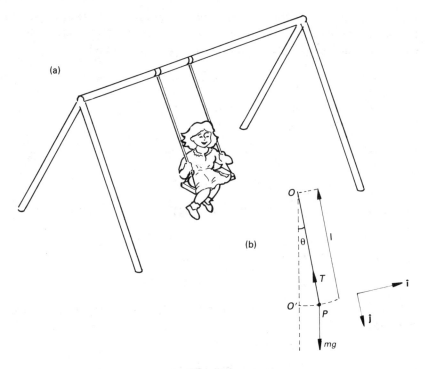

Fig. 9.4

In order to progress, we need to make some assumptions that simplify the situation yet keep the essentials. We are forced to neglect friction at the pivots, air resistance and so on. We must regard the swing as performing SHM. So, perhaps, we can also disregard the weight of the chain of the swing and treat the child and swing as a simple pendulum: a mass m on the end of a light inextensible string of length l, as in Figure 9.4(b).

In Figure 9.4(b), O is the origin, θ, the variable representing our single degree of freedom, is the angle the swing's chain makes with the vertical line through O, and P marks the position of the child and swing in a general position. The length of the chain is l and the mass of the child and swing combined is m. Note that $\theta = 0$ when the swing is in equilibrium: this makes the mathematics easier.

Because of the apparent two-dimensional nature of the problem, we briefly use vectors. Newton's second law is now applied to the mass m. In vectors, if $\mathbf{F_T} = -T\mathbf{j}$ is the tension in the chain and $\mathbf{F_g}$ $(= (-\mathbf{i} \sin \theta + \mathbf{j} \cos \theta) g)$ is the force due to gravity, then:

$$\mathbf{F_T} + \mathbf{F_g} = m \frac{d^2\mathbf{r}}{dt^2} \qquad (18)$$

is the statement of Newton's second law. To solve this, we resolve perpendicular to and parallel to the chain. There is no acceleration parallel to the chain, and the displacement, $O'P$ in Figure 9.4(b), is given by:

$$O'P = x = l\theta$$

Hence, the velocity of P, perpendicular to the chain, is the derivative of this with respect to time, which is given by:

$$v = \frac{dx}{dt} = l \frac{d\theta}{dt}$$

Acceleration is the second derivative of displacement with respect to time; hence:

$$\text{acceleration} = \frac{dv}{dt} = l \frac{d^2\theta}{dt^2}$$

With $\mathbf{i}$ and $\mathbf{j}$ as indicated in Figure 9.4(b), equation (18), when resolved, becomes:

$$-T\mathbf{j} + mg(\cos \theta \mathbf{j} - \sin \theta \mathbf{i}) = ml \frac{d^2\theta}{dt^2} \mathbf{i} \qquad (19)$$

which, equating coefficients of **i**, leads to the equation:

$$-mg \sin \theta = ml \, \frac{d^2\theta}{dt^2} \qquad (20)$$

and, equating coefficients of **j**, leads to the equation:

$$-T + mg \cos \theta = 0 \qquad (21)$$

This last equation is the one that enables us to determine the tension in the chain. This is, perhaps, important for designers of chains, but it does not concern us here. Equation (20) is an equation whose solution will describe θ in terms of t. Straight away, we observe that the mass, m, cancels. So, we can answer one of the questions posed at the outset. The mass of the child has *no* effect whatsoever on subsequent motion. To solve equation (20), we have to assume that θ is small, so that $\sin \theta$ is approximated by θ. For many applications, this approximation is sufficiently close for θ less than $10°$ $(0.1745°)$. Using this approximation, the equation for θ is:

$$\frac{d^2\theta}{dt^2} = -\frac{g\theta}{l} \qquad (22)$$

Equation (22) is of the same form as equation (4) with:

$$\omega^2 = \frac{g}{l} \qquad (23)$$

hence, we can use the earlier results. In particular, equation (13) with $x = l\theta$, $x_0 = l\theta_0$ and $\omega^2 = g/l$ yields:

$$v^2 = gl(\theta_0^2 - \theta^2) \qquad (24)$$

This equation gives a, the relationship between speed, v, and length of chain, l, and enables us to answer the second question. The length does affect the child's speed: v depends upon the square root of l, so, as l increases, so does v, but only slowly. The maximum speed of the child is $\theta_0 \sqrt{(gl)}$, which, for $\theta_0 = 10$ and $l = 2.5$ m ($g = 9.81$ ms^{-2}), is 0.87 ms^{-1} only. This problem can be solved using energy arguments, and indeed we have tackled a similar problem in Chapter 4, examples 4.3.1 (see also motion in a vertical circle, Chapter 8).

EXERCISES 9.2

1 A particle of mass m is hanging freely via a light piece of elastic from a fixed point O. If the piece of elastic is considered to be a spring of stiffness k and natural length l, find:

(a) the length of the elastic when the mass hangs in equilibrium;
(b) the period of oscillations of m about this equilibrium position if the mass is disturbed;
(c) the maximum distance the mass may be pulled down and released, if the motion is still to be simple harmonic.

2 A particle of mass 2 kg lies on a smooth inclined plane, whose angle with the horizontal is 30°. The mass is attached to the top of the plane by a light elastic string of stiffness 30 Nm and natural length 0.5 m.

(a) What is the length of the string in equilibrium?
(b) The mass is pulled 0.2 m and released. Find the period of the oscillation and calculate the maximum speed of the mass.
(c) How far does the mass have to be pulled down the plane for it just to reach O?

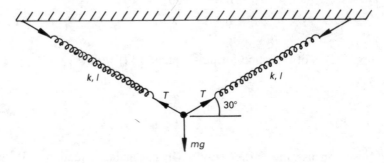

Fig. 9.5

3 A particle of mass m is connected to a ceiling by two identical springs as shown in Figure 9.5. Calculate the depth the mass hangs below the ceiling at equilibrium. Assuming that all displacements from equilibrium are small (so that the squares of them are negligible, and deviations are small enough that we can assume that the angle between the springs and the horizontal remains at 30°), find the period of small vertical oscillations and the period of small horizontal oscillations. Show that their ratio is $1:\sqrt{3}$.

4 A mass m is suspended vertically between two supports by two springs

of the same natural length l, but the upper spring has stiffness $mg/2l$ whereas the lower spring has stiffness mg/l. Find the equilibrium position if the supports are $3l$ apart. Calculate the periods of small oscillations about this position when (a) the particle is displaced vertically and (b) the particle is displaced horizontally.

The whole arrangement is rotated through 90° and placed on a horizontal table. What is the new equilibrium position? Have the periods of small oscillations along, and perpendicular to, the line of the springs changed?

9.3 DAMPED MOTION

In this section, we extend the mathematics of Section 9.2 to include damping.

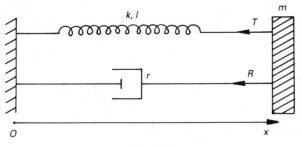

Fig. 9.6

Figure 9.6 is a mass–spring–damping system which reduces to Figure 9.2 if r, the dashpot constant, is zero. The dashpot can be thought of as a piston and cylinder (as the diagrammatic representation in Figure 9.6 indicates) which always resists motion. The perfect dashpot has a resistance R where:

$$R = r \left| \frac{dx}{dt} \right|$$

Here, r is a constant for a given dashpot, while the modulus sign indicates that R is positive (as long as it is drawn to oppose motion). We always assume x is increasing; therefore, R acts as in Figure 9.6. The equation of motion for m is:

$$-T - R = m \frac{d^2x}{dt^2} \qquad (25)$$

215

where:

$$T = k(x - l) \quad \text{and} \quad R = r \frac{dx}{dt}$$

Substituting these into equation (25) gives the following equation for x:

$$m \frac{d^2x}{dt^2} + r \frac{dx}{dt} + kx = kl \tag{26}$$

If the origin was chosen at the end of the spring, at the equilibrium position, the right-hand side of equation (26) would be zero rather than kl. However, we will work with the equation as derived.

We now introduce the two parameters ω and α, the first of which is already familiar:

$$\omega^2 = \frac{k}{m} \qquad \text{(the natural frequency)} \tag{27}$$

$$\alpha = \frac{r}{2\sqrt{(mk)}} \qquad \text{(the damping factor)} \tag{28}$$

Dividing equation (26) by m then gives:

$$\frac{d^2x}{dt^2} + 2\alpha\omega \frac{dx}{dt} + \omega^2 x = \omega^2 l \tag{29}$$

The solution to this equation, obtained by finding a particular solution and the complementary function (see for example R. Nagle and E. Saff, *Fundamentals of Differential Equations*, Benjamin Cummings, 1986), is:

$$x = Ae^{-\alpha\omega t} \cos\left(\sqrt{(1 - \alpha^2)}\omega t + \Phi\right) + l \tag{30}$$

where A, the amplitude, and Φ, the phase, are the two arbitrary constants determined by the initial conditions. We see that this reverts to SHM if $\alpha = 0$ (no damping). However, with damping, there are several important features. The term $e^{-\alpha\omega t}$ in equation (30) indicates that the vibration decays with time, and for large time t, x will be close to l, its equilibrium position. Obviously, the larger α is, the faster the vibration will decay. If $\alpha < 1$, the presence of $\sqrt{(1 - \alpha^2)}$ inside the cosine indicates that the period of oscillation is increased. As α approaches unity, this period gets longer. If $\alpha = 1$, there is no vibration and the damping is called *critical*, because x

becomes l in the shortest time. If $\alpha > 1$, the damping eliminates the vibration so completely that the mass only very slowly tends to its equilibrium position once displaced. In this latter case, equation (30) no longer holds and must be replaced by:

$$x = e^{-\alpha\omega t} (Ae^{-\sqrt{(\alpha^2 - 1)}\omega t} + Be^{\sqrt{(\alpha^2 - 1)}\omega t}) + l \tag{31}$$

At first sight, the second term in this equation looks as if it will grow. However, the $e^{-\alpha\omega t}$ outside will always dominate (since $\alpha > \sqrt{(\alpha^2 - 1)}$), so x still decays towards $x = l$. It is the second of these terms, in fact, that decays so slowly for large α. Having stated the mathematics, let us re-examine the child's swing introduced earlier with the addition of resistance.

Example 9.3

A child rides on a swing of length 4 m. The mass of the child and swing together is 40 kg. The air resistance is $-0.5x$, where x is the child's velocity. If the child has an initial amplitude of 1 m, find:

(a) the natural frequency of the oscillation;
(b) the damping factor;
(c) the time elapsed before the child has amplitude 0.5 m.

(Take $g = 9.81$ ms^{-2}.)

Solution   The axes and the angle θ are defined as shown in Figure 9.4(b). However, for very small angles ($<10°$), sin θ can be approximated by θ, and so we may write $x = l\theta$ and define quantities such as displacement, velocity and acceleration in terms of x. It is, in fact, as if all motion takes place along the line AB in Figure 9.7. As derived earlier, the restoring force due to the component of the child's weight is, to a good approximation, $-mgx/l$ (for angle of swing $<10°$). In addition to this, there is an additional force of -0.5 dx/dt due to air resistance. Newton's second law is thus:

$$m \frac{d^2x}{dt^2} = -0.5 \frac{dx}{dt} - \frac{mgx}{l}$$

with $l = 4m$ and $m = 40$ kg.

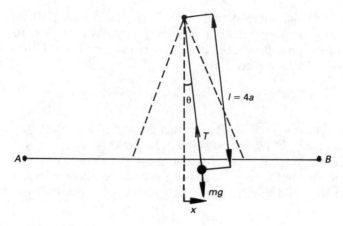

Fig. 9.7

(a) The natural frequency is:

$$\omega = \sqrt{\frac{g}{l}} = \sqrt{\frac{9.81}{4}} = 1.57 \text{ s}^{-1}$$

(b) The damping factor is: ·

$$\frac{r}{2\sqrt{(mk)}} = \frac{0.5}{2\sqrt{(40 \times 40 \times 9.81/4)}}$$

$$= \frac{0.5}{40\sqrt{9.81}} = 4 \times 10^{-3}$$

(c) The solution to the problem is:

$$x = Ae^{-\alpha t} \cos (\sqrt{(1 - \alpha^2)}\omega t + \Phi)$$

where A and Φ are arbitrary constants, $\omega = 1.57$ and $\alpha = 4 \times 10^{-3}$. Hence, A = amplitude = 1 m, and

$$Ae^{-\alpha t} = 0.5A \quad \text{when taking natural logarithms}$$

$$-\alpha t = \ln 0.5$$

$$t = \frac{0.693}{4 \times 10^{-3}} = 173.3 \text{ s (or} \approx 2.9 \text{ minutes)}$$

The foregoing example is in the range where the damping still allows the motion to be oscillatory. In most offices, there is a device on the top of the door called, appropriately enough, the damper, which stops the door from slamming. Here, the motion is such that no matter how hard we try, we can never slam the door, and it certainly never oscillates. Door dampers are therefore modelled using damping factors exceeding unity. Although to model the motion of a door accurately, rigid body dynamics outside the scope of this text are required, exercise 9.3.1 provides an idealised model.

EXERCISES 9.3

1 A door with a damper can be shown to be modelled by the equation:

$$\frac{d^2x}{dt^2} + 2.4 \frac{dx}{dt} + x = 0 \quad (t \geqslant 0)$$

where x is the distance between the edge of the door and the jamb. Calculate how long it takes the door to close ($x < 0.01$) if (a) it is released from rest when $x = 1$ m and (b) it is slammed with a speed $\dot{x} = -0.1$ ms^{-1} when $x = 1$ m. (*Hint*: Show that $x = Ae^{\alpha t} + Be^{\beta t}$, where α and β are the roots of $m^2 + 2.4m + 1 = 0$, and neglect the smaller exponential for large enough t.)

2 A scale pan is oscillating about its equilibrium position. Its frequency is ω and its amplitude is a at time $t = 0$, but b after one period has been executed. Prove that the damping factor α is given by:

$$\alpha^2 = \frac{\dfrac{1}{4\pi^2} \ln^2 \left(\dfrac{a}{b} \right)}{1 + \dfrac{1}{4\pi^2} \ln^2 \left(\dfrac{a}{b} \right)}$$

Calculate α if $a = 2b$ and hence write down the differential equation for x, the displacement of the scale pan from its equilibrium position.

9.4 FORCED OSCILLATIONS

Consider the system shown in Figure 9.8. The mass (particle) m is attached to the support at O via a dashpot with dashpot constant r, and a spring with

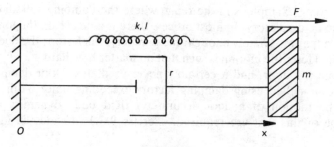

Fig. 9.8

natural length l and stiffness k. In addition, the mass m is subject to an external force F in the direction Ox. Newton's second law applied to the mass m gives:

$$F - r\frac{dx}{dt} - kx = m\frac{d^2x}{dt^2} \tag{32}$$

(external force + resistance due to dashpot + resistance due to spring = mass × acceleration). Remember when writing down the equation of motion to imagine that x is *increasing* and then write down the forces; this way, there should be no confusion about minus signs.

Remembering the definitions of ω and α, we can write equation (32) as:

$$\frac{d^2x}{dt^2} + 2\alpha\omega\frac{dx}{dt} + \omega^2 x = \frac{F}{m} \tag{33}$$

We have not yet said anything about the external force F: it could be a general function of time. It is most instructive to choose F to be sinusoidal, so let:

$$\frac{F}{m} = A_0\omega^2 \cos \sigma t \tag{34}$$

The constants A_0 and σ are chosen so that $\omega^2 A_0$ is the amplitude of the external force and σ is its frequency. The notation is a convenient one. We solve equation (33) with F given by equation (34) by choosing as a trial solution:

$$x = \alpha_0 \cos \sigma t + \beta_0 \sin \sigma t \tag{35}$$

The theory behind this can be found in standard texts that include second-order differential equations with constant coefficients and a sinusoidal right-hand side (see for example R. Nagle and E. Saff, *Fundamentals of Differential Equations*, Benjamin Cummings, 1986). Differentiation of equation (35) gives:

$$\frac{dx}{dt} = -\sigma\alpha_0 \sin \sigma t + \sigma\beta_0 \cos \sigma t \tag{36}$$

Differentiating again gives:

$$\frac{d^2x}{dt^2} = -\sigma^2\alpha_0 \cos \sigma t - \sigma^2\beta_0 \sin \sigma t \tag{37}$$

The following equation (derived from equations (33) and (34)):

$$\frac{d^2x}{dt^2} + 2\alpha\omega \frac{dx}{dt} + \omega^2x = A_0\omega^2 \cos \sigma t \tag{38}$$

is now used to find α_0 and β_0. Substituting from equations (35), (36) and (37) into equation (38) gives:

$$-\sigma^2\alpha_0 \cos \sigma t - \sigma^2\beta_0 \sin \sigma t + 2\alpha\omega(-\sigma\alpha_0 \sin \sigma t + \sigma\beta_0 \cos \sigma t) \\ + \omega^2(\alpha_0 \cos \sigma t + \beta_0 \sin \sigma t) = A_0\omega^2 \cos \sigma t \tag{39}$$

If we equate the coefficients of cos σt and sin σt on each side, we obtain the following two equations for α_0 and β_0:

$$-\sigma^2\alpha_0 + 2\alpha\omega\sigma\beta_0 + \omega^2\alpha = A_0\omega^2 \tag{40}$$

$$-\sigma^2\beta_0 - 2\alpha\omega\sigma\alpha_0 + \omega^2\beta_0 = 0 \tag{41}$$

These can be solved, either directly or using determinant methods, to obtain:

$$\alpha_0 = \frac{A_0\left(1 - \dfrac{\sigma^2}{\omega^2}\right)}{\left[\left(1 - \dfrac{\sigma^2}{\omega^2}\right)^2 + 4\alpha^2\dfrac{\sigma^2}{\omega^2}\right]^{1/2}} \tag{42}$$

221

$$\beta_0 = \frac{2A_0 \dfrac{\alpha\sigma}{\omega}}{\left[\left(1 - \dfrac{\sigma^2}{\omega^2} \right)^2 + 4\alpha^2 \dfrac{\sigma^2}{\omega^2} \right]^{1/2}} \tag{43}$$

We have thus determined one solution to equation (35). To this can be added the solution to the unforced equation (29) with zero right-hand side. The complete solution to the sinusoidally forced, damped vibration problem is thus:

$$x = \frac{A_0 \left(1 - \dfrac{\sigma^2}{\omega^2} \right) \cos \sigma t + 2A_0 \dfrac{\alpha\sigma}{\omega} \sin \sigma t}{\left[\left(1 - \dfrac{\sigma^2}{\omega^2} \right)^2 + 4\alpha^2 \dfrac{\sigma^2}{\omega^2} \right]^{1/2}}$$
$$+ Ae^{-\alpha\omega t} \cos \left(\sqrt{(1 - \alpha^2)}\omega t + \Phi \right) \tag{44}$$

Let us spend a little time discussing this solution. If there is damping, the $e^{-\alpha\omega t}$ term will tend to zero as time progresses. Hence, a long time after the motion has started, the displacement will, approximately, be given by the first purely sinusoidal term. Physically, this means that the long-term solution is completely determined by the forcing and is *independent* of the initial conditions. (The arbitrary constants A and Φ are determined by the initial conditions, but this term goes to zero.) The less the damping, the smaller is α, and so the longer the system 'remembers' the initial conditions. The decaying part of the total solution is sometimes called the *transient*. When $\alpha = 0$, the second term of equation (44) is also purely sinusoidal and hence never decays. Also, if $\alpha = 0$ the sin σt term is zero, so the solution is the sum of two different cosines:

$$x = \frac{A_0 \cos \sigma t}{\left(1 - \dfrac{\sigma^2}{\omega^2} \right)} + A \cos (\omega t + \Phi) \tag{45}$$

providing, of course, that $\sigma \neq \omega$. If both $\alpha = 0$ *and* $\sigma = \omega$, the solution to equation (38) is not given by equation (44), but by:

$$x = 0.5A_0\omega t \sin \omega t \tag{46}$$

This solution represents *resonance*, which is a crucial phenomenon in engineering. The important characteristic of equation (46) is that x has an increasing amplitude. If an engineering structure is displaced according to this type of function, it will fail, as the following examples will illustrate. Resonance occurs if the forcing frequency and the natural frequency are the same. If there is no damping ($\alpha = 0$), equation (46) shows that x increases without limit. If damping is present, the solution is given by putting $\sigma = \omega$ in equation (44), namely:

$$x = \frac{A_0}{2\alpha} \sin \omega t + Ae^{-\alpha\omega t} \cos (\sqrt{(1 - \alpha^2)}\omega t + \Phi) \tag{47}$$

With a non-zero damping factor, x no longer becomes infinite at resonance, but its amplitude, $A_0/2\alpha$, is close to its maximum, as long as α is not too large.

The ratio of the amplitude of the response to the amplitude of the forcing can be obtained by squaring and adding the coefficients of $\cos \sigma t$ and $\sin \sigma t$ in equation (44), then square rooting and dividing by A_0. The ratio is:

$$A_r = \frac{1}{\left[\left(1 - \frac{\sigma^2}{\omega^2}\right)^2 + 4\alpha^2 \frac{\sigma^2}{\omega^2}\right]^{1/2}}$$

$$= \frac{\left(\frac{\omega}{\sigma}\right)^2}{\left[\left(1 - \frac{\omega^2}{\sigma^2}\right)^2 + 4\alpha^2 \frac{\omega^2}{\sigma^2}\right]^{1/2}} \tag{48}$$

and is drawn in Figure (9.9) for various values of α. It can be shown that the peak for fixed α is given by:

$$\omega_{max} = \frac{\sigma}{(1 - 2\alpha^2)^{1/2}} \tag{49}$$

so we must have $\alpha < 1/\sqrt{2}$ for there to be a maximum amplitude of response. The following two examples highlight the practical use of the previous mathematics. Some of the algebra is, unavoidably, tedious, but this too mirrors real life.

Example 9.4.1

The suspension system in a car is modelled using the simple mass–spring–damping system shown in Figure 9.8. For the system, the natural frequency

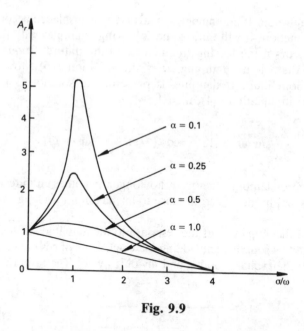

Fig. 9.9

is 10 Hz and the damping factor is 0.5. At what frequency does the system respond if the input frequency is 5 Hz? Calculate the ratio of the input amplitude to the output amplitude in this case. For arbitrary input frequency, find the maximum value of this ratio. What does this tell the designer? (*Note*: The unit of frequency used here is the Hertz, named after one of the pioneers of electromagnetic theory Heinrich Rudolph Hertz (1857–94). 1 Hertz = 1 cycle per second = 2π radians per second = 360 degrees per second.)

Solution For this problem, the mechanics, in the form of Newton's laws, has already been solved. The equation of motion is:

$$\frac{d^2x}{dt^2} + 2 \times 0.5 \times 10 \, \frac{dx}{dt} + (10)^2x = \text{forcing}$$

(cf. equation (38) with $\alpha = 0.5$, $\omega = 10$) and again the forcing is sinusoidal. We have already solved this equation with general sinusoidal forcing of amplitude ωA_0 and frequency σ: the solution is shown in equation (44). Using this solution, we can answer the first part of the problem. The solution consists of a 'steady state' part which does not decay and is an oscillation at the same frequency as the input frequency, 5 Hz in this case. The second part is the 'transient' which has frequency $(1 - \alpha^2)^{1/2}\omega$ where $\omega = 10$ and $\alpha = 0.5$. Hence, the transient has response frequency 8.66 Hz.

224

However, we must not forget the factor $e^{-\alpha\omega t}$ (which is e^{-5t}), which ensures that the transient decays very rapidly. The amplitude ratio is given by equation (48) with $\sigma = 5$ and $\omega = 10$, that is:

$$A_r = \frac{1}{[(1 - (0.5)^2)^2 + (2 \times 0.5 \times 0.5)^2]^{1/2}} = 1.109$$

According to the theory (equation (49)), the value of A_r achieves a maximum when $\sigma = \omega(1 - 2\alpha^2)^{1/2}$, if we treat σ as arbitrary. Now, $\omega = 10$ Hz and $\alpha = 0.5$; hence:

$$\sigma = 10(1 - 2(0.5)^2)^{1/2} = 7.071 \text{ Hz}$$

This is the 'resonant' frequency that makes A_r a maximum. In fact, α is large enough for this not to be of importance in this example. As Figure 9.9 shows there is hardly a peak for this value (calculations show that $A_r = 1.155$). However, in general, a designer of suspension systems would have to change the stiffness or dashpot constant of the system if the forcing frequency (which is not under the designer's control) turned out to be near the resonant frequency of the system.

The next example involves two particles. We shall therefore tackle the mechanics from first principles.

Example 9.4.2

Figure 9.10(a) shows a two-particle model of the tone arm and stylus of a record player (old fashioned not CD):

(a) Indicate all the forces acting on the system.
(b) Write down the two equations of motion using the coordinates shown if there is also a contact force between record and stylus (m_2).
(c) Now assume that there is an external force acting on m_2 such that:

$$x_2 = a + A_0 \cos \omega t$$

Find a condition on ω that will predict whether the stylus will jump on the record (assume $m_2 \ll m_1$).

Solution   Figure 9.10(b) shows the forces that are acting on masses m_1 and m_2. The tension in the spring and the force in the dashpot are drawn

225

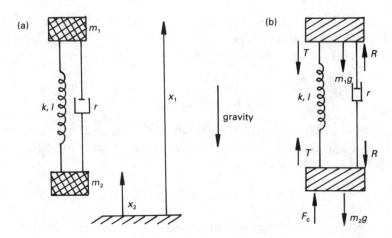

Fig. 9.10

assuming that the spring is in tension, and so the masses want to move together. Therefore, T, the tension in the spring, acts to bring the masses together. The dashpot force, R, depends in sign on whether the masses are actually moving together or not. It does not matter whether we take T and R in these directions, or whether we assume another direction for either T or R (or both). The crucial thing to remember is to be consistent. If it turned out that T is in compression all the time, it will be negative. Similarly, R may be negative. Pick on a convention and remain with it. F_c is the contact force between record and stylus.

The equations of motion for the two particles, using Newton's second law, are:

$$m_2 \frac{d^2x}{dt^2} = T - R - m_2g + F_2 \qquad \text{(for } m_2\text{)} \qquad (50)$$

$$m_1 \frac{d^2x}{dt^2} = R - T - m_1g \qquad \text{(for } m_1\text{)} \qquad (51)$$

Adding these two equations of motion gives:

$$m_2 \frac{d^2x_2}{dt^2} + m_1 \frac{d^2x_1}{dt^2} = -(m_1 + m_2)g + F_c$$

or, rearranging:

$$F_c = m_2 \frac{d^2x_2}{dt^2} + g + m_1 \frac{d^2x_1}{dt^2} + g$$

$$\approx m_1 \frac{d^2x_1}{dt^2} + g$$

since m_2 is much less than m_1. To find x_1, we need to solve equation (51). To do this, we note that:

$$T = k \times \text{extension}$$

$$= k(x_1 - x_2 - l)$$

$$R = -r(\dot{x}_1 - \dot{x}_2)$$

(the negative sign being present only because we assume that the parenthesis is positive). Equation (51) is thus:

$$m_1\ddot{x}_1 + r\dot{x}_1 + kx_1 = r\dot{x}_2 + kx_2 + kl - m_1g$$

We follow the text and introduce the natural frequency ω_0 and the damping factor α, whence this equation may be rewritten:

$$\ddot{x}_1 + 2\alpha\omega_0\dot{x}_1 + \omega_0^2 x_1 = 2\alpha\omega_0\dot{x}_2 + \omega_0^2(x_2 + l) - g \tag{52}$$

(In both these equations, we have used the dot to denote differentiation with respect to t.) Now we insert:

$$x_2 = a + A \cos \omega t$$

This means that a is the mean distance of the stylus above the record. As in equation (33), we look for a solution that is sinusoidal. However, in this case the mean is not zero, but has value $a + l - m_1g/k$, arising from a plus the natural length of the spring minus the compression due to the weight of the tone arm. Hence, x_1 will be of the form:

$$x_1 = a + l - \frac{m_1g}{k} + B \cos \omega t + C \sin \omega t$$

Substituting for x_1 and x_2 into equation (52) yields:

$$-\omega^2(B \cos \omega t + C \sin \omega t) + 2\alpha\omega_0\omega(-B \sin \omega t + C \cos \omega t)$$

$$+ \omega_0^2(B \cos \omega t + C \sin \omega t)$$

$$= -2\alpha\omega_0 A \sin \omega t + \omega_0^2 A \cos \omega t$$

227

Equating coefficients of cos ωt and sin ωt gives the following two equations for B and C:

$$\left(1 - \frac{\omega_0^2}{\omega^2}\right) B + \frac{2\alpha\omega_0 C}{\omega} = A$$

$$\frac{-2\alpha\omega_0 B}{\omega} + \left(1 - \frac{\omega_0^2}{\omega^2}\right) C = \frac{-2\alpha\omega_0 A}{\omega}$$

Solving these by determinant methods or otherwise gives:

$$B = \left[\frac{\left(1 - \frac{\omega_0^2}{\omega^2}\right) + \left(\frac{2\alpha\omega_0}{\omega}\right)^2}{\left(1 - \frac{\omega_0^2}{\omega^2}\right)^2 + \left(2\alpha\frac{\omega_0}{\omega}\right)^2} \right] A$$

$$C = \left[\frac{\frac{-2\alpha\omega_0^3}{\omega^3}}{\left(1 - \frac{\omega_0^2}{\omega^2}\right)^2 + \left(2\alpha\frac{\omega_0}{\omega}\right)^2} \right] A$$

The amplitude ratio equivalent to A in equation (48) is $(B^2 + C^2)^{1/2}/A$. The algebra looks worse than it actually is. Writing $p = 1 - \omega_0^2/\omega^2$ and $q = 2\alpha\omega_0 \omega$ means that $B^2 + C^2$ is given by:

$$B^2 + C^2 = \frac{A^2}{(p^2 + q^2)^2} [(p + q^2)^2 + q^2(1 - p)^2]$$

$$= \frac{A^2}{(p^2 + q^2)^2} (p^2 + 2pq^2 + q^4 + q^2 - 2pq^2 + q^2 p^2)$$

$$= \frac{A^2}{(p^2 + q^2)^2} (p^2 + q^2 + q^4 + q^2 p^2)$$

$$= \frac{A^2}{(p^2 + q^2)^2} (p^2 + q^2)(1 + q^2)$$

$$= \frac{A^2(1 + q^2)}{(p^2 + q^2)}$$

Hence, the amplitude ratio is:

$$\frac{(B^2 + C^2)^{1/2}}{A} = \left(\frac{1 + q^2}{p^2 + q^2}\right)^{1/2}$$

$$= \left[\frac{1 + \left(2\alpha \dfrac{\omega_0}{\omega}\right)^2}{\left(1 - \dfrac{\omega_0^2}{\omega^2}\right) + \left(2\alpha \dfrac{\omega_0}{\omega}\right)^2}\right]^{1/2}$$

The denominator should look familiar. It tends to be the same in all these mass–spring–damping problems.

Now, we derived earlier that:

$$F_c \approx m_1 \frac{d^2 x_1}{dt^2} + g$$

Using the fact that:

$$x_1 = a + l - \frac{m_1 g}{k} + B \cos \omega t + C \sin \omega t$$

and differentiating twice gives that:

$$\frac{d^2 x_1}{dt^2} = -\omega^2 (B \cos \omega t + C \sin \omega t)$$

$$= -\omega^2 (B^2 + C^2)^{1/2} \cos (\omega t - \Phi)$$

where $\cos \Phi = B/(B^2 + C^2)^{1/2}$ and $\sin \Phi = C/(B^2 + C^2)^{1/2}$. Substituting for this acceleration into our expression for F_c yields:

$$F_c \approx m_1(-\omega^2 (B^2 + C^2)^{1/2} \cos (\omega t - \Phi) + g)$$

Now $\cos (\omega t - \Phi)$ always has values between -1 and $+1$. This means that F_c is at its smallest when $\cos (\omega t - \Phi) = 1$, at which time:

$$F_c \approx m_1(-\omega^2 (B^2 + C^2)^{1/2} + g)$$

229

Hence, F_c is positive if:

$$-\omega^2(B^2 + C^2)^{1/2} + g > 0 \quad \text{or} \quad \omega^2(B^2 + C^2)^{1/2} < g = 9.81$$

Using our expression for $(B^2 + C^2)^{1/2}$, this inequality can be put in terms of the amplitude and frequency of the system, thus:

$$\omega^2 A \left[\frac{1 + \left(2\alpha \dfrac{\omega_0}{\omega}\right)^2}{\left(1 - \dfrac{\omega_0^2}{\omega^2}\right)^2 + \left(2\alpha \dfrac{\omega_0}{\omega}\right)^2} \right]^{1/2} < 9.81 \qquad (53)$$

This inequality must hold if the stylus is not to jump (and ruin your listening pleasure).

Having developed the mathematical solution to the problem, let us examine equation (53) in some detail. For small values of α (low damping factor), which is entirely realistic for record tone arms, we see that we must avoid $\omega \simeq \omega_0$, our old friend resonance. If the frequency of the stylus, ω, which may be thought of as a forcing frequency, is near the natural frequency of the spring, the stylus and tone arm will jump off the record. It also pays to have a low value of A, the amplitude of the oscillation of the stylus, and a low value of ω, its frequency. This is what we would expect from experience. Warped records are more likely to jump the grooves, as are records containing high frequencies (for example sopranos).

As we have already suggested, there are many consequences arising out of the mathematics of this section that have important real-life implications. Here, we shall discuss two of them: the operation of hi-fi systems, generalising example 9.4.2, and the vibration of engineering structures.

The force F in equation (33) is not usually a sinusoidal function. However, theory, which is outside the scope of this book, exists that can be used to prove that all functions that are well enough behaved can be split into a sum of sinusoids called a *Fourier Series*. Briefly, any function, and F is just a function varying with time, can be generated by adding together cosines and sines in much the same way as any colour can be generated from the three primary colours, red, green and blue. The pattern of how each cosine and sine goes to make up a particular force is called its *spectrum*. As far as we are concerned, the usefulness of this lies in the fact that we can use the analysis for a purely sinusoidal force to understand how a mass–spring–damping system like that depicted in Figure 9.8 responds to a more general force. From the analysis, we can look at the spectrum of

$x(t)$, the response function, and decide what to do. We can perhaps change the spring or the damper (corresponding to altering ω or α), or have a different configuration of masses, springs and dampers. If we are designing a hi-fi system and $x(t)$ represents the response of the speakers, then we would like $x(t)$ to reproduce the vibrations from a record (or compact disc) faithfully. If we are designing a bridge or building, then we have less control. The materials and shape will affect α and ω, but the forcing function comprises the forces of nature, mainly wind, which have to be analysed but cannot be controlled. In the latter case, $x(t)$, the response, needs to be minimised. It was clearly not in the design of the Tacoma Narrows bridge, which exhibited large responses and eventually collapsed. In such engineering designs, it is vital to make sure that the natural frequency (or natural frequencies – there are more than one for complex systems) of the engineering structure is very different from the frequency of the forcing. This engineering problem has by no means been solved, and many collapsing buildings, bridges and other structures that feature on today's news are due to the response, $x(t)$, to the forcing, F, being too large.

EXERCISES 9.4

1 Figure 9.11 shows a simple model of a suspension system. By examining the forces on m, show that the equation obeyed by x is:

$$\ddot{x} + 2a\omega\dot{x} + \omega_0^2 x = 2a\omega_0\dot{y} + \omega_0^2 y - \omega_0^2 l - g$$

where $\alpha = r/2\sqrt{(mk)}$, $\omega_0^2 = k/m$ and g is the acceleration due to gravity. Assuming that $l = 1$ m, $\alpha = 0.5$, $\omega_0 = 1\ \text{s}^{-1}$, $g = 9.81\ \text{ms}^{-2}$ and $y = 10.81 + a \cos \omega t$, where a and ω are constants, find the steady state response in terms of a and ω. Is resonance possible here?

2 By writing $A_r = 1/\sqrt{g}$, where g is considered to be a function of ω and A_r is given by equation (48), use that $dg/d\omega = 0$ for an extremum to

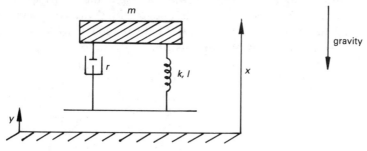

Fig. 9.11

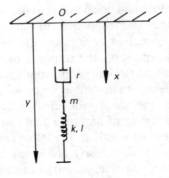

Fig. 9.12

prove equation (51), $\omega_{max} = \sigma/(1 - 2\alpha^2)^{1/2}$. Hence, deduce the maximum value of A_r, the amplitude ratio, for a pure cosine forcing of frequency σ. Deduce also that this value itself is a minimum when $\alpha = 0.7071$.

3 Figure 9.12 shows a mass–spring–damping system hanging vertically. If the natural frequency of the system is 2 s^{-1}, the damping factor is 0.1 Nm^{-1}s and the natural length of the spring is 2.453 m, show that x, the displacement of m below the support at O, obeys the equation:

$$\ddot{x} + 0.4\dot{x} + 4x = 4y$$

Write down the complete solution of this equation and distinguish between the transient response and the steady state response, given that:

$$y = 0.25 \sin \omega t \qquad (\omega = \text{a constant})$$

Determine the amplitude of the steady state response for each of the cases $\omega = 2$ s^{-1} and $\omega = 3$ s^{-1}, and comment accordingly.

4 You are pushing a child on the swing with parameters as specified in example 9.3. Find the resonant frequency. Find the (theoretical) response amplitude at this frequency. What would actually happen if you forced the child and swing with this frequency?

10 VARIABLE MASS PROBLEMS

10.1 INTRODUCTION

In Chapter 5, the term impulse was introduced. In this chapter, we renew our acquaintance with it via some revision of ideas. Perhaps the most rewarding way to think of an impulse is in terms of an external agent that alters momentum. Common such agents are baseball or cricket bats striking, and significantly changing, the momentum of a moving ball. The batter (usually) feels a jolt in the wrists, and this is the impulse. This type of impact, collisions, forms part of Chapter 5.

Impulse, I, a vector quantity, is formally defined as:

$$I = m\mathbf{v}_2 - m\mathbf{v}_1 \tag{1}$$

where $\mathbf{v}_1$ is the velocity before I was applied and $\mathbf{v}_2$ is the velocity after I was applied. Now, Newton's second law tells us that:

$$\mathbf{F} = m\,\frac{d\mathbf{v}}{dt}$$

where $\mathbf{F}$ is the external force, and the mass is constant. If we integrate this with respect to t between t_1 and t_2, we obtain:

$$\int_{t_2}^{t_1} \mathbf{F}\,dt = \int_{t_1}^{t_2} m\,\frac{d\mathbf{v}}{dt}\,dt$$

$$= m(\mathbf{v}_2 - \mathbf{v}_1)$$

$$= I \quad \text{from equation (1)}$$

Impulse is therefore the integral of the force over a time interval. This definition is quite general, but an impulse is usually considered as a force integrated over a *very short* time interval, hence $t_2 - t_1$ is usually small, ultimately infinitesimally small (see next section). This being the case, the integral of $\mathbf{F}(t)$ between t_1 and t_2 can be replaced by $(t_2 - t_1)\mathbf{F}(t)$ with minimal loss of accuracy. (Those readers familiar with Taylor's Series can estimate the error involved by using the Taylor Series for $\mathbf{F}$ about $t = t_1$, then integrating term by term, then setting $t = t_2$.) Hence, writing $t_2 - t_1$ as δt, equation (1) becomes:

$$\mathbf{F}\,\delta t = m\mathbf{v}_2 - m\mathbf{v}_1 \qquad (2)$$

It is this form of Newton's second law that will be utilised in the next section. The SI units of impulse are the same as those of momentum, that is, kgms^{-1} or Ns. In terms of fundamental units, impulse is MLT^{-1}.

10.2 DERIVING THE EQUATIONS

A simplistic view of the situation is as follows. In a changing mass problem, either the body is losing mass, for example in rockets or guns, or gaining mass, for example in raindrops passing through clouds or snowballs rolling down slopes. We will derive, separately, equations for each case. The reason we do this is for clarity. (The reason, hopefully, for all approaches in this text.) The crucial difference is that, for rocket-type problems, the ejected matter still has momentum and so has to be accounted for. On the other hand, for raindrop-type problems the matter to be absorbed is stationary and so has no momentum.

Consider a rocket, travelling with velocity $\mathbf{v}$, which has mass m at time t. The mass, of course, depends on t since it is being ejected. At time δt later, $t + \delta t$, the rocket has moved on. It now has velocity $\mathbf{v} + \delta\mathbf{v}$ but mass $m - \delta m$ (having lost δm as ejected matter). Further, we assume that this ejected matter, δm, has velocity $\mathbf{u}$. All velocities are measured relative to a fixed origin. Figure 10.1 displays the situation.

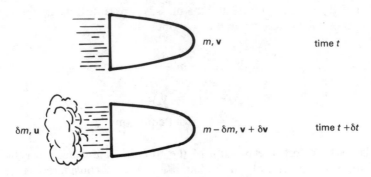

m, v   time t

δm, u   m − δm, v + δv   time t + δt

Fig. 10.1

The momentum of the rocket at time t is:

$$m\mathbf{v} \tag{3}$$

The momentum of the mass m (rocket, together with the ejected matter) at time $t + \delta t$ is:

$$(m - \delta m)(\mathbf{v} + \delta\mathbf{v}) + \delta m\mathbf{u} \tag{4}$$

Subtracting equation (3) from equation (4) then gives the change in momentum in time δt. For small δt, this is just the impulse (see equation (2)), which is $\mathbf{F}\,\delta t$, where $\mathbf{F}$ is the external force on the rocket. Hence:

$$\text{impulse} = \text{change in momentum}$$

leads to:

$$\mathbf{F}\,\delta t = (m - \delta m)(\mathbf{v} + \delta\mathbf{v}) + \delta m\mathbf{u} - m\mathbf{v}$$
$$\approx m\,\delta\mathbf{v} + (\mathbf{u} - \mathbf{v})\delta m$$

Dividing by δt and taking the limit as $\delta t \to 0$ renders the approximation exact, so that:

$$\mathbf{F} = m\,\frac{d\mathbf{v}}{dt} + (\mathbf{u} - \mathbf{v})\,\frac{dm}{dt} \tag{5}$$

Equation (5), often called the rocket equation, is the equation we must use instead of the more usual:

$$\mathbf{F} = m\,\frac{d\mathbf{v}}{dt}$$

Note also that the second term on the right-hand side takes into account $\mathbf{u}$, the velocity of the ejected matter. It is common to call $\mathbf{u} - \mathbf{v}$ the 'relative velocity of the ejected matter to the rocket'. Strictly, this is $\mathbf{u} - (\mathbf{v} + \delta\mathbf{v})$, but the ignored term is infinitesimal and can be ignored. Common usage is therefore correct.

We shall now derive a similar equation for accretion problems. It will turn out to be adequate to use Newton's second law straight away, but for comparison we shall use the impulse–momentum argument again.

Suppose we have a raindrop of mass m which, at time t, is travelling with velocity $\mathbf{v}$. At time $t + \delta t$, its velocity is now $\mathbf{v} + \delta\mathbf{v}$ and it has absorbed a mass δm, so that its mass is $m + \delta m$. Figure 10.2 shows the situation.

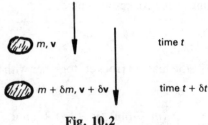

time t

time $t + \delta t$

Fig. 10.2

The momentum at time t is, simply, $m\mathbf{v}$. The momentum of the raindrop at time $t + \delta t$ is, equally simply, $(m + \delta m)(\mathbf{v} + \delta\mathbf{v})$. The δm which has been absorbed should have been accounted for in the expression for the momentum at time t, but of course it had zero velocity. The change in momentum in time δt is therefore:

$$(m + \delta m)(\mathbf{v} + \delta\mathbf{v}) - m\mathbf{v} = m\,\delta\mathbf{v} + \mathbf{v}\,\delta m$$

Applying the impulse = change in momentum equation with, once more, impulse $\mathbf{F}\,\delta t$, where $\mathbf{F}$ is the external force, gives:

$$\mathbf{F}\,\delta t \approx m\,\delta\mathbf{v} + \mathbf{v}\,\delta m$$

Dividing this by δt and letting $\delta t \to 0$, as before, yields:

$$\mathbf{F} = m\,\frac{d\mathbf{v}}{dt} + \mathbf{v}\,\frac{dm}{dt} \qquad (6)$$

Equation (6) can be derived from Newton's second law in the form of:

force = rate of change of momentum

$$\mathbf{F} = \frac{d(m\mathbf{v})}{dt} = m\,\frac{d\mathbf{v}}{dt} + \mathbf{v}\,\frac{dm}{dt}$$

Let us now cement these ideas through some examples.

Example 10.2.1

A rocket of mass M is travelling vertically upwards with speed v ms^{-1} and is burning fuel at a constant rate of r kgs^{-1} and ejecting mass at a constant speed of u ms^{-1} relative to the rocket. If $M = M_0$ at time $t = 0$, find an expression for v in terms of time.

Solution We could derive an equation for this problem by considering change in momentum. However, the circumstances are identical to those which led to the derivation of equation (5). All we need to do is to interpret the symbols. Equation (5) is:

$$\mathbf{F} = m \, \frac{dv}{dt} + (\mathbf{u} - \mathbf{v}) \, \frac{dm}{dt}$$

In this problem, $\mathbf{F}$ is due to gravity alone and is given by:

$$\mathbf{F} = -Mg\mathbf{k}$$

taking the origin on the ground, $\mathbf{k}$ is the axis pointing up along the path of the rocket and dm/dt, the rate of change of the mass, is simply r. In fact, we have that the mass of the rocket M must be such that:

$$\frac{dM}{dt} = -r$$

or, integrating with respect to t:

$$M = -rt + A$$

When $t = 0$, $M = M_0$, hence $A = M_0$, so that:

$$M = M_0 - rt$$

This is our equation for mass m in equation (5). Finally, in our interpretation, $\mathbf{u} - \mathbf{v}$ is simply $u\mathbf{k}$. We can omit $\mathbf{k}$, since all this motion is in this direction. Equation (5) is thus:

$$-(M_0 - rt)g = (M_0 - rt) \, \frac{dv}{dt} - ru$$

Dividing this equation by $(M_0 - rt)$ and rearranging gives:

$$\frac{dv}{dt} = -g + \frac{ru}{M_0 - rt}$$

Integrating this with respect to t gives:

$$v = -gt - u \ln (M_0 - rt) + A$$

If we assume that $v = 0$ when $t = 0$, then:

$$A = u \ln M_0$$

so that:

$$v = u \ln \left(\frac{M_0}{M_0 - rt} \right) - gt \tag{7}$$

Hence, theoretically, equation (7) gives the velocity (speed) of the rocket at any subsequent time t.

A little thought and some searching questions will soon display the short-comings of this model. Obviously, equation (7) will cease to hold some time before $t = M_0/r$, since at this time the rocket will have zero mass! We know that, at some time prior to this, all the fuel will be used up and the rocket will in fact move as a particle under gravity (Chapter 6). If the rocket is realistic, then it will get far enough from the surface of the Earth for two effects, which have so far been ignored, to become important. At large distances above the surface of the Earth, an inverse square law of attraction replaces the assumption of constant gravity (this is at distances comparable with the radius of the Earth – see Chapter 8). Also, and perhaps more importantly, we must consider the Earth as a rotating, not a stationary, body. However, the example serves as an introduction to rockets, and is reasonable for rockets of firework scales.

Example 10.2.2

If the rocket in the previous example runs out of fuel after a time $t = M_0/2r$, find the maximum height reached by the rocket given that it started from the ground. (Ignore variation in gravity and the Earth's rotation.)

Solution   Equation (7) holds for times up to $t = M_0/2r$. Hence, at the time the fuel runs out, $v = v_1$, where:

$$v_1 = u \ln \left(\frac{M_0}{M_0 - \dfrac{rM_0}{2r}} \right) - \frac{gM_0}{2r}$$

$$v_1 = u \ln 2 - \frac{gM_0}{2r} \qquad (8)$$

To find the distance travelled in this time, we need to integrate equation (7) with respect to time. Writing $v = dx/dt$, equation (7) is the differential equation:

$$\frac{dx}{dt} = u \ln \left(\frac{M_0}{M_0 - rt} \right) - gt$$

which integrates to:

$$x = -\frac{u}{r} (M_0 - rt) \ln \left(\frac{M_0}{M_0 - rt} \right) + ut - \frac{1}{2} gt^2 \qquad (9)$$

(To perform this integration, we need the integral:

$$\int \ln x \, dx = x \ln x - x$$

It is messy, but not difficult.) When $t = M_0/2r$, equation (9) becomes $x = x_1$:

$$x_1 = -\frac{uM_0}{r2} \ln 2 + \frac{uM_0}{2r} - \frac{1}{2} g \left(\frac{M_0}{2r} \right)^2$$

$$= \frac{uM_0}{2r} (1 - \ln 2) - \frac{gM_0^2}{8r^2}$$

A mass which is projected vertically with speed v_1 reaches a height $h = v_1^2/2g$ (see Chapter 1), so that the extra height is:

$$h = \frac{1}{2g} \left(u \ln 2 - \frac{gM_0}{2r} \right)^2$$

giving the total height reached as x_1 plus this height which, after some simplification, is:

$$x_1 + h = \frac{u^2 (\ln 2)^2}{2g} - \frac{uM_0}{r} \ln 2 + \frac{uM_0}{2r}$$

Finally, in this section, here is an accretion problem.

Example 10.2.3

A raindrop falls from rest under gravity through a stationary cloud. The mass of the raindrop increases by absorbing small droplets from the cloud. The rate of increase is mrv, where m is the mass, v is the speed and r is a constant. Show that, after the raindrop has fallen a distance x:

$$rv^2 = g(1 - e^{-2rx})$$

Also find x as a function of time.

Solution For accretion problems, equation (6) is available. In non-vector form (all motion here is in a straight vertical line), this is:

$$F = m\,\frac{dv}{dt} + v\,\frac{dm}{dt}$$

Under gravity, positive downwards, $F = mg$. We are also given $dm/dt = mrv$ (positive because m is increasing with time). Inserting this information into our equation gives:

$$mg = m\,\frac{dv}{dt} + v \cdot mrv$$

$$g = \frac{dv}{dt} + rv^2 \tag{10}$$

The problem asks for v in terms of x; hence, we use $v\,dv/dx$ instead of dv/dt. Equation (10) thus becomes:

$$g = v\,\frac{dv}{dx} + rv^2$$

which, on rearrangement, is:

$$\frac{d(v^2)}{dx} + 2rv^2 = 2g$$

This equation is linear in v^2 vs x with integrating factor e^{2rx}. Multiplying by e^{2rx} gives:

$$\frac{d(v^2 e^{2rx})}{dx} = 2ge^{2rx}$$

Integrating with respect to x yields:

$$v^2 e^{2rx} = \frac{g}{r} e^{2rx} + A \tag{11}$$

where A is a constant of integration. When $x = 0$, $v = 0$, hence:

$$0 = \frac{g}{r} + A \quad \text{or} \quad A = -\frac{g}{r}$$

Inserting this value of A back into equation (11) gives the desired relationship:

$$rv^2 = g(1 - e^{-2rx}) \tag{12}$$

We now write $v = dx/dt$ and rearrange this equation:

$$\left(\frac{dx}{dt}\right)^2 = \frac{g}{r}(1 - e^{-2rx})$$

$$\text{or} \quad \int \frac{dx}{\sqrt{(1 - e^{-2rx})}} = \int \sqrt{\frac{g}{r}}\, dt$$

Multiplying the numerator and denominator by e^{rx}:

$$\int \frac{e^{rx}\, dx}{\sqrt{(e^{2rx} - 1)}} = \int \sqrt{\frac{g}{r}}\, dt$$

Integrating this (by substituting $u = e^{rx}$ and the standard form $\int du/\sqrt{(u^2 - 1)} = \operatorname{arccosh} u$) gives:

$$\frac{1}{r}\operatorname{arccosh}(e^{rx}) = \frac{g}{r}t + B$$

when $x = 0$ and $t = 0$ (taking $x = 0$ to be the initial position of the raindrop) $B = 0$ so that:

$$\operatorname{arccosh}(e^{rx}) = t\sqrt{(rg)}$$

Making x the subject by inverting, followed by using natural logarithm gives:

$$x = \frac{1}{r} \ln \cosh (t\sqrt{(rg)}) \tag{13}$$

Although the formulae given in equations (12) and (13) have been derived exactly, this is due principally to the judicious choice of how the raindrop's mass changes with velocity. As the raindrop falls, the velocity gets nearer $\sqrt{(g/r)}$ ($x \rightarrow \infty$ in equation (12)), which is the terminal velocity. For large values of the argument, $\cosh \theta$ behaves like $(1/2)e^{\theta}$. Hence, equation (13) implies that, for large times:

$$x \approx \frac{1}{r} \ln \left(\frac{1}{2} \, e^{t\sqrt{(rg)}} \right)$$

$$x \approx t \sqrt{\frac{g}{r}}$$

This linear variation of x with time is consistent with the terminal velocity. In reality, the raindrop will emerge from the cloud, possibly to start evaporating again. The problem here applies to raindrops in cloud that is very deep.

In the next section, we shall extend the ideas introduced here to practical problems like soft landing a spacecraft on a planet and a rope sliding off the deck of a ship.

EXERCISES 10.2

1 A rocket of mass m at time t is travelling in a zero gravity environment. Initially, its mass is m_0 and its speed is v_0. If it emits matter with a constant speed u relative to the rocket, show that its speed v at any subsequent time t is given by:

$$v = v_0 + u \ln \left(\frac{m_0}{m} \right)$$

Show also that, if $m = m_0 e^{-kt}$, k = constant, then distance travelled must be a linear function of time. If $v_0 = 0$, comment on the consequences of Newton's third law.

2 A rocket is fired upwards. Matter is ejected downwards at a constant relative velocity gT and at a constant rate $2M/T$. At time $t = 0$, the mass of the rocket is $2M$ and half of this is fuel. Show that:

(a) the greatest speed of the rocket is attained when all the fuel has just been exhausted, and that this speed is $gT(\ln 2 - 0.5)$;
(b) the height the rocket reaches is $0.5gT^2(1 - \ln 2)^2$.

(You will find example 10.2.2 useful reference for this question.)

3 A rocket is moving in a straight line in outer space where there are no forces acting. An alien observes that its displacement from a fixed point, $x(t)$, obeys the law:

$$x(t) = \frac{1}{3} ut^3$$

where u is the speed of the ejected fuel relative to the rocket. Find how the mass of the rocket must vary with time if its mass is 10^4 kg initially. When will it have a mass of 10^2 kg?

4 A snowball is rolling down a slope which makes an angle of 30° with the horizontal. It starts with zero speed, travels in a straight line with negligible resistance, and gathers snow at a constant rate k. Determine k, in terms of the snowball's mass m_0 at time $t = 0$, if its mass doubles after 10 s. Find a general expression for the speed of the snowball and show that, after 10 s, its speed is three-quarters of the value it would have had if it were moving freely down the slope not gathering any mass ($k = 0$). (You may ignore all inertial effects – rolling and sliding may be treated synonymously here.)

5 A spherical raindrop is falling in a constant gravitational field through a stationary cloud. Its volume increases at a rate which is proportional to its instantaneous surface area. The raindrop starts from rest with a small radius r_0. Show that, initially, the acceleration of the raindrop is g. Show also that the velocity at time t is given by:

$$\frac{g}{4k} (r_0 + kt) - \frac{gr_0^4}{4k} (r_0 + kt)^{-3}$$

where k is a constant. Hence deduce that the eventual acceleration of the raindrop is $g/4$.

10.3 PROBLEMS OF A PRACTICAL NATURE INVOLVING VARYING MASS

In the last section, we dealt with some rocket problems and one problem of accretion where the emphasis was only on the varying mass. Here, we tackle more realistic problems. For this kind of problem, we normally rely on numerical techniques to solve the equations that arise from applying Newton's laws. To prevent the application of these underlying dynamical principles from being obscured by the use of messy numerical methods unfamiliar to most readers, this has been avoided as much as possible. However, because the equations of motion for variable mass problems are, by their very nature, more complex, we must expect the number of analytical solutions to be less.

First, let us look at a problem that is amenable to exact solution. It resembles exercise 4.3.3 which was solved using energy arguments.

Example 10.3.1

A long uniform rope is coiled up on the deck of a ship. One end is drawn up over a pulley which is at a height l above the deck. Initially, a length $2l$ hangs freely on the other side of the pulley. If all friction at the pulley can be ignored, show that the speed of the rope, v, is given by:

$$3v^2 = 2g(x - 2l)$$

and that it accelerates at a constant value of $g/3$. (The rope does not reach the water.)

Solution To help with the visualisation, the situation is shown in Figure 10.3.

Let us assume that the rope has a mass ρ per unit length. Hence, at time t, the momentum of the rope is given by the product of mass and speed, which is $\rho \times$ length moving $\times$ speed, that is:

$$\rho(x + l)v$$

The momentum of the rope at the next instant, $t + \delta t$, is:

$$\rho(x + \delta x + l)(v + \delta v)$$

(As in accretion problems, although the portion of the rope, length δx, which is on the deck at time t should have its own momentum included in

244

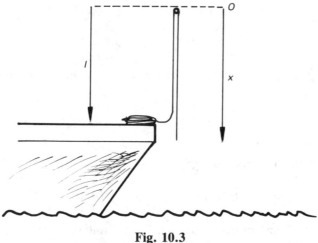

Fig. 10.3

the expression for momentum at time t, because it is not moving the contribution is in fact zero.) To find the change in momentum at time δt, we subtract these two expressions to obtain:

$$\text{change in momentum} = \rho(x + l)\delta v + \rho v\, \delta x$$

The force on the rope is now calculated.

On the left of the pulley is a length l, which has mass ρl. On the right of the pulley is a length x which has mass ρx. Therefore, there is a weight of rope $\rho l g$ pulling on the left of the pulley and a weight of rope $\rho x g$ pulling on the right of the pulley. Since $x > l$, the pulley rotates clockwise under the resultant force $\rho g(x - l)$. In the time δt, the impulse is $\rho g(x - l)\delta t$. Hence, equation (2) gives:

$$\rho g(x - l)\delta t \approx \rho(x + l)\delta v + \rho v\, \delta x$$

Dividing by δt and letting $\delta t \to 0$ gives the differential equation:

$$\rho g(x - l) = \rho(x + l)\frac{dv}{dt} + \rho v\frac{dx}{dt} \qquad (14)$$

Now, $dv/dt = v\, dv/dx$ and $dx/dt = v$, hence we can rewrite equation (14) entirely in terms of v and x as follows:

$$\rho g(x - l) = \rho(x + l)v\frac{dv}{dx} + \rho v^2 \qquad (15)$$

Inspection of this equation reveals that it is a linear differential equation in

245

v^2 against x. Cancelling ρ and writing $y = v^2$ gives:

$$\frac{1}{2}(x - l)\frac{dy}{dx} + y = g(x - l) \tag{16}$$

The integrating factor for this equation is $(x + l)^2$, hence reinstating v^2 for y:

$$\frac{d(v^2(x + l)^2)}{dx} = 2g(x + l)(x - l) = 2g(x^2 - l^2)$$

Integrating with respect to x gives:

$$v^2(x + l)^2 = 2g\left(\frac{1}{3}x^3 - xl^2\right) + A \tag{17}$$

where A is a constant of integration. We are told that, initially, $v = 0$ and $x = 2l$. Inserting these values into equation (17) gives the value for A as:

$$A = -\frac{4}{3}l^3 g$$

If this value is substituted into the right-hand side of equation (17), it becomes:

$$v^2(x + l)^2 = \frac{2}{3}g(x^3 - 3l^2x - 2l^3)$$

$$= \frac{2}{3}g(x + l)^2(x - 2l)$$

$$3v^2 = 2g(x - 2l) \tag{18}$$

as required, after cancelling $(x + l)^2$. Note that factorising the right-hand side is not magic, since we know that $v = 0$ when $x = 2l$; hence, $(x - 2l)$ must be a factor. We admit, however, to some good fortune in the cancellation of $(x + l)^2$!

To complete the problem, we use equation (18) to compute the acceleration. More precisely, we use equation (14) to find dv/dt in terms of v^2, as follows:

$$(x + l)\frac{dv}{dt} = g(x - l) - v^2$$

and substituting for v^2 from equation (18) gives:

$$(x + l)\frac{dv}{dt} = g(x - l) - \frac{2}{3}g(x - 2l)$$

$$= \frac{g}{3}(x + l)$$

Hence:

$$\frac{dv}{dt} = \frac{1}{3}g$$

Is this surprising, that the acceleration of the rope should be constant? Does it depend on the special values of l, the height of the pulley, and $x = 2l$ initially? (See exercise 10.3.5.)

Next, we return to the vertically launched rocket. However, this time we look at the launch process itself.

Example 10.3.2

A scale model of a rocket sits on the launch pad. The total mass of the rocket and fuel is 1 kg. The mass of the rocket M satisfies the equation:

$$\frac{dM}{dt} = -\frac{t}{33}$$

If the exhaust gas is ejected at a constant rate of 95 ms^{-1} relative to the rocket, determine the reaction force on the ground and how long before the rocket takes off. Take $g = 10$ ms^{-2}.

Solution   In this problem, we are only concerned with the period of time when the rocket is stationary. Equation (5) remains valid and the external force is $R - Mg$, where R is the reaction and M is the mass of the rocket (plus fuel). Figure 10.4 displays the situation.

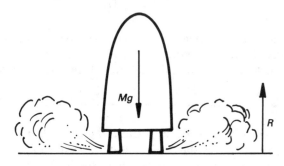

Fig. 10.4

The rocket is stationary, so that v, the speed of the rocket, is zero. However, exhaust gases are being emitted, so the second term on the

247

right-hand side of equation (5) is non-zero. In fact:

$$R - Mg = 0 + 95 \frac{dM}{dt}$$

$$R = Mg + 95 \frac{dM}{dt} \tag{19}$$

We can calculate M by integrating the equation given in the problem. We have that:

$$\frac{dM}{dt} = -\frac{t}{33}$$

and integrating with respect to time gives:

$$M = -\frac{t^2}{66} + C$$

When $t = 0$, $M = 1$ kg, hence $C = 1$, so that:

$$M = 1 - \frac{t^2}{66}$$

Inserting these expressions for M and dM/dt into equation (19), and setting $g = 10$, gives:

$$R = \left(1 - \frac{t^2}{66}\right) 10 - 95 \frac{t}{33}$$

which is the required expression for the reaction, R. This expression factorises as follows:

$$R = \frac{10}{66} (66 - 19t - t^2)$$

$$= \frac{10}{66} (3 - t)(22 + t)$$

When $t < 3$, $R > 0$, and when $t = 3$, R vanishes. We therefore deduce that the rocket lifts off after 3 s. When $t > 3$, R is, of course, zero, so equation (19) no longer holds, $v \neq 0$ and we have rocket motion as discussed in Section 10.2.

When a body as large as a rocket is travelling through the air, it is surely bad practice to ignore resistance. Equation (5) with the external force as gravity and resistance R_0, if the rocket is ascending vertically, is:

$$-R_0 - mg = m \frac{dv}{dt} + (u - v) \frac{dm}{dt} \tag{20}$$

Let us pose perhaps the simplest problem. A rocket is ascending vertically. It starts from rest at time $t = 0$. The resistance is mkv^2 (see Chapter 6 – this is reasonable for large bodies), where m is the mass of the rocket, v its speed and k is a constant. Let the mass be ejected at a constant speed U relative to the rocket, so that $u - v = U$ in equation (20). Finally, suppose also that the mass of the rocket is changing at a constant rate r and that its initial mass is m_0. This latter piece of information means that:

$$\frac{dm}{dt} = -r$$

or, integrating with respect to t and setting $m = m_0$ when $t = 0$:

$$m = m_0 - rt \tag{21}$$

Under all these simple assumptions, equation (20) becomes:

$$-mkv^2 - mg = m\frac{dv}{dt} - rU$$

or, making dv/dt the subject and substituting for m from equation (21):

$$\frac{dv}{dt} = -g - kv^2 + \frac{rU}{m - rt} \tag{22}$$

We cannot solve equation (22) exactly. The tactic of setting $dv/dt = v$ dv/dx gets us nowhere because of the t on the right-hand side. Other methods fail because the differential equation is neither separable nor linear. In fact, the only option open to us is to write equation (22) as:

$$\frac{dv}{dt} = f(v, t) \tag{23}$$

with $v = 0$ when $t = 0$, the initial condition, and $f(v, t)$ a shorthand for the right-hand side. We then turn to books on numerical methods and use Runge-Kutta, Taylor or some other method to march forwards in time from $t = 0$. However, these methods have two major drawbacks. First, they are not exact, and for many rocket problems precision is absolutely essential. Secondly, and more importantly for students, we have to assign specific numbers for all the constants in $f(v, t)$ which, together with all the 'number crunching', detracts from insight, especially at this initial learning stage.

Here is another rocket problem which is not amenable to exact solution, but at least we can solve the differential equation. It is the problem of soft landing on a planet. We will couch the problem in the form of an example.

Example 10.3.3

A rocket is descending vertically towards Mars. It is using its rockets to achieve a soft landing, and the gases are being ejected at a constant rate of 50 ms^{-1} relative to the rocket. The motors are started when the speed of the rocket is 100 ms^{-1}. Find the time of descent if the fuel is burnt at a rate equal to 0.1 times the mass at time $t = 0$. Find also the distance travelled during this descent. (The acceleration due to Martian gravity is 3.71 ms^{-2}.)

Solution   Figure 10.5 shows how we define the origin and the x-axis. The origin ($x = 0$ and $t = 0$) is chosen to be at the level when the speed of the rocket is 100 ms^{-1}.

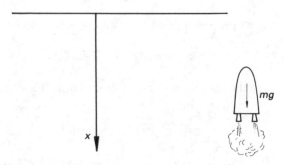

Fig. 10.5

Let M_0 denote the mass of the rocket at time $t = 0$, then:

$$\frac{dm}{dt} = -0.1M_0$$

Integrating this with respect to time, and setting $m = M_0$ when $t = 0$, gives:

$$m = M_0(1 - 0.1t) \tag{24}$$

For the notation in this problem, neglecting resistance, equation (5) is:

$$+3.71m = m\frac{dv}{dt} + 50\frac{dm}{dt}$$

remembering we are on Mars, where g is 3.71 ms^{-2}. Using equation (24) and rearranging gives the following equation for v, the speed of the rocket:

$$\frac{dv}{dt} = +3.71 - \frac{5}{1 - 0.1t}$$

which can be integrated immediately with respect to t to give:

$$v = 3.71t + 50 \ln (1 - 0.1t) + A$$

where A is a constant of integration. From the conditions given, $v = 100$ when $t = 0$, therefore $A = 100$ and hence:

$$v = 3.71t + 100 + 50 \ln (1 - 0.1t) \tag{25}$$

Now, at time $t = T$, say, we wish the rocket to soft land, that is, v to be equal to zero. For this to be true, we thus require:

$$0 = 3.71T + 100 + 50 \ln (1 - 0.1T) \tag{26}$$

Unfortunately, this is a transcendental equation, without an analytic solution. However, at least it is quite easy to find a root numerically. Most of us have calculators that can compute the right-hand side of equation (26) readily for various values of T. (Some can draw its graph, in which case simply find where the curve crosses the x-axis on the displayed Ox vs Oy Cartesian graph, where x is T of course.) The calculator (reinforced by substitution) gives $T = 9.32$ as the only positive solution to equation (26). It may come as some surprise to see that over 90% of the rocket's initial mass is used as fuel, and this is despite the landing, reducing the speed of the rocket from 100 ms^{-1} to 0 ms^{-1} in under 10 s, a deceleration comparable to our g. A 'softer' landing would mean keeping the rocket 'airborne' even longer, using more fuel. This points to the difficulty in soft landing, even on small planets.

Equation (25) can be integrated again with respect to t to give:

$$x = 0.5(3.71)t^2 + 100t + 500(1 - 0.1t) \ln (1 - 0.1t) - 500(1 - 0.1t)$$

which, when $t = 9.32$ s, gives $x = 824$ m, a very respectable landing distance.

Finally, here is a rather different example involving changing mass. A machine gun delivers single bullets very rapidly; however, for our purposes, it may be regarded as a continuous ejection of mass. For this case, the discrete treatment that was used in the derivations of equations (5) and (6) is particularly appropriate. In fact, the approximately equal sign in the equation preceding equation (5) can be replaced by equality if δm is a single bullet. Another point to mention here is the verification of Newton's *third* law that emerges from this next example. In fact, it is a good link between the continuously varying mass problems of this chapter and the collision problems of Chapter 5.

Example 10.3.4

A man carrying a machine gun stands in an ice rink and fires all of his bullets in a continuous stream at a fixed target. He wears ice skates, hence, as he fires, the recoil sends him back with a speed v. There is no friction. The mass of the man plus gun is 100 kg initially, the speed of each bullet is 100 ms^{-1} relative to a fixed origin, the gun fires 10 bullets each second and there are 1000 of them. Assuming that the mass of the man plus gun changes continuously:

(a) find the recoil speed v, relative to the same fixed origin, at any time t;
(b) find the distance the man has travelled by the time he has fired his last bullet;
(c) comment on Newton's third law applied to this example.

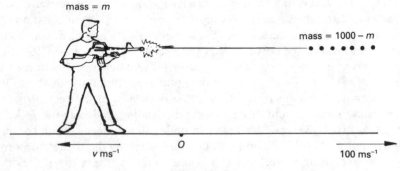

Fig. 10.6

Solution In fact, we could use the rocket equation (5) to obtain v in terms of m. However, there is an easier way to look at this example. Before the man starts firing, he, his gun and all his bullets are stationary. Now, momentum cannot be created out of nothing; therefore, at any subsequent time t, the total momentum must be zero, so that the momentum of the man plus gun must be equal and opposite to the sum of the momentum of all the bullets that have been fired. Figure 10.6 summarises the position at time t. This consideration means that we must have:

$$mv + (m - 100)100 = 0 \quad \text{or} \quad v = \left(\frac{100}{m} - 1\right)100 \text{ ms}^{-1} \qquad (27)$$

In order to find m, the mass of the man plus gun at any time t, we use the information that 10 bullets per second weighing 10^{-3} kg each are ejected. Hence:

$$m = 100 - 10 \times 10^{-3} = 99.99 \text{ kg}$$

after 1 s. Since dm/dt is constant:

$$\frac{dm}{dt} = -100 + 99.99 = -0.01$$

so that, integrating this equation with respect to t, and using $m = 100$ when $t = 0$, we obtain:

$$m = 100 - 0.01t$$

Substituting this into equation (27) gives the following answer to (a):

$$v = \left(\frac{100}{100 - 0.01t} - 1 \right) 100 \text{ ms}^{-1} \tag{28}$$

Note that, in this example, no calculus has yet been required. For problems concerned with conserving momentum (see Chapter 5), this is common. However, in order to answer (b), we put $v = dx/dt$ in equation (28) and integrate with respect to t. This gives:

$$x = -10^6 \ln (100 - 0.01t) - 100t + B \tag{29}$$

If we take $x = 0$ when $t = 0$ (distance is measured from the initial position of the gun man), then:

$$0 = -10^6 \ln 100 + B$$

so that $B = 10^6 \ln 100$. Substituting back into equation (29) gives the following equation for x:

$$x = -10^6 \ln (1 - t \times 10^{-4}) - 100t \tag{30}$$

Since there are 1000 bullets being fired at 10 every second, the gun fires for 100 s. Substituting $t = 100$ into equation (30), making sure to retain as many numbers in the decimal representation of the logarithm as possible, gives:

$$x = -10^6 \ln (0.99) - 100 \times 100$$

$$= -10^6 x - (0.0100503) - 10^4$$

$$= 50.3 \text{ m}$$

Hence the man and gun recoil a distance of 50.3 m. Note that x is positive here because v is positive and we have used $v = dx/dt$. This means that x points to the left in Figure 10.6.

Finally, Newton's third law implies that, for the force given by the gun to every bullet fired, an equal and opposite force is given to the gun (plus man) by the bullet. It is this force that eventually pushes the man back across the ice. The equation preceding equation (27) is the mathematical statement of this. Note that we have used Newton's third law to solve this problem, not his second, as is normally the case.

More problems involving Newton's third law can be found in Chapter 5.

EXERCISES 10.3

1 Reconsider the problem of example 10.3.1 involving a coil of rope lying on the deck of a ship. One end runs up and over a frictionless pulley, at a distance l above the deck, and down the other side. Initially, a length $2l$ hangs down towards the sea. The rope is then released. Suppose the rope is $5l$ in length, and that the sea is a distance $2l$ below the deck of the ship. Assume that the rope is neutrally buoyant (that is, has zero weight) in sea water. Determine an equation for the velocity:

(a) before the rope is fully uncoiled, but after the other end is in the water;
(b) when the end is in the air between the deck and the pulley, that is, no rope remains on the deck;
(c) when all the rope has passed over the pulley, and is partially submerged, but the end has yet to reach the sea surface. What is the velocity when the end is just disappearing beneath the waves?

(*Hint*: When the rope is under water, it contributes nothing to the force, but it still has momentum.)

2 A rocket has mass at time t given by $m_0(1 - \alpha t)$, where m_0 is the initial mass and α is the rate of ejection of gas, and both are constant. The ejected matter has a speed $4g/\alpha$, a constant, relative to the rocket. The atmosphere imposes a resistance $2m_0 v\alpha$, where v is the speed of the rocket. The rocket travels upwards, starting from rest at $t = 0$. Show that its speed v, at time t, obeys the equation:

$$v = 3gt - g\alpha t^2$$

Hence, show that half of the original mass is left when the rocket has reached a height of $g/3\alpha^2$.

3 A rocket of initial mass 80 tonnes is to be launched vertically. Sixty tonnes is available as fuel. Fuel is burnt at the constant rate of 780 kgs^{-1} and is ejected at a relative velocity of 2500 ms^{-1}. Use the rocket equation (5) to calculate:

(a) the acceleration on the launch pad at $t = 0$ (take-off);
(b) the velocity of the rocket at burn-out;
(c) the height at burn-out (all the fuel has been used);
(d) the maximum height reached;
(e) the impulse (thrust) of the rocket on the launch pad.

4 A man and machine gun together have mass M_0. The bullets in the gun each have mass m and the gun fires, for a time T, bullets with speed u relative to the man and gun. The coefficient of dynamic friction between the man and gun and the ice on which he is standing is μ. Show that, at time t, the frictional force between the man's feet and the ice is:

$$\mu\left(M_0 + m - \frac{mt}{T}\right)g$$

Hence, show that the speed of the man and his gun when the bullets have gone is:

$$u \ln\left(1 + \frac{m}{M_0}\right) - \mu g T$$

Explain why the conservation of momentum in the form of Newton's third law cannot be used here, as it was in example 10.3.4.

5 A final return to the coil of rope on the ship's deck. Rework example 10.3.1 with the pulley at a distance a above the deck, but all other parameters as in example 10.3.1. Answer the problem posed in the text by finding an expression for v and a general expression for the acceleration. Is there another value of a, apart from $a = l$, which leads to the acceleration being constant?

11 ROTATING AXES

11.1 INTRODUCTION

So far in this text, we have made a great deal of fuss about choosing a fixed origin and axes before trying to solve mechanics problems. At first thought, this seems a straightforward requirement to satisfy. Further thought will, however, reveal the difficulty. The Earth is rotating about its axis, and the centre of the Earth rotates once a year around the Sun. Hence, in absolute terms, one is hard pressed to find a point that is not moving; there are, in reality, no absolutely fixed points. Well, do we discard the majority of the first ten chapters of this book? Of course not. In most applications, the fact that the origin is not truly stationary may be safely ignored on the grounds of scale. When we do the mathematics, we will make this clearer (see Section 11.4). It turns out that, only for a small class of problems, but a very important class of problems, it is mandatory to use axes that rotate. These are problems involving distances and times comparable to the radius of the Earth and the period of rotation of the Earth respectively. For a second class of problems, it is more convenient, and perhaps constructive, to use a rotating coordinate system. Problems that fall into this category include cars rounding corners and children throwing balls while on a roundabout. The use of a rotating coordinate system brings out well-known, but often poorly understood, concepts such as Coriolis 'force' and 'centrifugal force'. The quotation marks are used here because the words 'centrifugal' and 'force' are, in fact, often wrongly used. In Section 11.3, we will derive some basic relationships between rotating and non-rotating coordinate Cartesian axes.

11.2 PRELIMINARY NOTIONS OF ROTATING FRAMES

Rather than plunging headlong into the mathematics of rotating frames of reference, we will first consider an everyday situation that will illustrate some of the problems.

256

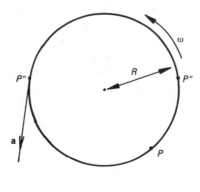

Fig. 11.1

Imagine a roundabout in a children's play area. A child sits on the roundabout near its rim holding a ball. You stand still, on the ground, watching. The child throws the ball vertically upwards. Let us examine the path of the ball, both from your 'truly fixed' viewpoint and from the point of view of the child. First, we need to define a few parameters.

Let the roundabout have a radius R and be rotating with a constant angular velocity ω. Let the ball be thrown vertically with velocity u. Figure 11.1 shows the situation. O indicates your position, that of a fixed observer. Of course, since the ball was launched vertically, you, at O, see the ball go directly up, and fall back down again according to the mathematics of Chapter 6. If the child launched the ball when she was at point P, then by the time the ball returned to the point of launch, the child will have moved on to point P' (as seen by you at O). What then would be the child's view of the ball?

As the ball was thrown, the child would see the ball move horizontally, as if under the action of some force. After all, Newton's laws have been insisting that bodies move in straight lines unless acted upon by some force, and (from the child's point of view) here is a ball blatantly moving off line! Now, the sensible child realises that it is she that is moving, for there is the rest of the world whizzing around her. There is no doubt who is still and who is moving. It would be less obvious if the rest of the world was screened from view. Let us scale up the problem: instead of a roundabout we think of the Earth spinning about the north pole; think only of the polar cap if the curvature of the Earth concerns you; instead of a child and a ball, we think of a rocket launcher and a missile – it is launched vertically, but the Earth 'revolves under it'. The big difference here of course is that the fixed point O has no meaningful analogy. All of us are on the roundabout. What force moves the missile off the vertical line?

257

Here is another problem. Let us get back to the child on the roundabout. Suppose she lets go of the ball at the point P''. You, at O, apply Newton's first law. The ball has a velocity of magnitude equal to the speed of the child, which is ωR, and in the direction of **a**, the tangent to the path of the child at P''. Further, if we ignore resistance, the distance the ball travels horizontally in a time t will be ωRt. The child will travel the same distance, ωRt, but as the arc of a circle. Figure 11.2 shows the geometry in more detail.

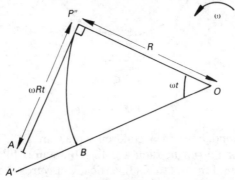

Fig. 11.2

The child is at B and the ball is at A. A is to the right and slightly behind the child. A little trigonometry reveals that:

$$AA' = R(\tan \omega t - \omega t)$$

$$A'B = R(\sec \omega t - 1)$$

Pythagoras' theorem gives the distance between the child (at B) and the ball (at A) as AB, where:

$$(AB)^2 = R^2(2 - 2 \sec \omega t + 2\omega t \tan \omega t - \omega^2 t^2)$$

If $t \ll 1$, then we have:

$$AB \approx \frac{1}{2} R\omega^2 t^2$$

The details apart, the main thrust is that the child sees the ball move away from her, apparently for no reason. Of course, as the ball is released, it falls to Earth under gravity, but the fact that it also moves horizontally from the viewpoint of the child means that there must be a horizontally acting force, again from the child's viewpoint only. If a bomb is dropped towards the Earth, the rotation of the Earth has a similar effect. However, in this case, gravity is so dominant that it is hardly felt, there are additional effects such as the airplane's motion and friction. We will discuss the effect of rotation on missiles and bombs in Section 11.4.

If we swing an object on a string around our heads and the string breaks, then the object flies off. This was considered in Chapter 8. We call this 'centrifugal force'. It is misnamed, but it is essentially the effect that moves the ball, bomb or object off the vertical.

In the next section, we shall derive equations that are valid in a rotating coordinate system where we do not have the privilege of choosing a fixed origin.

EXERCISES 11.2

1 A girl is on the rim of a roundabout of radius 2 m. It is rotating with a constant angular velocity of 1 rad s^{-1}. She throws a ball vertically upwards at a speed of u ms^{-1}.

   (a) How far does she travel before the ball returns to the level of the roundabout?
   (b) For what values of u will she be able to catch the ball?

2 In exercise 11.2.1, **k** is vertically upwards, and the angular velocity of the roundabout is ω**k**. From the girl's viewpoint, describe qualitatively the direction of the 'force' that moves the ball off the **k** direction, if she is facing her direction of travel and **i** is (to her) forwards. Does this direction change if the angular velocity of the roundabout is $-\omega$**k**?

3 The girl now projects the ball horizontally, directly away from the axis of rotation of the roundabout. Neglecting resistance, qualitatively describe the type of curve the ball traces in the horizontal, from the girl's viewpoint. (Neglect the fact that the ball falls to the ground; consider only its horizontal motion.)

11.3 ROTATING COORDINATE SYSTEMS

In this section, we shall formally obtain a relationship between the rate of change of a vector quantity observed relative to a fixed origin, and the rate of change of the same quantity referred to a coordinate system that is rotating. The vector quantity in question is arbitrary, but it is normally the displacement or velocity of a particle. We will also assume that the origins of both the fixed and rotating coordinate systems are the same. This is perfectly valid since there is at least one fixed point in all rotations. (In fact, unless there are infinitely many, there is *only* one.)

Now, normally there is no confusion between rates of change of quantities referred to different origins. However, in this section, we have to distinguish between these different rates. We shall use d/dt to denote the rate of change referred to fixed axes, and $\partial/\partial t$ to denote the rate of change referred to rotating axes. Finally, the treatment here is only two dimensional. This is for two very good reasons. First, it is easier to understand. Secondly, and more importantly, we only deal with problems involving rotation in two dimensions. Exercise 11.3.4 displays the generalisation to three dimensions.

We define $\mathbf{i}$ and $\mathbf{j}$ as unit vectors in the plane of rotation (x–y plane). Let $\mathbf{A} = A_1\mathbf{i} + A_2\mathbf{j}$ be a vector quantity, then the rate of change of this quantity is simply:

$$\frac{d\mathbf{A}}{dt} = \frac{d(A_1\mathbf{i} + A_2\mathbf{j})}{dt} \tag{1}$$

with respect to the fixed axes. However, the axes we have labelled $\mathbf{i}$ and $\mathbf{j}$ rotate with angular velocity ω, as shown in Figure 11.3(a). Expanding the right-hand side of equation (1), we obtain:

$$\frac{d\mathbf{A}}{dt} = \frac{dA_1}{dt}\mathbf{i} + \frac{dA_2}{dt}\mathbf{j} + A_1\frac{d\mathbf{i}}{dt} + A_2\frac{d\mathbf{j}}{dt} \tag{2}$$

The only way the unit vector $\mathbf{i}$ changes with time is that it rotates anticlockwise. The same is true for the unit vector $\mathbf{j}$. Figure 11.3(b) shows the changes in $\mathbf{i}$ and $\mathbf{j}$ in the small time δt. The small angle that $\mathbf{i}$ and $\mathbf{j}$ rotate through is $\delta\theta$, say. However, $\omega = d\theta/dt$, hence $\delta\theta = \omega\,\delta t$.

From Figure 11.3(b), $\delta\mathbf{i}$ is in the $\mathbf{j}$ direction and $\delta\mathbf{j}$ is in the $-\mathbf{i}$ direction. Also, we have that:

$$\left|\frac{\delta\mathbf{i}}{\delta t}\right| = \left|\frac{\delta\mathbf{j}}{\delta t}\right| = \omega$$

since $|\delta\mathbf{i}| = |\mathbf{j}\omega\,\delta t|$ and $|\delta\mathbf{j}| = |-\mathbf{i}\omega\,\delta t|$ from the infinitesimal arcs of Figure 11.3(b). Taking the limit as $\delta t \to 0$, we have therefore derived that:

$$\frac{d\mathbf{i}}{dt} = \omega\mathbf{j} \quad \text{and} \quad \frac{d\mathbf{j}}{dt} = -\omega\mathbf{i}$$

Inserting these into equation (2) gives:

$$\frac{d\mathbf{A}}{dt} = \frac{dA_1}{dt}\mathbf{i} + \frac{dA_2}{dt}\mathbf{j} + \omega A_1\mathbf{j} - \omega A_2\mathbf{i} \tag{3}$$

The first two terms on the right-hand side describe the rate of change of $\mathbf{A}$ as if $\mathbf{i}$ and $\mathbf{j}$ were fixed. We said we would label this $\partial\mathbf{A}/\partial t$. Now, since the axes are rotating as indicated in Figure 11.3(a), the vector angular velocity is in the $\mathbf{k}$ direction (out of the paper – remember the right-hand screw rule). Hence:

(a)

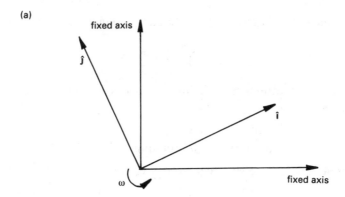

(b)

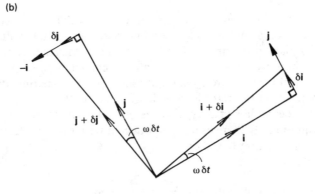

Fig. 11.3

$$\boldsymbol{\omega} = \omega\mathbf{k} \tag{4}$$

This enables us to tidy up the rest of the terms on the right-hand side of equation (3). Recall that:

$$\mathbf{j} = \mathbf{k} \times \mathbf{i} \tag{5}$$

$$-\mathbf{i} = \mathbf{k} \times \mathbf{j} \tag{6}$$

where $\times$ is the vector cross-product. Equations (5) and (6) mean that:

$$A_1\mathbf{j} - A_2\mathbf{i} = \mathbf{k} \times (A_1\mathbf{i} + A_2\mathbf{j})$$
$$= \mathbf{k} \times \mathbf{A} \tag{7}$$

261

Finally, equations (7) and (4) substituted into equation (3) gives:

$$\frac{d\mathbf{A}}{dt} = \frac{\partial \mathbf{A}}{\partial t} + \boldsymbol{\omega} \times \mathbf{A} \tag{8}$$

Equation (8) is the required relationship. It is sometimes more explicitly written:

$$\frac{d\mathbf{A}}{dt}\bigg|_{\text{fixed}} = \frac{d\mathbf{A}}{dt}\bigg|_{\text{rotating}} + \boldsymbol{\omega} \times \mathbf{A}$$

or, since $\mathbf{A}$ is in a sense simply a dummy vector:

$$\frac{d}{dt}\bigg|_{\text{fixed}} \equiv \frac{d}{dt}\bigg|_{\text{rotating}} + \boldsymbol{\omega} \times \tag{9}$$

where the three lines indicate an operator identity. The identity in equation (9) is in fact, as has already been indicated, universally valid and not just true for plane problems. This relationship also means that, in practical situations where we cannot measure rates of change with respect to fixed axes, we can still use Newton's laws, as long as we replace time derivatives by the operator on the right-hand side of equation (9).

Newton's second law usually involves second derivatives. We shall now see how equation (9) changes its appearance if we let $\mathbf{A} = \mathbf{v}$, the velocity of a particle, in equation (8), then:

$$\text{acceleration} = \frac{d\mathbf{v}}{dt} = \frac{\partial \mathbf{v}}{\partial t} + \boldsymbol{\omega} \times \mathbf{v} \tag{10}$$

If, on the other hand, we let $\mathbf{A} = \mathbf{r}$, the position vector of a particle, in equation (8), we obtain:

$$\text{velocity} = \mathbf{v} = \frac{d\mathbf{r}}{dt} = \frac{\partial \mathbf{r}}{\partial t} + \boldsymbol{\omega} \times \mathbf{r} \tag{11}$$

Finally, therefore, we substitute for $\mathbf{v}$ from equation (11) into equation (10) and we derive an equation for acceleration in terms of the position vector $\mathbf{r}$:

$$\text{acceleration} = \frac{d^2\mathbf{r}}{dt^2} = \frac{\partial}{\partial t}\left(\frac{\partial \mathbf{r}}{\partial t} + \boldsymbol{\omega} \times \mathbf{r}\right) + \boldsymbol{\omega} \times \left(\frac{\partial \mathbf{r}}{\partial t} + \boldsymbol{\omega} \times \mathbf{r}\right)$$

For simplicity, we use the dot notation so that $\partial \mathbf{r}/\partial t = \dot{\mathbf{r}}$ and we can expand the right-hand side of this equation to obtain:

$$\text{acceleration} = \ddot{\mathbf{r}} + \dot{\boldsymbol{\omega}} \times \mathbf{r} + \boldsymbol{\omega} \times \mathbf{r} + \boldsymbol{\omega} \times (\dot{\mathbf{r}} + \boldsymbol{\omega} \times \mathbf{r})$$

$$= \ddot{\mathbf{r}} + \dot{\boldsymbol{\omega}} \times \mathbf{r} + 2\boldsymbol{\omega} \times \mathbf{r} + \boldsymbol{\omega} \times (\boldsymbol{\omega} \times \mathbf{r})$$

For all of our applications, $\boldsymbol{\omega}$ is constant, hence the $\dot{\boldsymbol{\omega}}$ on the right of this last equation is zero. We thus arrive at the following expression for acceleration relative to a fixed frame:

$$\text{acceleration} = \ddot{\mathbf{r}} + 2\boldsymbol{\omega} \times \dot{\mathbf{r}} + \boldsymbol{\omega} \times (\boldsymbol{\omega} \times \mathbf{r}) \tag{12}$$

where all the terms on the right-hand side of equation (12) are measured on the rotating frame of reference, unaware that they are rotating.

We see that there are two extra terms. The term $2\boldsymbol{\omega} \times \dot{\mathbf{r}} = 2\boldsymbol{\omega} \times \mathbf{v}$, where $\mathbf{v}$ is the velocity measured in the rotating frame of reference, is called the Coriolis acceleration (after Gustave Gaspard de Coriolis (1792–1843) the French engineer and mathematician). It is of considerable importance in meteorology and oceanography, and is indeed responsible for the momentum balance that gives rise to the familiar low pressure centre on our weather maps. The term $\boldsymbol{\omega} \times (\boldsymbol{\omega} \times \mathbf{r})$ is called the centripetal acceleration and was encountered in Chapter 8 when we discussed circular motion. We have been careful to use the term acceleration here. If acceleration is multiplied by mass, we get a force. Newton's second law in a rotating coordinate system which has constant angular velocity $\boldsymbol{\omega}$ when a force vector $\mathbf{F}$ acts is thus:

$$\mathbf{F} = m\ddot{\mathbf{r}} + 2m\boldsymbol{\omega} \times \mathbf{v} + m\boldsymbol{\omega} \times (\boldsymbol{\omega} \times \mathbf{r})$$

It is common to write this as:

$$\mathbf{F} - 2m\boldsymbol{\omega} \times \mathbf{v} - m\boldsymbol{\omega} \times (\boldsymbol{\omega} \times \mathbf{r}) = m\ddot{\mathbf{r}}$$

and to consider the extra terms as 'fictitious forces'. The common terminology is:

$$\text{Coriolis force} \quad = 2m\boldsymbol{\omega} \times \mathbf{v}$$

$$\text{centripetal force} \ = m\boldsymbol{\omega} \times (\boldsymbol{\omega} \times \mathbf{r})$$

$$\text{centrifugal force} \ = -m\boldsymbol{\omega} \times (\boldsymbol{\omega} \times \mathbf{r})$$

Professionals tend to eschew these phrases and stick to Coriolis acceleration and centripetal acceleration as defined earlier. This way, one does not forget the origin of the terms. One further point before tackling an example, do not forget the parentheses in the expression $\boldsymbol{\omega} \times (\boldsymbol{\omega} \times \mathbf{r})$; vector products are not associative so the parentheses are essential. (In fact, $(\boldsymbol{\omega} \times \boldsymbol{\omega}) \times \mathbf{r} \equiv 0$!)

263

Example 11.3.1

Calculate the equations of motion valid relative to a child on the rim of a roundabout of radius R rotating with a constant angular velocity $\omega\mathbf{k}$. Verify that the expressions:

$$x = R(\omega t \sin \omega t + \cos \omega t)$$

$$y = R(\omega t \cos \omega t - \sin \omega t)$$

satisfy these equations.

Solution Apart from setting $\boldsymbol{\omega} = \omega\mathbf{k}$, the problem is quite general, and the equation of motion from equation (12) is:

$$-mg\mathbf{k} = m[\ddot{\mathbf{r}} + 2\omega\mathbf{k} \times \mathbf{r} + \omega\mathbf{k} \times (\omega\mathbf{k} \times \mathbf{r})] \tag{13}$$

We cancel the ms in this equation, write:

$$\mathbf{r} = x\mathbf{i} + y\mathbf{j} + z\mathbf{k}$$

and compute the vector cross-products as follows:

$$\mathbf{k} \times \mathbf{r} = x\mathbf{k} \times \mathbf{i} + y\mathbf{k} \times \mathbf{j} + z\mathbf{k} \times \mathbf{k}$$
$$= x\mathbf{j} - y\mathbf{i}$$

therefore:

$$\mathbf{k} \times \dot{\mathbf{r}} = \dot{x}\mathbf{j} - \dot{y}\mathbf{i}$$

Taking the second cross-product:

$$\mathbf{k} \times (\mathbf{k} \times \mathbf{r}) = x\mathbf{k} \times \mathbf{j} - y\mathbf{k} \times \mathbf{i}$$
$$= -x\mathbf{i} - y\mathbf{j}$$

which is simply the projection of $\mathbf{r}$ on to the x–y plane, but negative. Hence, equation (13) in component form is:

$$0 = \ddot{x} - 2\omega\dot{y} - \omega^2 x \tag{14}$$

$$0 = \ddot{y} + 2\omega\dot{x} - \omega^2 y \tag{15}$$

$$-g = \ddot{z} \tag{16}$$

The last of these equations merely expresses the fall of the ball under gravity. Let us insert the given expressions for x and y into equations (14) and (15) and verify them as correct solutions, then we can discuss them further.

We are given that:

$$x = R(\omega t \sin \omega t + \cos \omega t) \tag{17}$$

$$y = R(\omega t \cos \omega t - \sin \omega t) \tag{18}$$

Differentiating both of these with respect to t, twice, gives:

$$\dot{x} = \omega^2 R t \cos \omega t$$

$$\dot{y} = -\omega^2 R t \sin \omega t$$

and:

$$\ddot{x} = \omega^2 R(\cos \omega t - \omega t \sin \omega t)$$

$$\ddot{y} = \omega^2 R(-\sin \omega t - \omega t \cos \omega t)$$

Substituting these six expressions into equations (14) and (15) shows these latter two equations to be valid.

In fact, the reader can quite easily derive equations (17) and (18) from Figure 11.2 using triangle BAA'. The triangle is shown again in Figure

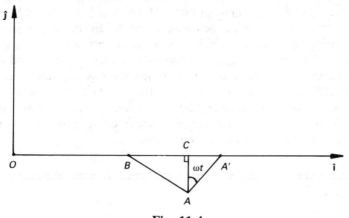

Fig. 11.4

11.4, but this time O is the centre of the roundabout and the child is at B, stationary with respect to the rotating axes. We derived previously that:

$$AA' = R(\tan \omega t - \omega t)$$

$$A'B = R(\sec \omega t - 1)$$

Of course, the coordinates of the ball at A are OC and $-CA$, where C is the perpendicular from A to $A'B$. It is easy to see that:

$$
\begin{aligned}
OC &= OB + BC \\
&= OB + A'B - A'C \\
&= OB + A'B - AA' \sin \omega t \\
&= R + R(\sec \omega t - 1) - R(\tan \omega t - \omega t) \sin \omega t \\
&= R(\omega t \sin \omega t + \cos \omega t)
\end{aligned}
$$

$$
\begin{aligned}
AC &= AA' \cos \omega t \\
&= R(\sin \omega t - \omega t \cos \omega t)
\end{aligned}
$$

from which equations (17) and (18) follow.

In this example, the Coriolis acceleration and centripetal acceleration are of similar magnitude to each other and of similar magnitude to the horizontal accelerations $\ddot{x}$ and $\ddot{y}$. Typical magnitudes for R and ω might be 2 m and 1 rad s^{-1} respectively. In contrast to this, since $\ddot{z} = -g$ and $g \approx$ 10 ms^{-2}, z is much larger in magnitude. Hence, the ball will still be seen to drop, and some care needs to be taken to observe the horizontal motion. It is interesting, and quite typical, that vertical and horizontal motion is uncoupled. This decoupling also happens when we consider motion on a rotating Earth. Much more significant simplifications take place due to the fact that the rate of rotation of the Earth is 7.29×10^{-5} rad s^{-1}, which renders the velocity and acceleration small when distances are not typically hundreds or thousands of kilometres. Before considering motion on the Earth in some detail, let us do an example.

Example 11.3.2

A toy consists of a light hollow hoop of radius a and a plug of mass m which slides along it without friction. The hoop is spun about a vertical axis with a constant angular velocity ω. Find any points of equilibrium, investigate their stability and discuss what happens if $\omega^2 = g/a$.

Solution   For this problem, we have axes fixed in the hoop. Let **k** and **j** be defined as indicated in Figure 11.5. The **i** direction is therefore out of the paper.

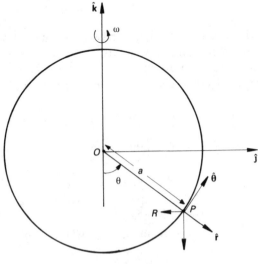

Fig. 11.5

Newton's second law for this problem, remembering that the coordinates are rotating with angular velocity ω, is:

$$m[\ddot{\mathbf{r}} + 2\boldsymbol{\omega} \times \dot{\mathbf{r}} + \boldsymbol{\omega} \times (\boldsymbol{\omega} \times \mathbf{r})] = -mg\mathbf{k} + R \qquad (19)$$

An important point to make here is that, although the reaction R is perpendicular to the tangent to the hoop at P, the location of the plug, it is not in the plane of the hoop. This is due to the rotation, in particular, the component of acceleration in the **i** direction. We are not interested in R, so we resolve equation (19) in the direction of the tangent at P in order to eliminate it. We have that:

$$\boldsymbol{\omega} = \omega\mathbf{k} \qquad \text{and} \qquad \mathbf{r} = a\hat{\mathbf{r}}$$

hence:

$$\boldsymbol{\omega} \times \mathbf{r} = \omega \mathbf{k} \times a\mathbf{r}$$
$$= \omega \mathbf{k} \times (-a \cos \theta \mathbf{k} + a \sin \theta \mathbf{j})$$
$$= -a\omega \sin \theta \mathbf{i}$$

so that:

$$\boldsymbol{\omega} \times (\boldsymbol{\omega} \times \mathbf{r}) = a\omega^2 \sin \theta \mathbf{k} \times \mathbf{i}$$
$$= -a\omega^2 \sin \theta \mathbf{j}$$

This result, that the acceleration of a mass performing a horizontal circle radius l is $l\omega^2$ directed towards the axis, was derived in Chapter 8 and should therefore come as no surprise ($l = a \sin \theta$ here). Differentiating $\mathbf{r} = a\hat{\mathbf{r}}$ with respect to time gives, from Section 8.9:

$$\dot{\mathbf{r}} = a\dot{\theta}\hat{\boldsymbol{\theta}}$$

$$\ddot{\mathbf{r}} = a\ddot{\theta}\hat{\boldsymbol{\theta}} - a\dot{\theta}^2\hat{\mathbf{r}}$$

Finally:

$$\boldsymbol{\omega} \times \mathbf{r} = \omega\dot{\theta}a\mathbf{k} \times \boldsymbol{\theta}$$
$$= \omega a\dot{\theta}\mathbf{k} \times (\sin \theta \mathbf{k} + \cos \theta \mathbf{j})$$
$$= -\omega a\dot{\theta} \cos \theta \mathbf{i}$$

and we see that the Coriolis term has no component in the θ direction. However, for clarity, we write out again the full equation of motion (equation (19)):

$$m(a\ddot{\theta}\hat{\boldsymbol{\theta}} - a\dot{\theta}^2\mathbf{r} - 2\omega a\dot{\theta} \cos \theta \mathbf{i} - a\omega^2 \sin \theta \mathbf{j}) = -mg\mathbf{k} + R \qquad (20)$$

We know that R has no component in the $\hat{\boldsymbol{\theta}}$ direction, hence $R \cdot \hat{\boldsymbol{\theta}} = 0$. Also, $\mathbf{k} \cdot \hat{\boldsymbol{\theta}} = \sin \theta$ and $\mathbf{j} \cdot \hat{\boldsymbol{\theta}} = \cos \theta$ ($\mathbf{i} \cdot \hat{\boldsymbol{\theta}} = 0$ of course), so taking the dot product of equation (20) with $\hat{\boldsymbol{\theta}}$ gives:

$$ma\ddot{\theta} - ma\omega^2 \sin \theta \cos \theta = -mg \sin \theta$$
$$a\ddot{\theta} = \sin \theta (a\omega^2 \cos \theta - g) \qquad (21)$$

We therefore have an equation that is amenable to stability techniques. The general theory is outside the scope of this text, however we outline its application in this particular problem here.

The equilibrium positions are given by setting $\ddot{\theta} = 0$, that is:

$$\sin \theta = 0 \qquad (22)$$

$$\cos \theta = \frac{g}{a\omega^2} \qquad (23)$$

which give distinct values of θ, provided $g \neq a\omega^2$. Ignoring, for the moment, this special value of ω, consider first equation (22) which leads to $\theta = 0, \pi$.

Near $\theta = 0$, let $\theta = \varepsilon$, a small angle. At these small values, $\sin \theta \approx \varepsilon$, $\cos \theta \approx 1$, hence equation (21) implies:

$$a\ddot{\varepsilon} \approx \varepsilon(a\omega^2 - g)$$

which indicates unstable equilibrium if $a\omega^2 > g$ and stable equilibrium if $a\omega^2 < g$ (remember $a\omega^2 \neq g$). For the stable range, valid for small values of ω ($< \sqrt{(g/a)}$), the period of oscillations is $2\pi(a/(g - a\omega^2))^{1/2}$. Note that when $\omega = 0$, this is the period of oscillation of a simple pendulum of length a.

Near $\theta = \pi$, $\theta = \pi + \varepsilon$, where ε is small. Hence, we can use the relationships $\sin \theta \approx -\varepsilon$ and $\cos \theta \approx -1$, and equation (21) becomes:

$$a\ddot{\varepsilon} \approx \varepsilon(a\omega^2 + g)$$

which, to no one's surprise, is always unstable.

Equation (23) gives small oscillations about $\theta = \theta_0$, where:

$$\cos \theta_0 = \frac{g}{a\omega^2}$$

Hence, if we set $\theta = \theta_0 + \varepsilon$, where ε is small, so that:

$$\cos \theta = \cos (\theta_0 + \varepsilon)$$

$$\approx \frac{g}{a\omega^2} - \varepsilon \sin \theta_0$$

$$\sin \theta = \sin (\theta_0 + \varepsilon)$$

$$\approx \sin \theta_0 + \frac{\varepsilon g}{a\omega^2}$$

hence:

$$\sin \theta \, (a\omega^2 \cos \theta - g) \approx \left(\sin \theta_0 + \frac{\varepsilon g}{a\omega^2} \right)(g - \varepsilon a\omega^2 \sin \theta_0 - g)$$

$$\approx -\varepsilon a\omega^2 \sin^2 \theta_0$$

If $\cos \theta_0 = g/a\omega^2$, then:

$$\sin^2 \theta_0 = 1 - \frac{g^2}{a^2\omega^4}$$

Equation (21) then gives:

$$\ddot{\varepsilon} \approx -\varepsilon\omega^2 \left(1 - \frac{g^2}{a^2\omega^4}\right)$$

$$= -\frac{\varepsilon}{a^2\omega^2}(a^2\omega^4 - g^2)$$

which indicates stability if $a\omega^2 > g$, that is, if ω is large enough. The period of small oscillations is:

$$2\pi a\omega(a^2\omega^4 - g^2)^{-1/2}$$

Finally, we examine the special case $g = a\omega^2$. With $\omega^2 = g/a$, equation (21) becomes:

$$a\ddot{\theta} = g \sin \theta (\cos \theta - 1)$$

$$= -2g \sin \theta \sin^2 \tfrac{1}{2}\theta$$

(on using the trigonometric identity $\cos \theta = 1 - 2 \sin^2 \tfrac{1}{2}\theta$) which near $\theta = 0$ gives a non-linear equation:

$$a\ddot{\theta} \approx -\frac{1}{2}g\theta^3$$

the analysis of which is outside the scope of this book. However, the negative sign and cube of θ on the right-hand side ensure a stable equilibrium position. It is not, however, simple harmonic motion and the term 'period' is not well defined for this kind of problem (see for example D.W. Jordan and P. Smith, *Non-linear Differential Equations*, Oxford University Press, 1989).

In summary, we have concluded that:

For $0 < \omega^2 < g/a$:

$$\theta = 0 \text{ is stable}$$

$$\theta = \cos^{-1}(g/a) \text{ is unstable}$$

For $\omega^2 = g/a$:

$\theta = 0$ is stable, but not SHM

For $\omega^2 > g/a$:

$\theta = 0$ is unstable

$\theta = \cos^{-1}(g/a\omega^2)$ is stable

For *all* values of ω, $\theta = \pi$ is an unstable equilibrium position.

EXERCISES 11.3

1 By writing $z = x + iy$ ($i = \sqrt{-1}$), show that equations (14) and (15) in example 11.3.1 can be written:

$$\ddot{z} + 2i\omega z - \omega^2 z = 0$$

with boundary conditions $z = R$, $\dot{z} = 0$ at time $t = 0$. Use the theory of second-order differential equations with constant coefficients to show that:

$$x = R(\cos \omega t + \omega t \sin \omega t)$$

$$y = R(-\sin \omega t + \omega t \cos \omega t)$$

as in the text.

2 A boy rides on a roundabout which has radius a. His father stands on firm ground and observes he has a constant speed v. He pulls from his pocket a simple pendulum which has period T_0 and passes it to his son who measures the period to be T. Establish that the pendulum, when held by the boy on the roundabout, swings not about $\theta = 0$ but about $\theta = \theta_0$, where:

$$\tan \theta_0 = \frac{v^2}{ag}$$

(θ is the angle the pendulum string makes with the vertical.) Show further that:

$$T = T_0(ag)^{1/2} (v^4 + a^2g^2)^{1/4}$$

3 A mass lies on a horizontal plane that rotates about a vertical axis such that its position vector, $\mathbf{r}$, satisfies:

$$\dot{\mathbf{r}} = \boldsymbol{\omega} \times \mathbf{r}$$

where $\boldsymbol{\omega}$ is the angular velocity. Show that:

$$\ddot{\mathbf{r}} = -\omega^2 \mathbf{r}$$

and hence that:

$$\mathbf{r} = \mathbf{c} \cos \omega t + \frac{1}{\omega} \boldsymbol{\omega} \times \mathbf{c} \sin \omega t$$

where $\mathbf{c}$ is a constant vector. (You will need the identity $\mathbf{a} \times (\mathbf{b} \times \mathbf{c}) = (\mathbf{a} \cdot \mathbf{c})\mathbf{b} - (\mathbf{a} \cdot \mathbf{b})\mathbf{c}$.)

4 An observer at a point that is fixed relative to a Cartesian coordinate system $Oxyz$ observes a particle moving with velocity $\mathbf{v}$. His colleague is watching the same particle, but observes its velocity to be $\mathbf{V}$. He also considers that the first observer's coordinate rotates with respect to his axes.

(a) Let $\mathbf{r} = x\mathbf{i} + y\mathbf{j} + z\mathbf{k}$, where $\mathbf{i}$, $\mathbf{j}$ and $\mathbf{k}$ are in the x, y, z directions respectively. Show that:

$$\frac{d\mathbf{i}}{dt} = \alpha_1 \mathbf{j} + \alpha_2 \mathbf{k}$$

$$\frac{d\mathbf{j}}{dt} = \alpha_3 \mathbf{k} - \alpha_1 \mathbf{i}$$

$$\frac{d\mathbf{k}}{dt} = -\alpha_2 \mathbf{i} - \alpha_3 \mathbf{j}$$

and hence deduce the existence of a vector $\boldsymbol{\omega}$ such that:

$$x\frac{d\mathbf{i}}{dt} + y\frac{d\mathbf{j}}{dt} + z\frac{d\mathbf{k}}{dt} = \boldsymbol{\omega} \times \mathbf{r}$$

(b) Show that:

$$\mathbf{V} = \mathbf{v} + \boldsymbol{\omega} \times \mathbf{r}$$

11.4 THE ROTATING EARTH

An obvious example of motion involving axes that rotate is the motion of a particle relative to axes fixed in the surface of the Earth. Indeed, since virtually all mechanics takes place on Earth, and we have to work with such rotating axes, it is a sensible question to ask why we do not always have to consider motion relative to rotating axes. The answer has already been hinted at in the last section: it is one of scale. Consider the equations (14 and 15) we derived in example 11.3.1, for horizontal motion in the x–y plane, of a mass under no (horizontal) forces but referred to axes that rotate with angular velocity ω about the z-axis. These are:

$$\ddot{x} - 2\omega\dot{y} - \omega^2 x = 0$$

$$\ddot{y} + 2\omega\dot{x} - \omega^2 y = 0$$

Suppose now that these express motion relative to the following axes, x points east and y points north (the usual geophysicist's convention), and that they are sufficiently close to the North Pole that the axis can be considered vertical. (We will have more to say about this later.) It is usual to use capital omega Ω for the Earth's rotation, where:

$$\Omega \approx \frac{2\pi}{1 \text{ day}} = 7.27 \times 10^{-5} \text{ rad s}^{-1}$$

More accurately, the Earth takes 86 164 s to perform one revolution (rather than 24 h which is 86 400 s). This leads to a change in the second decimal place and gives the widely accepted value:

$$\Omega = 7.29 \times 10^{-5} \text{ rad s}^{-1} \tag{24}$$

The main point, however, is the smallness of Ω. Letting $\omega = \Omega$ in equations (14) and (15) and inserting some large but everyday sport (baseball, football) magnitudes of $\ddot{x}$, $\ddot{y}$, $\dot{x}$, $\dot{y}$, x and y into the equations, namely $\ddot{x}$, $\ddot{y} \approx 1 \text{ ms}^{-2}$, $\dot{x}$, $\dot{y} \approx 100 \text{ ms}^{-1}$, x, $y \approx 400$ m, gives the following magnitudes of the terms:

acceleration	$\ddot{x}$, $\ddot{y} \approx 1 \text{ ms}^{-2}$
Coriolis acceleration	$2\Omega x$, $2\Omega y \approx 10^{-2} \text{ ms}^{-2}$
centripetal acceleration	$\Omega^2 x$, $\Omega^2 y \approx 10^{-6} \text{ ms}^{-2}$

This shows immediately that centripetal acceleration can virtually always be neglected as infinitesimal in magnitude, and for most applications Coriolis acceleration can also be neglected. However, certain quite small ballistic applications, where x and y are very large and where small errors are very important to eliminate, could involve consideration of Coriolis acceleration (see example 11.4.4). One rather bizarre fact is that, in the era of the ULCC (Ultra Large Crude Carrier – the huge oil tanker) in the early and mid-1970s, the tankers were so large that the handling of these vessels involved consideration of the Coriolis effect.

As mentioned earlier, on a rotating Earth, we commonly choose Cartesian axes, fixed relative to the Earth's surface. Usually, if O is an arbitrary point on the Earth's surface taken as the origin, then x points east, y points north and z points up. Of course, O itself is not only rotating but moving. We therefore need to relate the equation of motion:

$$m(\ddot{\mathbf{R}} + 2\boldsymbol{\omega} \times \mathbf{R} + \boldsymbol{\omega} \times (\boldsymbol{\omega} \times \mathbf{R})) = \mathbf{F} \tag{25}$$

to $Oxyz$ as defined. As written, in equation (25), $\mathbf{R}$ is referred to a fixed origin but rotating axes. These are labelled X, Y and Z in Figure 11.6. In Figure 11.6, $O'XYZ$ are rotating with angular velocity $\Omega\mathbf{K}$, hence O is fixed relative to O'. This implies that there is an easy relationship between an arbitrary point P referred to O' and the same point referred to O.

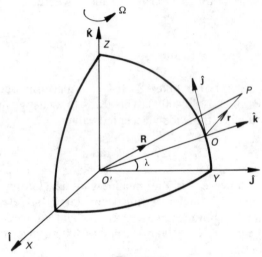

Fig. 11.6

If the radius of the Earth is a (in vectors, $a\mathbf{k}$), then writing:

$$\mathbf{R} = X\mathbf{I} + Y\mathbf{J} + Z\mathbf{K}$$

$$\mathbf{r} = x\mathbf{i} + y\mathbf{j} + z\mathbf{k}$$

leads to:

$$\mathbf{R} = \mathbf{r} + a\mathbf{k}$$

Hence:

$$\frac{d\mathbf{R}}{dt} = \frac{d\mathbf{r}}{dt}$$

$$\frac{d^2\mathbf{R}}{dt^2} = \frac{d^2\mathbf{r}}{dt^2}$$

Therefore, only the centripetal acceleration term is different, and equation (25) becomes:

$$m(\ddot{\mathbf{r}} + 2\boldsymbol{\omega} \times \dot{\mathbf{r}} + \boldsymbol{\omega} \times (\boldsymbol{\omega} \times \mathbf{r}) + \boldsymbol{\omega} \times (\boldsymbol{\omega} \times a\mathbf{k})) = \mathbf{F}$$

On the Earth:

$$\Omega\mathbf{K} = \Omega \cos \lambda\mathbf{j} + \Omega \sin \lambda\mathbf{k}$$

hence:

$$\boldsymbol{\omega} \times (\boldsymbol{\omega} \times a\mathbf{k}) = \boldsymbol{\omega} \times (\Omega a \cos \lambda\mathbf{i})$$

$$= \Omega^2 a \cos \lambda\mathbf{j}$$

so that, for a mass subject only to gravity, the equation of motion is:

$$m(\ddot{\mathbf{r}} + 2\boldsymbol{\omega} \times \mathbf{r} + \boldsymbol{\omega} \times (\boldsymbol{\omega} \times \mathbf{r}) + \Omega^2 a \cos \lambda\mathbf{j}) = -mg\mathbf{k} \qquad (26)$$

We now make use of the smallness of Ω to simplify equation (26). The relevant data is:

$$|\boldsymbol{\omega}| = |\Omega| = \Omega = 7.29 \times 10^{-5} \text{ rad s}^{-1}$$

$$a = 6.378 \times 10^6 \text{ m}$$

hence, $\Omega^2 a \cos \lambda < 0.04$. Also, if $|\mathbf{r}|$ is not of the same order of magnitude as the radius of the Earth:

$$|\boldsymbol{\omega} \times (\boldsymbol{\omega} \times \mathbf{r})| < 0.01$$

hence, to a high degree of accuracy:

$$\ddot{\mathbf{r}} + 2\boldsymbol{\omega} \times \mathbf{r} = -g\mathbf{k} \qquad (27)$$

(Another standard practice is to combine gravity with the centripetal acceleration to form apparent gravity. This is sensible because apparent gravity is what is actually measured – we cannot stop the Earth to perform experiments. However, the difference between apparent gravity and true gravity is too small to concern us here.) Let us now look at an example with meteorological relevance.

Example 11.4.1

A particle moves on the Earth with its horizontal speed much greater than its vertical speed. If we take the standard geophysical axes as x points east, y points north and z points up with the origin north of the equator at latitude λ, show that to a good degree of approximation:

$$\ddot{x} - f\dot{y} = 0$$

$$\ddot{y} + f\dot{x} = 0$$

$$\ddot{z} = -g$$

where $f = 2\Omega \sin \lambda$ (called the Coriolis parameter by meteorologists and oceanographers).

Solution   Figure 11.7 repeats Figure 11.6 but is less crowded.

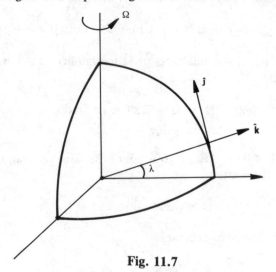

Fig. 11.7

The Coriolis term is quite easily calculated. Since:

$$\Omega = \Omega \cos \lambda \mathbf{j} + \Omega \sin \lambda \mathbf{k}$$

$$\dot{\mathbf{r}} = \dot{x}\mathbf{i} + \dot{y}\mathbf{j} + \dot{z}\mathbf{k}$$

we have:

$$2\Omega \times \mathbf{r} = \begin{vmatrix} \mathbf{i} & \mathbf{j} & \mathbf{k} \\ 0 & 2\Omega \cos \lambda & 2\Omega \sin \lambda \\ \dot{x} & \dot{y} & \dot{z} \end{vmatrix}$$

$$= (\dot{z}2\Omega \cos \lambda - \dot{y}2\Omega \sin \lambda)\mathbf{i} + (\dot{x}2\Omega \sin \lambda)\mathbf{j}$$
$$+ (-\dot{x}2\Omega \cos \lambda)\mathbf{k}$$

Equation (27) in component form is thus:

$$\ddot{x} + \dot{z}2\Omega \cos \lambda - \dot{y}2\Omega \sin \lambda = 0 \tag{28}$$

$$\ddot{y} + \dot{x}2\Omega \sin \lambda = 0 \tag{29}$$

$$\ddot{z} - \dot{x}2\Omega \cos \lambda = -g \tag{30}$$

We will now examine each of these equations.

Equation (28) is approximately:

$$\ddot{x} - f\dot{y} = 0$$

since $f = 2\Omega \sin \lambda$ and $z \ll y$, which implies that the middle term of equation (28) is negligible.

Equation (29) is:

$$\ddot{y} + f\dot{x} = 0$$

as required.

Equation (30) has $-g$ on the right-hand side which is of magnitude (approximately) 10 ms^{-2}. On the other hand, even for high speeds, $\dot{x}2\Omega \cos \lambda$ will not be of this magnitude. For example, if $x = 10^2$ ms^{-1}, then:

$$|\dot{x}2\Omega \cos \lambda| \approx 0.01$$

hence, to a good approximation:

$$\ddot{z} = -g$$

as required.

Following directly on, here is another example relevant to geophysical fluid dynamics.

Example 11.4.2

A floating platform is in the Pacific Ocean at latitude λ and is given a velocity $\dot{x} = U$, $\dot{y} = V$ at time $t = 0$. Assuming no vertical motion, and no other external forces act, determine the path of the platform, assuming that it is free to move horizontally and that frictional forces are negligible. (You may take $f = 2\Omega \sin \lambda$ as a constant.)

Solution The horizontal equations of motion are:

$$\ddot{x} - f\dot{y} = 0$$

$$\ddot{y} + f\dot{x} = 0$$

or, writing $u = \dot{x}$, $v = \dot{y}$, we obtain:

$$\dot{u} - fv = 0 \qquad (31)$$

$$\dot{v} + fu = 0 \qquad (32)$$

Differentiating equation (32) with respect to t and eliminating u using equation (31) gives:

$$\ddot{v} + f^2v = 0$$

with solution $v = A \sin ft + B \cos ft$. Given that $v = V$ at time $t = 0$, $B = V$, hence:

$$v = A \sin ft + V \cos ft \qquad (33)$$

and differentiating:

$$\dot{v} = fA \cos ft - fV \sin ft$$

which, from equation (32), gives:

$$u = V \sin ft - A \cos ft$$

We find the constant A by setting $u = U$ when $t = 0$, whence:

$$u = V \sin ft - U \cos ft \qquad (34)$$

Setting $\dot{x} = u$, $\dot{y} = v$, then integrating equations (33) (with $A = U$) and (34) with respect to time gives the following two equations for x and y:

$$x = \frac{1}{f} (-V \cos ft - U \sin ft) + X \tag{35}$$

$$y = \frac{1}{f} (-U \cos ft + V \sin ft) + Y \tag{36}$$

where X and Y are constants. The informed reader may already realise the curve that equations (35) and (36) represent. However, we can readily establish the answer by using the technique described in Chapter 9, example 9.4.2, obtaining the following expressions:

$$f(x - X_0) = (U^2 + V^2)^{1/2} \sin (ft + \Phi)$$

$$f(y - Y_0) = (U^2 + V^2)^{1/2} \cos (ft + \Phi)$$

where $\cos \Phi = -U/\sqrt{(U^2 + V^2)}$, $\sin \Phi = -V/\sqrt{(U^2 + V^2)}$. Hence, squaring and adding (and then dividing by f^2) gives:

$$(x - X_0)^2 + (y - Y_0)^2 = \frac{U^2 + V^2}{f^2}$$

which is a circle, centre (X_0, Y_0), radius $\sqrt{(U^2 + V^2)}/f$.

The result obtained in the foregoing example means that a parcel of neutrally buoyant (no net vertical force) salt water that does not readily mix with its environment will travel in a circle, radius $|\mathbf{u}_0|/f$, where $\mathbf{u}_0$ is the initial velocity of the parcel and f is the local value of the Coriolis parameter. This type of motion is called an *inertial oscillation*, and much of the energy of the ocean is tied up in such oscillations. Near boundaries, they are suppressed, but they persist in the deep ocean, because frictional effects, which would eliminate them, are virtually absent there. Near the sea surface, friction leads to the parcel being slowed down and spiralling in towards the point (X_0, Y_0), the centre of the inertial oscillation. More about these spirals (called *Ekman spirals*) and other dynamically interesting oceanographic phenomena can be found in oceanography texts.

In Chapter 2, we discussed the force due to a mass on a slope. In Chapter 7, this was generalised to include two-dimensional motion of a particle on an inclined plane. The force that is directed down the plane in both cases is a component of that due to gravity. In the atmosphere, air pressure varies from place to place. Pressure maps, with their isobars and fronts, are displayed on weather forecasts. Indeed, the barometer in the hall measures this pressure – it varies with time as well as location. Most of us are familiar with lows (cyclones) and highs (anti-cyclones) – these are local minima and maxima respectively of air pressure. A difference in pressure between two adjacent points leads to a force towards the lesser pressure proportional to the gradient of the pressure. The following example illustrates this idea.

Example 11.4.3

A cloud is travelling horizontally at a constant speed in mid-latitudes. It is subject to a constant pressure force which is directed towards a point O with magnitude p per unit mass. If the cloud is at a distance a from O, calculate its path and direction of travel in the northern hemisphere. (Assume that the cloud is neutrally buoyant and that $2\Omega = f\mathbf{k}$ with $f = 2\Omega \sin \lambda$, a constant (see exercise 11.4.2).)

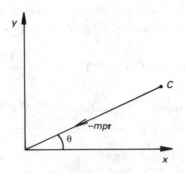

Fig. 11.8

Solution   If the cloud is at position vector $\mathbf{r}$ relative to O and $\mathbf{r} = 0$, then approximately:

$$2m\Omega \times \mathbf{v} = -mp\mathbf{r} \qquad (37)$$

Figure 11.8 shows the cloud at C, and our standard axes x pointing east and y pointing north. Equation (37) shows a balance between Coriolis effects and pressure gradient force. This is called geostrophic balance by meteorologists. Expanding the vector products, we use plane polar coordinates in which:

$$\mathbf{v} = \dot{r}\hat{\mathbf{r}} + r\dot{\theta}\hat{\boldsymbol{\theta}}$$

since we are assuming that all motion takes place at a constant level and that the cloud is neutrally buoyant. Therefore:

$$2\Omega \times \mathbf{v} = \begin{vmatrix} \mathbf{r} & \theta & z \\ 0 & 0 & f \\ \dot{r} & r\dot{\theta} & 0 \end{vmatrix}$$

$$= -fr\dot{\theta}\hat{\mathbf{r}} + f\dot{r}\hat{\boldsymbol{\theta}}$$

Hence, equation (37) leads to:

$$-fr\dot{\theta} = -pr \tag{38}$$

$$f\dot{r} = 0 \tag{39}$$

Integrating equation (39) with respect to t gives:

$$r = \text{constant} = a$$

Hence, the path is a circle of radius a. Equation (38), in turn, gives, after cancellation of r:

$$\dot{\theta} = \frac{p}{f} \quad \text{or} \quad \theta = \frac{pt}{f} + \text{constant}$$

That is, θ increases with time. In the northern hemisphere, f is positive so θ is positive, hence the cloud moves in the direction of θ increasing, which is anti-clockwise.

The result just obtained can be used practically. If it is a day when there is a reasonably consistent wind direction, the clouds will be moving reasonably steadily. Stand with your back to the wind and the low pressure is to your left (Buys Ballots law). This is only true in northern latitudes. Since, most of the time, in the UK, we experience winds from the south-west or west, this is consistent with a low pressure centre near Iceland, which is the climatologically average position for a cyclone.

We now leave meteorology and look at a ballistic example where vertical motion is important.

Example 11.4.4

A bomb of mass m is dropped from a stationary helicopter which is at a height that is small compared to the radius of the Earth. Find an expression for the easterly deflection of the bomb by Coriolis acceleration. What is the value of this deflection for a bomb that takes 30 s to reach the Earth at latitude 60°N? (Assume squares of the Earth's rotation can be ignored.)

Solution Since we can ignore squares of the Earth's rotation, the equation of motion is equation (27):

$$\ddot{\mathbf{r}} + 2\boldsymbol{\omega} \times \mathbf{r} = -g\mathbf{k}$$

where:

$$\boldsymbol{\omega} = (0, \quad \Omega \cos \lambda, \quad \Omega \sin \lambda) \quad \text{and} \quad \mathbf{r} = (x, y, z)$$

(Again, x points east, y points north and z points up.) Hence:

$$\boldsymbol{\omega} \times \mathbf{r} = \begin{vmatrix} \mathbf{i} & \mathbf{j} & \mathbf{k} \\ 0 & \Omega \cos \lambda & \Omega \sin \lambda \\ \dot{x} & \dot{y} & \dot{z} \end{vmatrix}$$

$$= (\dot{z}\Omega \cos \lambda - \dot{y}\Omega \sin \lambda)\mathbf{i} + (\dot{x}\Omega \sin \lambda)\mathbf{j}$$
$$+ (-\dot{x}\Omega \cos \lambda)\mathbf{k}$$

Hence, equation (27) leads to the three scalar equations:

$$\ddot{x} = \dot{y}2\Omega \sin \lambda - \dot{z}2\Omega \cos \lambda \tag{40}$$

$$\ddot{y} = -\dot{x}2\Omega \sin \lambda \tag{41}$$

$$\ddot{z} = -g + \dot{x}2\Omega \cos \lambda \tag{42}$$

To solve these exactly is very unwieldy. However, a systematic neglect of Ω^2 (and higher powers) is quite easy. First of all, we integrate all three of these equations with respect to time:

$$\dot{x} = y2\Omega \sin \lambda - z2\Omega \cos \lambda + A \tag{43}$$

$$\dot{y} = -x2\Omega \sin \lambda + B \tag{44}$$

$$\dot{z} = -gt + x2\Omega \cos \lambda + C \tag{45}$$

with $x = 0, y = 0, z = 0, \dot{x} = 0, \dot{y} = 0, \dot{z} = h$ (the height of the bomb). The boundary conditions give:

$$A = 2\Omega h \cos \lambda \qquad B = 0 \qquad C = 0$$

Inserting the expression for x in equation (43) into equation (42) gives:

$$\ddot{z} = -g + (y2\Omega \sin \lambda - z2\Omega \cos \lambda + 2\Omega h \cos \lambda)2\Omega \cos \lambda$$

and we see that the complicated expression involving parentheses is of order Ω^2 and so may be ignored. Hence:

$$\ddot{z} \approx -g$$

and integrating gives:

$$\dot{z} = -gt + D$$

$D = 0$ since $\dot{z} = 0$ when $t = 0$. Hence, $z = -gt$. This equation for $\dot{z}$, together with equation (44) for y, inserted into the equation for $\ddot{x}$, equation (40), will give the differential equation for x, the easterly deflection that the problem requires us to find. This is:

$$\ddot{x} = 2\Omega \sin \lambda(-x2\Omega \sin \lambda) - 2\Omega \cos \lambda(-gt)$$

or, ignoring the first term, which is of order Ω^2:

$$\ddot{x} = 2\Omega gt \cos \lambda$$

Integrating once with respect to time:

$$\dot{x} = \Omega gt^2 \cos \lambda + E$$

($E = 0$ since $\dot{x} = 0$ when $t = 0$.) Integrating again with respect to time gives:

$$x = \frac{1}{3} \Omega gt^3 \cos \lambda + F$$

$F = 0$ since $x = 0$ when $t = 0$, hence, the final expression for the easterly deflection of the bomb is:

$$x = \frac{1}{3} \Omega gt^3 \cos \lambda$$

If $t = 30$ s, and with $g = 10$ ms^{-2}, $\Omega = 7.29 \times 10^{-5}$ rad s^{-1} and cos $\lambda = 60$, we obtain:

$$x = \frac{1}{3} \times 10 \times (7.29 \times 10^{-5}) \times (30)^3 \times \cos 60$$
$$= 3.28 \text{ m}$$

283

(Note that the initial height of the bomb must be $gt^2/2$, when with $t = 30$ and $g = 10$ this is 4500 m, which might be thought of as quite high.)

Another approach to the foregoing example is to use a numerical technique called *successive approximation* whereby equations (43), (44) and (45) are integrated again with respect to t to give:

$$x_n = 2\Omega \sin \lambda \int y_{n-1} \, dt - 2 \cos \lambda \int z_{n-1} \, dt + 2\Omega t h \cos \lambda$$

$$y_n = -2\Omega \sin \lambda \int x_{n-1} \, dt$$

$$z_n = \frac{1}{2}gt^2 + h + 2\Omega \cos \lambda \int x_{n-1} \, dt$$

If $n = 1$, the left-hand side is x_1, y_1, z_1, and we set $x_0 = 0$, $y_0 = 0$, $z_0 = h$. The quantities x_1, y_1 and z_1 will then give a better approximation. We then put $n = 2$ etc. to obtain better and better approximations.

Finally, as an additional comment on this example, it is said that mortar shells fired during the Battle of the River Plate, in the Second World War, always missed their target. The firing strategy would be based on northern hemisphere dynamics, with range finder, angle of launch etc. based on dynamics in the latitudes of Western Europe. (Perhaps the strategy completely ignored the effects of the rotating Earth.) Anyway, the River Plate is in Argentina and the Coriolis parameter is negative, being south of the equator. Hence, the mortars would be deviated the opposite way, resulting in them missing their targets (see exercise 11.4.7). It is assumed that, during the 1982 Falkland Islands dispute, the military got things right.

EXERCISES 11.4

1 A neutrally buoyant parcel of air of mass 10^6 kg is free to move horizontally. At time $t = 0$, it is at a location on the line of latitude 60°N, and is stationary. It is then subject to a constant southerly (*from* the south) wind force of magnitude 7 N. Assuming the horizontal acceleration is $(\ddot{x} - f\dot{y}, \ddot{y} + f\dot{x})$, where $f = 2\Omega \sin 60 = 1.26 \times 10^{-4}$ rad s^{-1}, find:

(a) x and y as functions of time;
(b) the time when the parcel first returns to latitude 60°N, and the distance east of the origin of this point;
(c) the highest latitude reached (to the nearest degree).

(Note that the parcel travels along a cycloid and travels in a net easterly direction. In fact, it is the difference in heat between equator and pole that causes north–south air flow, and the Coriolis effect that turns this through a right angle causing the trade winds and westerlies familiar to geographers. $1°$ latitude ≈ 111 km.)

2   Show that, for the study of motion in the atmosphere or ocean that is predominantly horizontal, the effects of the Earth's rotation can be successfully modelled locally by considering only its vertical component. Discuss the implications of this at the equator and compare the situations at equivalent latitudes north and south of the equator.

3   A cloud is at a distance r_0 from the centre of a low pressure centre around which the isobars are circular. If the cloud is subject to a frictional force of $c\mathbf{v}$ per unit mass, where c is a constant and $\mathbf{v}$ is its velocity, show that the motion of the cloud is approximately described by the equation:

$$f\hat{k} \times \mathbf{v} = -p\mathbf{r} - c\mathbf{v}$$

(You may assume that the pressure force is $-m p\mathbf{r}$. Work in plane polar coordinates.) Hence, show that:

$$\mathbf{r} = r_0 \exp\left(\frac{-cpt}{c^2 + f^2}\right)$$

and that the cloud moves with a constant angular velocity of magnitude $pf/(f^2 + c^2)$.

4   In example 11.4.3, the motion of a cloud around a low pressure centre was discussed. Consider a line of such clouds which are along $\theta = \theta_0$ at time $t = 0$. How will these line of clouds (a front) travel around the low pressure centre under the assumptions made in example 11.4.3? Replace the pressure force $-m p\mathbf{r}$ (proportional in distance from the centre of the low) by a pressure force $-m p\hat{\mathbf{r}}$ (constant in magnitude for all r). Calculate what happens to the line of clouds under this new assumption. Which do you think is more realistic?

5   Reconsider exercise 11.4.3 with the new assumption that the pressure is of constant magnitude so that the velocity $\mathbf{v}$ obeys the equation:

$$f\mathbf{k} \times \mathbf{v} = -p\hat{\mathbf{r}} - c\mathbf{v}$$

Find the new r and angular velocity of the cloud.

6 On a rotating Earth, assume that:

$$\ddot{r} = -g\mathbf{k} - 2\Omega \times \dot{r} - \Omega \times (\Omega \times r)$$

where $|\Omega| = 7.29 \times 10^{-5}$ rad s^{-1}. By assuming that, approximately:

$$\ddot{r} = -g\mathbf{k} \quad \text{and} \quad \dot{r} = \mathbf{u} - gt\mathbf{k}$$

and treating Ω as small in magnitude, show that:

$$\mathbf{r} \approx \mathbf{u}t - \frac{1}{2}gt^2\mathbf{k} - \Omega \times (\mathbf{u}t^2 - \frac{1}{3}gt^3\mathbf{k})$$

7 A missile is launched due east with speed u. Using the expression for $\mathbf{r}$ derived in the last exercise, show that:

$$x = ut - \frac{1}{3}\Omega gt^3 \, 1 \cos \lambda$$

$$y = -ut^2\Omega \sin \lambda$$

$$z = -\frac{1}{2}gt^2 - ut^2\Omega \cos \lambda$$

Use these to find the deflection southwards if $u = 400$ ms^{-1} and the time of flight is 10 s at 50°N. If the missile launcher was calibrated to hit a target 4000 m away but at 50°N, by how much would it miss the target if used at 50°S?

SOLUTIONS TO EXERCISES

CHAPTER 1

Exercises 1.4

3 (b). **4** 36 s, 12 s, 12 s. **5** $5\frac{1}{3}$ s.

Exercises 1.5

1 (a) 2 s; (b) $2 + 7t - t^2$; (c) $14\frac{1}{9}$ ms^{-1};
(d) $5\frac{1}{6}$ m. **2** $-\frac{1}{4}$ ms^{-1}, $\frac{3}{8}$ ms^{-2}.
3 14 ms^{-2}, 40 m.
4 (a) $\pm\sqrt{(28/3)} - 2/3(4 - x^2)^{3/2}$; (b)
never; (c) $\sqrt{(28/3)}$ ms^{-1}.

Exercises 1.6

1 257.2 m, 12.2 ms^{-1}. **2** 5 ms^{-1}.
3 50 s, 24.47 ms^{-2}. **4** 146.25 m.
5 $u^2/2(a + b)$.

Exercises 1.7

1 Particle 1: 3 ms^{-1}, 0.5 ms^{-2};
Particle 2: 8 ms^{-1}, -2 ms^{-2}. **2** Yes.

Exercises 1.8

1 4 s, 12 m, $\cos^{-1}$ (0.6) with
bank. **2** 30° to BA, 3.11 h.
3 16.39 ms^{-1}.

Exercises 1.9

1 (a) $20\sqrt{2}\mathbf{i} + 20\sqrt{2}\mathbf{j}$;

(b) $-6\sqrt{3}\mathbf{i} + 6\mathbf{j}$; (c) $20\mathbf{i}$; (d) $-3\sqrt{2}\mathbf{i}/2$
$+ 5\sqrt{2}\mathbf{j}/2$. **2** (a) 50 km/h, east;
(b) 15 km/h, 126.9°; (c) 14.1 km/h,
NW; (d) 12 km/h, south.

Exercises 1.10

1 (a) $2\mathbf{j}$, $-\mathbf{i} + 4\mathbf{j}$, $3\mathbf{i} + 3\mathbf{j}$; (b) B and
C, 1.30 pm. **2** 0.507 h, 69.4°.
3 2 minutes 33.5 s, 51.4 m.
4 3.74 km, 28 minutes 4.6 s.

CHAPTER 2

Exercises 2.2

1 Straight line. **6** $30t - 60$, 2.
8 (a) $0.25W$; (b) $0.25W$; (c) $0.25W$;
(d) $0.26W$.

Exercises 2.3

1 (a) L^{-3}; (b) ML^{-3}; (c) ML^{-1}T^{-2};
(d) MLT^{-2}. **2** L^{-1}.
3 MT^{-2}. **4** 4000.

CHAPTER 3

Exercises 3.4

1 $\cos^{-1}$ (97/100) = 28.1°,
$\cos^{-1}$ (145/154) = 19.7°.
2 $6g/(1 + \sqrt{3})$. **3** AC, DB: 6.25 g,
CD: 4.25 g. **4** AB, AD, CD, BC: W
(thrust), DB: $W\sqrt{3}$ (tension).

Exercises 3.5

1 $4\mathbf{j} - 8\mathbf{k}$.　**2** $(100g\sqrt{2}\sin 50°)/\sin 75° = 1099$ N, $(100g\sin 30°)/\sin 75° = 777$ N.　**3** $\sqrt{6}W/6$.

Exercises 3.6

1 17.6 N.　**2** $5(t-1)\mathbf{i} - 10\mathbf{k}$, $t = 1$. **3** 42.33 N along the line of the lead (154.11° to the +ve x-axis).

CHAPTER 4

Exercises 4.2

1 (a) 30 J; (b) 0 J; (c) -30 J. **2** $Wh/3(1 - (2a/\sqrt{(2a^2 + h^2)}))$. **3** 76 ms^{-1}.

Exercises 4.3

2 $\frac{1}{3}\sqrt{(gl)}$.　**4** 2.68 ms^{-1}.　**5** (a) 9509.5 × mass; (b) 8517.6 × mass.

Exercises 4.4

1 3.4 kg.　**2** 3.22 ms^{-1}, 24.2 ms^{-1}.　**3** 20 ms^{-1}.

CHAPTER 5

Exercises 5.2

1 (a) 125 Ns, $39\frac{2}{3}$ ms^{-1}; (b) $\frac{1}{3}$ Ns, $2\frac{1}{6}$ ms^{-1}; (c) $187\frac{1}{2}$ Ns, $56\frac{1}{6}$ ms^{-1}. **2** 15 Ns. **3** $mV/2\sqrt{2}$, A: $\frac{1}{2}\sqrt{(5/2)}v$, $\tan^{-1} 2$ with BA, B: $\frac{1}{2}\sqrt{2}v$, along BA. **4** (a) MV; (b) $(MV + mv)/(M + m)$.

Exercises 5.4

2 $u/3$ in direction of $2m$ mass's original direction, $4mu^2/3$. **3** $mV/(M + m)$, $\frac{1}{2}MV^2[1 + (Mm/(M + m)^2]$.　**4** 5 ms^{-1}.

Exercises 5.5

1 $4m$: $-0.5u$, $5m$: u, $7.5\ mu^2$.　**2** $3 + \sqrt{5} = 5.236$ s, 2 s.　**4** $m_1, m_2 \gg m_3$, $u \gg 1$, $e = e' = 1$.

Exercises 5.6

1 0.5.　**2** $[\sqrt{(5g^2h^2 + 2ghu^2)} - gh/(u^2 + gh)]^{1/2}$.　**5** $M \gg m$, $e = e' = 1$.

Exercises 5.7

1 (a) 1.75 ms^{-1}, $\tan^{-1}(\sqrt{3}/4)$; (b) $1/\sqrt{3}$, 6.25 J.

Exercises 5.8

1 Same, $\tan^{-1}(4(6 + \sqrt{3})/39)$. **2** $(1 + 3\tan^2 \theta)/2$ with $\theta \leq \pi/6$.

CHAPTER 6

Exercises 6.2

1 125 m.　**2** 5 m.　**3** $t = 0.5$ s, $x = 8.75$ m.　**4** $t = H/u$, $x = gH^2/2u$.　**5** 245 m.

Exercises 6.3

1 $t = 40.25$ s, 1110 m.　**2** (a) 500 m; (b) 368 m; (c) 484 m.　**3** 368 m, 83.3 ms^{-1}.

Exercises 6.4

1 (a) 29.4 ms^{-1}; (b) 5.24 s. **2** 31.3 ms^{-1}, $t = 8.3$ s.　**3** $k = 1/40$, $t = 11.4$ s.

Exercises 6.5

1 (a) kv, $k = 1.6$; (b) kv^2, $k = 0.036$.　**2** (a) $(g/k)^{1/3}$; (b) v_0e^{ag}; (c) $v = $ constant at initial velocity if $k = g$, otherwise no terminal velocity.

CHAPTER 7

Exercises 7.4

1 (a) 20 m; (b) 25 m. **2** (a) $U^2/2g$; (b) U^2/g. **3** (b) $\sqrt{(3/5)} = 0.78$ s.

Exercises 7.5

1 $5\sqrt{(89)}/2 = 23.6$ ms^{-1}, tan^{-1} (5/8) below horizontal. **2** $U\sqrt{2}$, $\pi/4$ above horizontal. **3** $10\sqrt{(31)} = 55.7$ ms^{-1}, tan^{-1} ($\sqrt{60}/50$) below horizontal.

Exercises 7.6

1 20 ms^{-1}, $2\sqrt{2} = 2.83$ s. **2** 0.5 sin^{-1} (44/45) = 38.9°. **3** (a) $5\sqrt{(15)} = 19.4$ m; (b) 14.4 m.

Exercises 7.9

1 tan^{-1} (1/3), $\pi/4$. **2** No values. **3** (a) 1/3; (b) 50 ms^{-1}; (c) $\sqrt{(10)} = 3.16$ s; (d) 150 m; (e) $3\sqrt{(35)} = 17.7$ ms^{-1}. **5** $[(2gh \sec^2 \alpha)/(2 \tan \alpha + 1)]^{1/2}$, $[2h (2 \tan \alpha + 1)/g \sec^2 \alpha]^{1/2}$.

Exercises 7.10

1 Yes.

Exercises 7.12

1 75°, 0°. **2** $\tan \theta = 2 \tan \alpha$. **3** tan^{-1} (3/2).

Exercises 7.13

2 $2880\sqrt{41} = 18441$ m, $60\sqrt{61} = 468.6$ ms^{-1}, tan^{-1} (1/30) below horizontal.

Miscellaneous Exercises 7

1 $-6\mathbf{i} - 8\mathbf{j}$, 20 s, $400\mathbf{i} - 1000\mathbf{j}$. **2** (a) 0.4 m; (b) $8\sqrt{(3/5)} = 2.77$ m. **3** (a) $y = 0.312x - 0.053x^2$; (b) 7.25 m; (c) 5.29 ms^{-1}, 25.7° below horizontal. **4** No non-zero

values. **5** $U \sin \alpha = V \sin \beta$, $U \cos \alpha + V \cos \beta$. **6** 5, 7.40 ms^{-1}, tan^{-1} (1 + $\sqrt{5}$) = 72.8°. **7** $3\sqrt{3}v^2/2g$. **8** 2.58 ms^{-1} to 6.74 ms^{-1}.

CHAPTER 8

Exercises 8.6

1 $4000\pi^2 = 39\,480$ N. **2** $3ma\omega^2$, $2ma\omega^2$. **3** 0.2892. **4** tan^{-1} (v^2/rg).

Exercises 8.7

1 $(g/l)^{1/2}$. **2** $(15ag)^{1/2}/2$. **3** $(ag\sqrt{3})^{1/2}$. **4** $(3ag)^{1/2}$. **5** $(g \cos \alpha)/(l \sin^2 \alpha)$. **6** (a) (i) $m(a\omega^2 - g)$, $m(a\omega^2 + g)$; (ii) $m(2g - a\omega^2)$.

Exercises 8.8

2 $((2g/a) \sin \theta)^{1/2}$. Full swing: period = $7.04\sqrt{(a/g)}$. Small oscillations: period = $6.283\sqrt{(a/g)}$. **3** $23a/27$. **4** $5a(4\sqrt{2} + \sqrt{5})/27$.

Exercises 8.9

1 $3mg(1 - \cos \theta + \sin \theta)/2$, $g(3 \sin \theta - \cos \theta)/4a$. **2** $2T\theta + mg(3 \cos \theta - 2)$, $(T/ma) - (g/a) \sin \theta$.

Exercises 8.14

1 (a) $-\mathbf{i} - \mathbf{k}$; (b) $9\mathbf{k}$. **2** $-2\mathbf{i} + 2\mathbf{j} - 2\mathbf{k}$.

Miscellaneous Exercises 8

1 (b) $\sqrt{3}/5$.

CHAPTER 9

Exercises 9.2

1 (a) $l + (mg/k)$; (b) $2\pi\sqrt{(m/k)}$; (c) $l + (2mg/k)$. **2** (a) 0.8 m; (b) 1.62 s, 0.77 ms^{-1}; (c) 0.87 m. **3** Vertical period = $2\pi\sqrt{(2m/k)}$, horizontal period = $2\pi\sqrt{(2m/3k)}$. **4** Equilibrium position = $7l/3$.

(a) Vertical period = $2\pi\sqrt{(2l/3g)}$;
(b) Horizontal period = $2\pi\sqrt{(2l/3g)}$.
New equilibrium position = $5l/3$,
periods the same.

Exercises 9.3

1 9.2 s; (b) 9.15 s. **2** $\alpha = 0.11$, $\ddot{x} +$
$0.22\omega\dot{x} + \omega^2 x = 0$.

Exercises 9.4

1 $x = a \cos \omega t/(1 - \omega^2 + \omega^4) + a\omega^3$
$\sin \omega t/(1 - \omega^2 + \omega^4)$.
Large damping, therefore little
resonance. **2** Maximum value of A_r
= 1. **3** $x = e^{-0.2t}(A \cos 2t + B \sin 2t)$
$- 0.4\omega \cos \omega t/((4 - \omega^2)^2 + 0.16\omega^2$,
$\omega = 3, 0.045$. $\omega = 2, 1.25$ (near to
resonant frequency). **4** Resonant
frequency = 1.99 s^{-1}, response
amplitude = 1.25. Small amplitude,
response correctly modelled. Larger
amplitude: (a) large θ, model not
valid; (b) child could go over the top;
(c) swing's chains would probably go
slack.

CHAPTER 10

Exercises 10.2

3 $m = 10^4 e^{-t^2}$, $t = 2.15$ s.

4 $k = 0.1m_0$, $v = [(20 + t^2)/(40 +$
$4t)]g$.

Exercises 10.3

1 (a) $3v^2(x + l)^2 = 6gl(x^2 + 2lx) -$
$13gl^3$; (b) $75v^2 l = g(15x^2 +$
$60lx - 382l^2)$;
(c) $75v^2 = g(90x - 163l)$, $75v^2 = 507gl$.
3 (a) 12.4 ms^{-2}; (b) 2696 ms^{-1}; (c)
2776 km; (d) 3140 km; (e) 6.346×10^7
Ns. **5** No, $v^2 = 2g(x^3 - 3a^2 x + 6a^2 l -$
$8l^3)/3(x + a)^2$.

CHAPTER 11

Exercises 11.2

1 (a) $4u/g$ m; (b) $N\pi g$ ms^{-1}, N is an
integer. **2** Yes, it reverses.

Exercises 11.4

1 (a) $x = 441(ft - \sin ft)$, $y = 441(1 -$
$\cos ft)$; (b) 2771 m; (c) 1385 m.
4 Pressure = $-mp\mathbf{r}$; line of cloud stays
linear, winding around the low (like a
radar). Pressure = $- mp\hat{\mathbf{r}}$; line of
cloud forms a logarithmic spiral (more
realistic). **5** $r = r_0 - pct/(c^2 + f^2)$,
$\theta = pf/(c^2 + f^2)[r_0 - pct/(c^2 + f^2)]^{-1}$.
7 2.2 m, 4.4 m.

INDEX